A STORY To Tell

FOR TEACHERS, PARENTS, AND CHILDREN

SECOND EDITION

DESERET
BOOK

SALT LAKE CITY, UTAH

Originally compiled by the General Board of the Primary Association and the Deseret Sunday School Union Board. © 1945 Deseret Book Company, Salt Lake City, Utah; reprinted 1946, 1956, 1959, 1963, 1966, 1968, 1971

© 2004 Deseret Book Company

Visit us at deseretbook.com

Library of Congress Cataloging-in-Publication Data

A story to tell.—2nd ed.
    p. cm.
  Summary: A collection of over 130 short stories first published in 1945 that illustrate such character traits as honesty, courage, and kindness, using examples from the lives of real people in order to build faith in Christ and encourage good works.
  ISBN 1-59038-359-1 (hardbound : alk. paper)
  1. Conduct of life—Juvenile fiction. 2. Children's stories, American. [1. Conduct of life—Fiction. 2. Christian life—Fiction. 3. Short stories.] I. Deseret Book Company.
  PZ5.S89253 2004
  [Fic]—dc22
                               2004018916

Printed in the United States of America   18961
R. R. Donnelley and Sons, Crawfordsville, IN

10 9 8 7 6 5 4 3

CONTENTS

Once Upon a Time

PIONEERS OF THE WEST

Holiday Time

PREFACE TO THE SECOND EDITION

A Story to Tell is a "book of virtues" for young children that features fables, parables, and exceptionally well-told stories. First published in 1945, the book was compiled by the General Boards of the Primary Association and the Deseret Sunday School Union of The Church of Jesus Christ of Latter-day Saints to help parents and teachers inspire children to live the standards of the Church and to acquire Christian virtues.

Once again available after three decades, due in large measure to the efforts of Sterling H. Redd, the nearly one hundred forty stories in this well-loved Latter-day Saint children's classic will delight and teach a whole new generation. Along with an alphabetical index, this edition offers a greatly expanded subject index of some one hundred thirty headings, painstakingly created by Brother Redd to give parents, teachers, grandparents, and anyone who teaches children easy access to a large array of stories appropriate for specific occasions and for teaching outstanding character traits.

Such stories as "The Lost Wallet," "Abraham Lincoln Keeps His Promise," "Ammon, the Son of a King," "The Three Little Goldfish," "How a Pioneer Boy Crossed the Plains," "The Selfish Giant," and "The Christmas Legend," along with dozens of others, portray a variety of desirable qualities of mind and heart. As the years pass, the need will only increase for such stories of substance to assist adults in inspiring children and youth to live respectable, exemplary, worthwhile lives.

FOREWORD TO THE FIRST EDITION

Suitable stories are one of the greatest needs of teachers of children in the Primary Association and in Sunday School classes for children of corresponding ages. The committees and their assistants in charge of assembling and classifying the stories contained in this volume have done a very commendable service to the Church. The stories can be used in family gatherings on home night as well as in the auxiliary organizations in the wards and branches throughout the Church.

The teaching of religion to immature minds is most effective when introduced in the form of concrete examples of religious living. This has been demonstrated through many centuries in the use of fables, parables, and exceptionally well-told stories.

Stories taken from the lives of men and women outstanding for their character traits are especially valuable not alone for children but also for people of all ages. This fact is well illustrated in the biographical materials pertaining to the founder of the Christian faith and the great prophets both ancient and modern.

Many such inspiring stories may also be taken from sources not classified as scripture. In American history they are generally best known in connection with the lives of Washington and Lincoln. There are, however, thousands of other Americans of outstanding character qualities whose heroic achievements are an inspiration to all who become acquainted with them. In this class are the biographical sketches of numerous pioneers who laid the foundations upon which recent advancements are based.

In connection with the uses of these materials in teaching religion, in either the auxiliary organizations or the home, it should be remembered that the character of the teacher is very important. Does the teacher embody adherence to and enthusiasm for the principles expressed in the stories? If not, the emotional reaction in the children may be unfavorable toward character development. It may even be negative. Character grows out of the emotions no less than out of the intellect. Correct understanding and love and enthusiasm for the right, expressed in appropriate conduct in everyday life, are the goals of religious education.

MILTON BENNION
GENERAL SUPERINTENDENT OF THE SUNDAY SCHOOL.

Preface to the First Edition

Great credit is due the committees and those that assisted them in the selection and the classification, both by subject content and purpose for use of the stories in teaching the children. The outcome is the product of two committees working conjointly in behalf of the organizations that appointed them. LaVern W. Parmley, Ruth H. Chadwick, and Alta Miller represented the Primary Association General Board. Eva May Green, Melba Glade, and Margaret Ipson represented the Deseret Sunday School Union Board. The committees received very substantial and much appreciated assistance from members of their respective boards, from Marba C. Josephson [associate editor of the *Improvement Era*], and from others interested in story telling as an effective means in the education of children.

The thanks of the sponsors of the project are due the publishers of the magazines of the auxiliary organizations of the Church and to other writers and publishers of books approved by the Church. For other stories included in this volume, thanks are due the following:

John Martin, Mrs. Katherine H. Dent, David Lloyd, Ginn & Company, Lathrop, Lee & Shepard Company, Inc., Milton Bradley Company, Little Brown & Company, J. B. Lippincott Company, Scott, Foresman & Company, The Sunshine Press, and Educational Publishing Corporation.

The Primary Association
The Deseret Sunday School Union.

GROWING UP

Search me, O God, and know my heart:
try me and know my thoughts:
and see if there be any wicked way in me,
and lead me in the way everlasting.

—Psalm 139:23–24.

THE GREAT STONE FACE

In the mountains of New England there lived a little boy named Ernest. He loved to sit at the cottage door with his mother at the close of day and watch the sun set behind the western mountains. The rugged cliffs seemed to have been chiseled by the Master Sculptor into the form of a human face. So natural were the features that as Ernest gazed, they seemed to smile down upon him in a kindly way.

The people who lived in this mountain valley had been told by the Indians many years ago that some day a child would be born there who would grow to be a noble and great man, and whose face would resemble the face on the mountains. Little Ernest wondered if he should live to see this man.

As the years went on and Ernest grew to manhood, the Great Stone Face became more and more a part of his life. After the day's work was done, he would look hopefully at the face, and it never failed to give him encouragement and comfort. He could not do an unkind act or think an ignoble thought while the Great Stone Face was looking down upon him.

One day it was told in the town that Gathergold, a merchant who had gone to the city many years before and won a fortune, was to return to the place of his birth. Many people said he was the man who had been foretold so long ago. But when Ernest looked at his harsh, scheming countenance, from which the children shrank in fear, he sadly shook his head. This was not the man.

Then a great soldier, who had become known as General Blood and Thunder for his bravery, returned to the valley. Again the people said: "This is he who was foretold." But his stern countenance, bespeaking a man of iron will, lacked the understanding and sympathy of the Great Stone Face.

Years passed. A great statesman, who had lived in the valley as a boy, returned and was heralded as "Old Stony Phiz." His face was more nearly like that on the mountain than the others had been, but it lacked the courage and frankness which shone from the one of stone. Ernest began to wonder if he should live long enough to see the fulfillment of the old prediction.

Ernest was an old man, his hair silver with age. His neighbors had grown to love him and to seek his wise counsel. Even people from outside the valley heard of him and came to hear his words. One day a great poet came to visit him. As Ernest talked with him he wondered if at last this was not the man of the Great Stone Face. But no, the face on the mountain had a depth of character not shown by this man.

The last rays of the setting sun fell upon Ernest's calm face, lighting it with a radiance so beautiful the poet started in wonder. His features, so noble and kindly, were surely the same as those of the Great Stone Face. Ernest himself was the long-awaited man.

—Adapted from Nathaniel Hawthorne.

Bright Blanket

What a lovely bright blanket." Jimmy took a bite of cracker and cheese and looked again at the tall Indian leaning against a post nearby. The Indian had been standing in that exact spot since Jimmy had come to the agency over an hour ago. The man had a blanket around him, but the day was warm and comfortable. The blanket was bright with black and red zigzags. When Jimmy looked up again, the Indian was looking at the sack of lunch he had in his lap.

He must be hungry, Jimmy thought. Jimmy was sitting on a wooden platform in front of a small store.

He looked in his lunch sack. It held some crackers, a small piece of cheese, three sardines, and a big candy bar. Jimmy took the candy bar and slipped it in his pocket. He looked up again. The Indian was still watching him.

"Okay, I can do without it." Jimmy threw the candy back into the sack with the lunch. He rose to his feet slowly. There was no use trying to talk to this tall silent man, so Jimmy went up to him and handed him the sack. He rubbed his own stomach, which meant, "I am so full. You may have the rest." The Indian took the sack but did not speak.

Jimmy's father was building an Indian school in New Mexico and had taken Jimmy with him for the summer. It was nearly fall now and almost time for school to start. In a week or two Jimmy would be going back home. He was proud of the things he had learned during the summer. He had learned to ride horseback and often ran errands for his father.

This morning he had been sent to the agency for the mail. He was not afraid, but the road was long and lonesome. After it turned, he could see nothing but brown hills. He wished he was home with his mother for a good meal. He was still hungry, and the crackers had made him thirsty.

Jimmy went to the hitching post and untied his horse. Mounting it, he started down the long dusty road. When he looked back, the Indian was sitting on the platform opening the sack.

The road twisted and crawled around the brown hills. That made it much longer than if it had gone straight. It took longer to travel it. Jimmy thought he would take a short cut. He would go right over the hills instead of around them. He pulled on the reins, but the pony did not want to leave the road. Jimmy pulled again. So the horse turned into the brush.

"I can see by the sun that I am going in the right direction," Jimmy told himself when he had been going a long time. He wished he would come to the road again. The brush was strange and not friendly like the road.

Time passed. The hills crowded close to each other. On the top of each one Jimmy looked about for the road. He could not see it anywhere. He was as hungry as he had been before he ate his lunch. Then the sun hid behind the hills and darkness crept around through the hollows. It was getting cold too. In this high country the evenings and nights were always cold.

On the top of a low hill he stopped his pony and looked about. He should be going east, but he could not tell which way was east. He thought he had better go back to the road, but he could not tell which way to go.

Then darkness crept up to the top of the hills. Big black brush was all about. A coyote called out his lonesome tune. Jimmy knew he was lost. He almost wished he was a little boy so he could cry. He almost wished it—but not quite. Instead he thought about what he would do. He knew he must not get excited and rush about.

"Whoa," he cried and pulled on the bridle reins. "We will stay here." He slid to the ground and tied his horse to a bush. As he tied the pony, he talked to him. "If we go on in the dark, we might pass father's camp. We will stay here until morning and then follow our tracks back." The pony whinnied as if he understood.

Then Jimmy waited and waited and waited. It sounded as if that coyote had brought all his friends to bark at him. Jimmy sat as close to his horse as he could.

A big silence settled over the earth. It grew colder and colder. Maybe, he thought, there will never be another morning. Maybe it will stay night.

Then Jimmy thought about something his father had told him. When he had first started going to the agency store alone, his father said never to leave the road. If he stayed on the road he could never get lost, for it would take him back to the school.

The more he thought of it the more Jimmy wished he had obeyed his father. He would the next time. But he hoped morning would come soon.

Jimmy's eyes grew heavy. They would not stay open. He did not want to go to sleep, but he thought if he closed his eyes for just a second it would rest them. Then before he knew it he was fast asleep.

Jimmy had a dream. He dreamed he was on an iceberg without a coat and he was freezing. Then his dream changed. He dreamed he was at home in his own bed. His own blankets felt so warm and snug. He cuddled down among them and slept and slept.

Jimmy awoke suddenly. Morning was peeping over the brown hills. He looked for his pony.

"My horse is gone," he cried. "Now I am lost."

He still felt warm. Then he saw that he was covered with a bright Indian blanket. It had black and red zigzags on it. He turned quickly. An Indian was sitting near him, looking very cold and hungry. It was the man to whom he had given his lunch.

"Come," the Indian arose. "You lost. Your horse he go. Come."

Oh, how thankful Jimmy was for that Indian. Rising, he offered the man his blanket, but the Indian threw it around Jimmy's own shoulders. The air was still cold. Then he set off across the hills with Jimmy following him.

Jimmy knew he was starving to death, and his mouth was dry from thirst. Then right before them was the road. He had not been very far from it after all. They started walking down it in the direction of his father's camp.

Soon they met Jimmy's father and some soldiers. They had been hunting for him. Mr. Brown was so thankful to see Jimmy that he forgot to scold him. He hugged him tight, almost exactly as his mother would have done.

Then Mr. Brown took some money from his pocket. He offered it to the Indian. The Indian would not even see it. Jimmy handed him his bright blanket.

"Here is your blanket. Thank you very much for finding me and keeping me warm."

The man did not take his blanket. "Boy keep," he said and turned and marched away toward the agency. Tears came to Jimmy's eyes. He was not ashamed of them. How thankful he was that he had been kind to the man.

"I shall keep this blanket forever," he told his father. "And I shall always remember how I got it."

—DOROTHY CLAPP ROBINSON.

A Son's Faith

Some years ago a well-known man was accused of having taken for his own use certain money that did not belong to him. No real evidence could be found, so a group of the citizens called on the man to tell him of the accusation and to give him a chance to answer if he could.

Of course, the man was angry and very much hurt to think that his neighbors would listen to rumors that he was dishonest. For a little while he would not believe that the matter was serious; but when the visitors told him all that they had seen and heard, he realized that it would be very difficult to prove that he was not the guilty one. He could say that he had not taken the money, but who would believe him?

Just then his son, who had been listening, said: "I don't believe my father took the money. He has always been very careful to do what is right. He has always been honest with me and with all the members of the family, and I think you will agree that he has been honest with his neighbors. He has taught honesty to me as long as I can remember. I think someone else took the money and started these stories so that the real criminal could get away."

The young man told about his father so sincerely and so confidently that the men who were present were generally impressed. They began to look for some other person or cause of the shortage, and soon they found where the real trouble lay.

What a fine thing it was for the son to stand up and defend his father before the angry neighbors. Surely there could be no finer way to show honor to a parent.

A Night in the Mountains

Two young boys, ten and twelve years of age, driving a cow with a young calf ahead of their horse, rode up to the old dairy corral in the mountains just as the sun was setting. The elder boy dismounted and, letting down the bars, drove from the corral another cow with a young calf.

"I am glad we found them both," he said, "but Boss has given us such a long day's hunt, we will have to hurry to get out of the mountains before dark."

"If we don't, we'll get lost," said Frank, the younger of the two.

"Yes, Father always says for us to get out of the mountains before dark, or there is real danger of getting lost," said Tom.

To hurry was impossible, with the young calves traveling so slowly, and darkness crept rapidly upon them. There was no moon, and Tom realized soon that he was not sure of the way. There was no fear in his heart of spending a night in the mountains. He loved the mountains by day or night and knew there was no danger in spending the night in them; but there was real concern for their parents, who he knew would be filled with anxiety if they failed to return that night. They traveled along in silence, Frank trusting implicitly in the judgment of his elder brother, and Tom feeling less sure of the way as the darkness grew more intense. Finally Tom said: "I think we had better stop and make a fire and stay here all night."

"I'm awfully hungry," said Frank. "I wish there was something left in the dinner sack."

"I wish so too," answered Tom, "but we'll scout around,

and we may find a tree of pine nuts. This seems a good place for the cows to bed, and there is grass for the horses."

Dismounting, they unsaddled the horses, and while Frank watched them as they browsed, Tom gathered some wood and built a fire. The cows bedded soon, glad of rest for their young calves. A bright fire brought cheer to the boys' hearts; and leaving Frank to keep it burning and watch the horses while they fed, Tom hunted for a pine nut tree. He soon found one and, filling the dinner sack with cones, brought them to roast in the fire. The boys made an ample supper of the nourishing, palatable nuts and water from a mountain spring.

"It's fun to roast and eat these pine nuts, and I like to camp in the mountains," said Frank, "but I wish Father and Mother could see us here and know we are all right."

"You know they have always told us that there is a help that never fails, and while they are praying for us, we will pray that they will know we are all right," said Tom.

After tying the horses securely for the night, they prepared their bed. Scraping the remains of the fire away and spreading pine boughs for a pillow, they made their bed on the warm earth with their saddle blankets and, kneeling beside it, prayed that they would be protected from harm and that their parents would know they were safe for the night.

As soon as the sun was up so they could be sure of their directions, the boys made their way down the mountain and met their father well up the canyon road. After a happy greeting the father said: "Frank, you ride on ahead to tell your mother all is well, and I will help Tom drive the cows home."

When Frank rode in sight of the house, he could see his

mother standing at the gate, her hand shading her eyes, strain-
ing to see him.

"We are all right," he called, when he was within hearing
distance. "Father and Tom are coming with both cows and their
calves."

After explaining what kept them all night, he said: "Did
you sleep last night? We prayed that you would know we were
safe so you could sleep."

"Yes," his mother said, "and I saw you in my dreams,
snuggled together, fast asleep in your saddle blankets."

—Josephine Gardner Moench.

The Pig Brother

There was once a child who was untidy. He left his books
on the floor and his muddy shoes on the table; he put his
fingers in the jam pots and spilled on his best trousers; there
was really no end to his untidiness.

One day the Tidy Angel came into his nursery. "This will
never do!" said the angel. "This is really shocking. You must go
out and stay with your brother while I set things to right here."

"I have no brother!" said the child.

"Yes, you have," said the angel. "You may not know him,
but he will know you. Go out in the garden and watch for him,
and he will soon come."

"I don't know what you mean!" said the child, but he went
out into the garden and waited.

Presently a squirrel came along, whisking his tail.

"Are you my brother?" asked the child.

The squirrel looked him over carefully. "Well, I should hope not!" he said. "My fur is neat and smooth; my nest is handsomely made and in perfect order; and my young ones are properly brought up. Why do you insult me by asking such a question?"

He whisked off, and the child waited.

Presently a wren came hopping by.

"Are you my brother?" asked the child.

"No, indeed!" said the wren. "What impertinence! You will find no tidier person than I in the whole garden. Not a feather is out of place, and my eggs are the wonder of all for smoothness and beauty. Brother, indeed!" He hopped off, ruffling his feathers, and the child waited.

By and by large Tommy cat came along.

"Are you my brother?" asked the child.

"Go look at yourself in the glass," said Tommy cat haughtily, "and you will have the answer. I have been washing myself in the sun all morning, while it is clear that no water has come near you for a long time. There are no such creatures as you in my family, I am thankful to say."

He walked on, waving his tail, and the child waited.

Presently a pig came trotting along.

The child did not wish to ask the pig if he were his brother, but the pig did not wait to be asked.

"Hello, brother!" said the pig.

"I am not your brother!" said the child.

"Oh, yes, you are!" said the pig. "I confess I am not proud of you, but there is no mistaking a member of our family. Come along and have a good rolling in the barnyard! There is some lovely black mud there."

"I don't like to roll in mud!" said the child.

"Tell that to the hens!" said the Pig Brother. "Look at your hands and your shoes and your trousers! Come along, I say! You may have some of the pigwash for supper, if there is more than I want."

"I don't want pigwash!" said the child, and he began to cry.

Just then Tidy Angel came out. "I have set everything to rights," she said, "and so it must stay. Now, will you go with the pig brother, or will you come back with me and be a tidy child?"

"With you, with you!" cried the child, and he clung to the angel's dress.

The pig brother grunted. "Small loss!" he said. "There will be all the more wash for me!" And he trotted off.

—LAURA E. RICHARDS,
FROM *THE GOLDEN WINDOWS*, LITTLE, BROWN & CO.

THE LOST WALLET

It was snowing hard for the first time that winter, and the white flakes were piling up on Maple Street. Billy Gates grasped his shovel and put on his gloves. He wanted to clear the snow away from the front of his house before it got too deep.

Just then he saw three people coming toward him. When they drew near, he saw that they were old Mr. Judd and Tommy and Jackie Green. Tommy and Jackie were twins, eight years old and just one week younger than Billy.

Tommy called, "Hello, Billy. Come with us. Mr. Judd has lost his wallet with two dollars in it, and we're going to help find it."

Poor Mr. Judd didn't see very well, and whenever he mislaid anything, he asked the Green boys and Billy to go to his house to look for it with him. The boys were glad to help the kind old man. Then too they had a great deal of fun at his house.

Mr. Judd had been a sailor when he was young, and he told them many exciting stories of the sea whenever they visited him.

"Come on, Billy," Mr. Judd urged, "you're Maple Street's champion finder of lost articles."

Billy wished he could go with his friends. It was fun playing detective for old Mr. Judd. And it would be more fun to hear the stories that were sure to follow.

But then he remembered his father who had to work long hours at the busy creamery. If Billy went to help Mr. Judd, his father would have to shovel the snow himself that evening when he reached home. So Billy made his decision.

"I'm sorry, Mr. Judd," he said, "but I've got to finish this job so that Daddy won't have to do it tonight."

Mr. Judd patted Billy's shoulder. "That's right," he said. "You've got good parents, and I'm glad you want to help them. But I'm sorry you can't come with us."

Then they started down the street. Billy looked sadly after the three. What a great time they would have in Mr. Judd's warm, jolly, little house. The boys loved to be there, for it was full of the odd things that the old man had brought from the far places of the earth. And each one of these things had a story.

But it would be silly to stand fretting. So Billy set to work.

The snow had been falling heavily, and Billy had to push

hard to get it out into the road. It didn't seem possible that the light, airy flakes could weigh so much.

Soon his arms and shoulders were tired. He wanted to rest, but he had determined not to stop until the job was finished.

At last there was just one more strip to be cleared. Billy set the wide shovel down and pushed. He watched the soft snow as it crept up the wood of the shovel.

Then suddenly something black and square appeared in the whiteness. Billy stopped working and picked up the black object. He brushed it off and turned it over in his hands.

Why, it was a wallet and inside it were two single dollar bills. This must be the wallet that Mr. Judd had lost!

He crammed it into his pocket and quickly pushed the last strip of snow into the street.

"Mother," he called when this was done, "I'm going over to Mr. Judd's house. I've found his wallet."

Down the street he ran, and when he rang Mr. Judd's doorbell, Tommy Green opened the door. Tommy looked very sad.

"We haven't found the wallet yet," he said, "and Mr. Judd feels so bad about it that I don't think he'll be able to tell that story."

Just then the old man came into the room. Billy could see that he was worried. Mr. Judd didn't have a great deal of money, and two dollars was a large sum to him.

"Mr. Judd," said Billy with a grin, "guess what has happened!"

"You look so happy," said Mr. Judd, "that if you hadn't just come into the house, I'd say you'd found my wallet."

"Well, look at this," Billy cried.

Mr. Judd blinked with surprise when he saw what Billy had

in his hand. Then he laughed, "Why, Billy, we've turned the house upside down looking for that. Wherever did you find it?"

Of course, they all wanted to hear what had happened. Tommy and Jackie Green stood by with their eyes popping while Billy told his tale.

"That's odd," said Mr. Judd, when the story was finished. "I must have dropped it when I went for my walk this morning. I was sure I had lost that wallet in the house."

Then he brought the three boys into the kitchen. They sat at the table, and Mr. Judd gave each one a glass of the root beer that he made himself.

The boys agreed with Mr. Judd that it had been fine of Billy to give up having fun with his friends so that he could help his father. Billy thought that if they knew what a good father he had, they wouldn't think that what he had done had been so great.

Then they sat about the kitchen stove while Mr. Judd told them the exciting story of how his ivory elephant from India had lost one of its tusks.

—Ruth Cannon.

A Daring Deed

Everyone knows how necessary cooperation is in most things. In athletics and in business it is important that each does his own part. But here is a little story of a business in which perfect cooperation meant life or death to a man.

It occurred during one of New York's great fires. For hours the firemen had been fighting flames and rescuing the horror-stricken people. Finally they climbed an adjoining building and were turning water on the ruins from there. Suddenly Sergeant Vaughan saw a man standing on a window ledge just opposite him; his clothes were burnt and his face and hands were black with soot. The most amazing thing of all was the poor fellow's admirable calmness. When he saw the sergeant and knew that he was looking for someone to rescue, he shouted, "It's no use. Don't try. You can't do it."

The sergeant looked wistfully about him. Not a stick or piece of rope was in sight. There was absolutely nothing. "But I couldn't let him," he said months after, when he had come out of the hospital and was back at work, "I just couldn't let him die, standing there so quiet and so brave." To the man he said sharply, "I want you to do exactly as I tell you now. Don't grab me, but let me get the first grab." He had noticed that the man wore a heavy overcoat and had already laid his plan.

"Don't try," urged the man. "You cannot save me. I will stay here till it gets too hot; then I will jump."

"No, you won't," said the sergeant, as he lay full length on the roof looking over. "It's a pretty hard yard. I will get you or go dead myself."

The four firemen on the roof sat on the sergeant's legs as he swung free down to the waist, so he was almost able to reach the man on the window with outstretched hands.

"Now jump—quick!" he commanded, and the man jumped. The sergeant caught the man with a grip of both wrists on the collar of his coat.

"Hoist!" he shouted to the four on the roof, and they tugged with all their might. The sergeant's body did not move. Bending over till his back creaked, the sergeant hung over the edge, and a weight of two hundred and three pounds suspended from him was hanging down. A cold sweat started upon the men's foreheads as they tried and tried again, without gaining an inch.

But in a flash it came to Sergeant Vaughan, to relieve the terrible weight that wrenched and tore at his muscles, he would swing the man to and fro like a pendulum. He could swing him up! A smothered shout warned his men. They crept nearer the edge without letting go their grip on him and watched with staring eyes the human pendulum swing left and right, wider and farther, until now with a mighty effort, it swung within their reach. They caught the skirt of the coat, held on, pulled, and in a moment lifted him over the ledge.

The cooperation of six brave men had saved a life.

HE CAME OFF CONQUEROR

Pray always, that you may come off conqueror." During World War II the postman dropped me a letter from a former missionary companion of mine, John Boud. Some seven years before, we had worked together in the offices of the European and British Missions in London. John Boud, now a lieutenant, senior grade, was stationed at San Diego, California, and had the honor of being the first Latter-day Saint chaplain in the United States Navy, so far as is known.

Lieutenant Boud's letter carried the usual good cheer that his correspondence always exuded, but he related a particular war story which proved stimulating.

Each Wednesday, Chaplain Boud held a service at the

marine base for Latter-day Saint servicemen. Many of the sessions were in the form of testimony meetings. He related the experience of one young Mormon sailor who had been in the navy about a year. During that time he had baptized three friends. These were great thrills, but one of the most stirring moments came when this same sailor had a destroyer blasted from under him. The young man had been kidded, and perhaps even ridiculed a bit, during the wanderings of the destroyer because he always turned down the drinks and passed off the smokes. Some of this slur was tossed at him in the typical taunts of hardened tars.

Then one day the ship's captain bellowed out: "Stand by for torpedo!" All hands rushed to the fore of the ship. Some of the more frantic sailors dropped to their knees, calling in loud voices for the Lord to spare them. Walking about in the crisis, the boy from Idaho noticed among those with outstretched arms, calling to the heavens for mercy, the same fellows who had mocked him.

Then the crash came. The torpedo hit like a terrific bolt of thunder and lightning. The young Latter-day Saint was hurled into the ocean. Later he was rescued.

When other survivors of the sunken vessel gathered together to recount their thrills, one of the first questions popped was at the sailor who never drank or smoked: "Why, tell us," one of the seamen asked, "didn't you fall to your knees like the rest of us and pray?"

Then came the young man's classic reply: "Because, fellows, I had been doing some praying long before our lives were in danger."

—WENDELL J. ASHTON.

The Story of Donny
and the Bunny

Donny was a little boy who lived in a big red house on a hill. His real name was Donald, but his Aunt Jane started calling him Donny, and now even his mother and daddy call him Donny.

One day Grandmother came to visit, and she brought Donny a beautiful pair of bunny slippers. Now these slippers were a very special kind. They had soft wool all over inside and cunning little bunny heads right where you snuggle your toes. Donny loved them.

Before I go any further, I must tell you something very sad. You see, Donny had just one bad habit. He couldn't seem to remember to put his things away when he was through with them.

One night he left his tricycle out in the rain, and in the morning the red had all faded off the seat.

If you were to go into Donny's playroom some night without turning on the light, you might step on all sorts of things.

Grandmother knew all this, so it is no wonder that when she gave Donny the slippers, she said, "Now, Donny, do take care of these slippers or the bunnies might run away."

Donny was so very happy about the slippers that he put them right on his feet. He didn't take them off again until bedtime. When he undressed to take his bath, he patted them very lovingly and wiggled his hands in their ears; but I am sorry to have to tell you that when he got into the shower, he kicked them off. They landed in a puddle of water that the shower was making. Donny forgot all about them. He climbed into bed without a thought of putting them away.

He was so tired that he went to sleep with the first wink and was soon dreaming. He might have slept until morning had he not felt something pulling his covers, but he did feel it and sat right up in his bed. To his surprise, there on the bed he saw one of his bunny slippers, only it looked more like a real live bunny.

"Hello," said Donny in great surprise. "Where is your mate?"

"My mate?" said the bunny. "Young man, I'm not a ship."

"Of course not," answered Donny, "but I thought you were a pair."

"Are you trying to make fun of me? Do I smell like fruit?" asked the bunny.

"No, indeed," said Donny politely. "I was only trying to find out if you were the right or the left."

"I was left in the bathroom in a puddle of water," said the bunny, "but I don't like to be left as I really am right."

"Well, then if you are the right, where is the left?" said Donny.

"I suppose," said the bunny, "the left is still left."

"You are mixing me all up," said Donny.

"Well, that is just what you do with your toys," answered the bunny. "Indeed, I never have seen such a mixup as your playroom. I went in there to find someone to play with, but it was such a jumble that everyone was cross."

"Oh," said Donny in a surprised voice. "I didn't know they could tell the difference."

"Yes, indeed, they can." Replied the bunny. "I heard a great many things about you in the playroom. In fact, I had decided to run away and leave you."

"Oh, please don't do that!" said Donny in a frightened voice.

"Well," said the bunny, "I would have gone already, only I lost one of my eyes when you kicked me off last night. I came in here to see if you would help me find it."

"I'm dreadfully sorry about your eye, but I didn't know you could see out of it," replied Donny.

"What did you think they gave me eyes for if not to see with?" asked the bunny.

"To tell the truth, I didn't think," said Donny.

"That is just as I thought," replied the bunny in great disgust. "Little boys who do think never leave their playrooms in such a muddle."

"I'm truly sorry," said Donny in a sorrowful voice, "and if you will promise not to run away, I will clean my playroom right this minute."

"It is a bargain," said the bunny with a smile. "Only first help me find my eye."

"We will probably find it in the bathroom," said Donny.

Now Donny, himself, told me all this about the bunny, so I really don't know for sure if he dreamed it; but this I do know for sure: that next morning when Mary went into the playroom to clean, every toy was in its proper place.

What is more, I examined the bunny slippers myself, and I am very sure that both the eyes were in each slipper. To this day Donny puts his things away as nicely as any little boy I know.

—Mildred Tanner Pettit.

FRIENDSHIP

Listen to the story of the soldier who asked his officer if he might go out into the no-man's-land between the trenches to bring in one of his comrades who lay grievously wounded.

"You can go," said the officer, "but it's not worth it. Your friend is probably killed, and you will throw your own life away." But the man went. Somehow, he managed to get to his friend, hoist him onto his shoulder, and bring him back to the trenches. The two of them tumbled together and lay in the bottom of a trench. The officer looked very tenderly on the would-be rescuer, and then he said: "I told you it wouldn't be worth it. Your friend is dead, and you are wounded."

"It was worth it though, sir."

"How do you mean, 'worth it'? I tell you your friend is dead."

"Yes, sir," the boy answered, "but it was worth it, because when I got to him he said, 'I knew you'd come.'"

THERE IS A WAY

What a pretty smile!" A little boy stooped over the crib of his sleeping baby sister. "She must be dreaming of heaven and the angels!" He looked at the smiling face for a long time. "I am going to make that smile last forever!" he said.

From the table he took a pen, some red ink, black ink, and a sheet of paper and was busy drawing a picture of sister Sally when he heard his mother coming toward the room. He slipped the drawing under the crib and looked up guiltily.

"Benjamin West," his mother said, "what are you doing?"

Ben felt sure he would be punished for making the drawing, but he picked it up and handed it to his mother.

"A picture of Sally!" his mother cried happily and kissed him.

Then he knew that he need not be afraid to show his mother other drawings that he had made.

Benjamin West was ten years old before he ever saw a picture drawn by anyone except himself. He had no colored crayons or drawing paper, but because he loved to draw, he found ways of sketching without the things he really needed. With a piece of chalk he sketched bushes and trees, and figures of men and animals and birds, on the kitchen floor, and even on the barn doors.

He loved the beautiful pink and yellow and red and blue flowers that grew in the fields near his home in Springfield, Pennsylvania, and he longed to put color into his drawings of them, but two hundred years ago, when Ben was a little boy, colored paints were not plentiful, and he did not have a brush.

Ben did have a number of friends among the Mohawk Indians who used to visit his town, and they gave him some of the red and yellow paint that they used for coloring their faces, and Ben's mother added a piece of indigo.

"I have three colors now," Ben sang out. "I can make green, by mixing red and blue. I could paint pictures of the Indians and their feathers and could make my flowers and trees beautiful with these colors, if I had a brush," he finished sadly.

Seasons came and went, and Ben noticed the flowers and woods and birds change their colorings with the seasons and longed to make fine, colored pictures of them.

"Where can I get a brush?" he asked himself aloud one day, as he sat stroking the silky fur of his pet cat. Then Ben got a happy idea.

"Hold still, Kitty, please!" he said, and with a pair of sharp scissors he carefully clipped enough fur from the tip of the cat's tail to make a brush.

Many times after that his cat had to give up fur for Ben's brushes, not willingly, of course, because her coat became so thin that she had to stay close to the chimney corner to keep warm, while Ben was making colored sketches. Soon the walls of the West home were hung with drawings of wild flowers, of Indian chiefs in brilliant-colored dress and feathers, and of birds with beautiful plumage.

One day Mr. Pennington, a merchant from Philadelphia, came to visit Ben's parents.

"Where did you get all these fine pictures?" Mr. Pennington pointed to the walls.

"Ben made them," his father said, "with red and yellow paints and a piece of indigo—"

"And with a brush made from the cat's tail," his mother added.

"The boy has a fine gift," Mr. Pennington said.

After he went back to Philadelphia, Mr. Pennington sent Benjamin a letter and a gift. When he opened the package, the boy found a box of many-colored paints, several different-sized brushes, squares of canvas, and some fine engravings of landscapes.

Ben was too happy to say much about this great gift, but he wrote Mr. Pennington a letter of thanks and promised to make good use of everything his friend had given him. He put the paint box under his pillow at night and went to sleep thinking of the pictures he would make.

For the next two days Ben shut himself, alone, into the garret, and when his mother went up to ask what he was doing, he held up a beautiful landscape for her to see.

"Look, Mother," he said. "I copied parts from two of these new engravings and made up this picture with my own ideas."

When Ben's parents and their friends saw the fine piece of work he had done, they all agreed that he should have a chance to study art; and although they were not wealthy, they all contributed money to pay his expenses to Philadelphia to study, so that he might become a great artist. Benjamin, himself, was even more sure than they were that he would succeed, and because he had faith in himself, he became a famous artist.

In later years he went to London. There he served as chief artist to King George III and became president of the Royal Academy of Arts.

Among his paintings were many showing the miracles and sufferings of the Redeemer of mankind, with which he decorated the walls of a beautiful chapel near London. For a time one of his pictures, which he later gave to a hospital in Philadelphia, was exhibited at the Royal Academy in London. It was a painting titled *Our Lord Healing the Sick.* It contained many life-sized figures and covered a large wall. Beside it hung a small, faded, but still beautiful landscape—the painting that the young artist had made in his father's garret.

—FLORA FLAHERTY.

PAL AND PEEPER

Ned and Fred slipped quietly around a corner of the cow shed to where a ladder leaned against its roof. "Sh!" whispered Fred, as Ned began to follow him up the ladder. "You'd better stay down and take her when I hand her down." Ned obediently remained at the foot of the ladder.

"She's here, sure enough!" hissed Fred a moment later, from the top of the shed. Ned saw him stoop and thrust his hands into the hay which was heaped on the top of the shed. Then he was handing down Snowflake, the pet hen the boys had raised from a wee, yellow chick. They had missed her nearly a month ago and discovered her hiding place only this morning, while searching for eggs about the sheds and barns. Fred had heard a muffled clucking and instantly suspected it was Snowflake.

She was ruffled now and clucking in a scolding tone at being disturbed. "Now, wait, I'll show you something!" Fred said mysteriously, as Ned tucked the complaining hen under his arm.

"Baby chicks!" guessed Ned excitedly. Fred had taken off his cap and was filling it with little fluffs of down. "One, two, four, five, eight, ten, and all yellow like she used to be!" he announced, as he began to carefully descend the ladder.

"Go away, Pal! You are scaring Snowflake!" said Ned to the big, friendly dog who had come into the chicken yard, and whose intelligent brown eyes and wagging tail were asking plainly what the excitement was all about.

Fred showed him the hatful of wee, yellow babies, making their peeping, bird-like sounds.

"Be good, Pal, be good and don't hurt them," he said, and Pal wagged his tail understandingly.

It was fun putting Snowflake and the little chicks into the pen they had built and bringing water and the food Mother had prepared for them.

It was not long until the little chicks were squeezing out and running about near the pen, while Snowflake peered anxiously through the bars and called them to come and cuddle under her wings to rest.

Though the chicks were as alike as peas in a pod, there was one so wee that he could always be distinguished from the rest. He could not run so fast and was always getting left behind a big corn shock or fence post. It was easy to locate him by his frenzied peeping and catch and bring him back to his mother.

The boys named this little one Peeper and never covered the pen at night without making sure he was under his mother's wing.

One day Ned and Fred had been to town with their parents. As they neared home, they heard a terrible commotion in the chicken yard. "A hawk!" cried both boys at once, and the instant the car stopped they were racing for the sheds. Sure enough, a great black hawk was just circling away over the cornfields. The chickens were still hiding under the hedge and beneath corn shocks.

Snowflake, squawking excitedly, was hovering over the chicks she had so hurriedly called to safety. Fred opened the pen and lifted her off her brood to count them. "Oh, Ned, Peeper's gone!" he exclaimed a moment later. "The hawk has caught the poor little thing because he's so slow!" Pal crouched on the ground near the chicken's pen. He looked up eagerly into first

one boy's face, then the other, as if trying to speak. Ned said he
knew Pal understood the whole thing.

"Listen!" said Fred. "I thought I heard him peeping!"

"I know I did!" exclaimed Ned joyfully. "He's hidden somewhere. Let's hunt him!"

The boys looked everywhere, under the hedge, behind
every corn shock, in the haystacks, in every out-of-the-way corner in the yard. No Peeper was to be found. Strangely enough,
they could still hear his frantic peeping.

At last Mother called them to dinner, and they were forced
to give up the search.

They stopped for a moment at Snowflake's pen to explain.

"Well, Snowflake," said Ned, "we can't find him, but we
keep thinking we hear him, so maybe he'll come back yet!"

"Look!" cried Fred. Pal lifted his head and gently raised his
paws off the ground—and what do you think! Out jumped
Peeper good as new and ran peeping to his mother!

Pal stood up and looked eagerly at the boys as though to
say, "What do you think of my way of saving little Peeper from
the hawk?" And the boys laughed and gave him the praise he
wanted.

—Estelle Webb Thomas.

A Race against Death

A log house of five rooms nestling in a recess of a deep
canyon where the sunbeams always came late and
departed early, a log stable and a corral standing off to one side,
a rusty-looking wagon, a few chickens feebly scratching at the

unimpressionable ground, and a dog lazily out before the open door of the house—these constituted the most noticeable outer features of Ray Morton's home on the Fourth of July, 1887.

Not exactly the most noticeable, either, for Ray himself was swinging an ax at the woodpile with a vigor that spoke well for the power of his young muscles and the industry of the spirit behind them. He was a well-knit, supple-looking boy of fifteen, with a face burned brown by the western sun and lighted by a pair of honest, hazel eyes that seemed troubled this particular morning.

A man stepped out of the open door and watched him chop for a few moments. The man's face also was overcast by anxiety, and he had the appearance of one who had been keeping a long and weary vigil not yet concluded.

"Ray!"

"Yes, Father!"

"You had better quit chopping, son, and go and catch Hawk; your mother is so much worse that I must send for the doctor."

The ax fell with a ring against the chopping log, and the boy stepped onto the rough porch and took down a heavy bridle, hanging against the side of the house.

"Do you think Mother is going to leave us, Father?" he asked, with a tremor in his voice and his eyes full of unused tears.

"Whether she does or not, Ray, is in the hands of Eternal Providence!" his father answered reverently. "We must do what we can to save her; the issue is in the keeping of him who ordereth all things well."

Mrs. Morton had been ill for a week, but during the past

two days she had seemed to improve, and no doctor had been called. It was fifty miles to the little town on the railroad—the nearest point where a physician could be obtained, and the fee for attending was a very heavy one.

Hawk, a magnificent black stallion, and the best saddle horse for a hundred miles around, was grazing in the pasture above the house. He seemed to know there was urgent need for his services, for he did not cut up in his usual tantalizing way when Ray stepped hastily up to him and displayed the bridle.

"Your mother has just had a slight convulsion, which, I am afraid, will return in a more severe form," said Mr. Morton, stepping out of the house and assisting the boy to adjust the saddle with trembling hands. "Ride, ride, my son, as you've never ridden before, for your mother's life probably hangs on the speed you make!"

A hasty visit to the sick room, and a long, trembling pressure of his mother's fevered lips to his own, a few rapid words of caution and advice from his father, and he was into the saddle and away.

The tears coursed rapidly down his cheeks as Hawk settled into a long, swinging lope down the dusty road. His mother— the playmate of his childhood and the never-failing friend to whom he still confided his every doubt and trouble—his mother was in danger of dying, and his father had told him that her life, in all probability, depended upon how quickly he rode the fifty miles before him.

"I'll get there in time if Hawk will only hold out," he sobbed to himself, dashing the tears from his eyes and settling himself more firmly in the saddle.

On, on down the winding mountain road the black horse

steadily galloped. The mouth of the canyon, where begin the great plains that stretch to the banks of the Missouri with hardly a break, would come into view around the next turn; and he looked at his handsome silver watch—a kindly remembrance from the little mother on his last birthday—to see how fast Hawk was traveling.

"Forty-five minutes—and the mouth of the canyon is ten good miles from home," he muttered. "It was just ten o'clock when I started; counting breathing spells for Hawk—and Father said I was to breathe him five minutes at the end of every ten miles—this gate would take me into town between two and three this afternoon. I must beat that. Come, come, Hawk, we are riding for Mother."

Hawk responded with a quickened stride and a toss of his shapely head that scattered foam from the heavy bit in a shower of snowy flakes.

Out on the sun-baked plain swept the noble horse and his sorrowful little rider. The sweat was slowly dripping from the broad cinches now, and the foam of it rose in white streaks in the creases of Hawk's powerful muscles, two snowy lines decorating his shoulders and haunches where the heavy saddle chafed him at each swing of his broad back.

The sun glared down on the parched plain with scorching fervor, and the dust rose and rolled in gray billows under the stallion's feet, settling on his foam-flecked coat and transforming his ebon hue into a shade of somber drab.

Miles ahead, where the road crossed the bed of an ancient lake—a league of heavy sand that Ray dreaded, but which he knew he could not avoid—there suddenly sprang into view a glistening sheet of water, bordered by tall trees whose airy branches appeared to tremble in a cool breeze from the distant mountains.

"If only it was water!" he gasped, as the illusive mirage slowly dissolved.

When the border of the sandy stretch was reached, Hawk was panting heavily, the proud arch of his neck had disappeared, and he looked at his rider questioningly when he dismounted for a few minutes and loosened the cinches so that the horse might breathe more freely.

"Twenty-five miles from home—halfway to town, and Hawk has made it in an hour and fifty minutes," Ray muttered as he consulted his watch.

Unslinging a small canteen hanging at his side, he carefully washed out Hawk's mouth with a part of the water it contained and then spent the remaining part of the allotted ten minutes in rubbing his steed's legs and shoulders vigorously with his bare hands.

"Now, Hawk, old boy, another twenty-five miles for Mother!" he said, and once more swung himself into the saddle.

Hawk responded gallantly to the call; but Ray noticed that the springy heave of two hours before was missing from the broad back under him, and the stallion seemed to put down and pick up his feet with a heavier motion.

"Don't fail me, Hawk!" he cried, with a sob in his voice, as he reached forward and patted the horse's reeking neck. "Mother was always kind to you, and she needs the best there is in you now."

The miles sped steadily behind, and before one o'clock Ray caught sight of the mound marking the site of the old well, close to the left of the road—the hole in which old man Norcross had sunk a small fortune, endeavoring to strike water where no water is.

"Fifteen miles yet, and Hawk is awful tired!" he moaned as they swept by it.

No cruel spurs disfigured his heels, nor would he have used them if they had. He knew Hawk would continue the wild race until he dropped exhausted, and there was no need to urge him with steel or quirt.

Forward, good Hawk! That faint sound stirring the waves of sultry air is the whistle of a horse of iron approaching the goal for which you strive. Eight miles more—a short eight miles, and the lifelong gratitude of a husband and wife, a father, mother, and son awaits you!

Ray's heart, already full of anxiety for his mother, now commenced to ache for Hawk. The pace had been fearful—forty-two miles in a little over three hours—and the noble animal's breath was coming and going in sobbing gasps that sounded like the breaking of his gallant heart. He lurched heavily every few minutes, and the boy felt the overtaxed muscles quivering spasmodically under him at every stride.

"I can't kill him!" Ray moaned, "and Mother would not wish me to do so even to save her own life."

Four miles more, and at the top of a rise in the road the tall tank at the depot came into view. It seemed so near in the clear air at that altitude that Ray imagined he could distinguish the white stains on its side made by the alkali water slopping over the top.

"Come, Hawk!" he coaxed. "Three miles more, and Mother will say we did our best!"

But Hawk was almost done. Galloping down the next slight descent, he suddenly pitched heavily forward, made a desperate effort to recover himself, and fell in a heap to the ground, throwing his rider ten feet down the slope. He tried to rise, but the effort was too great for his weakness, and he sank back with a moan almost human in its distress.

Staggering giddily to his feet, Ray walked over to the horse and removed the saddle and bridle, washed his mouth with the water remaining in the canteen, gave him an affectionate pat or two, and started for town as fast as he could run.

His high-heeled cowboy boots impeded his progress, and he stopped and took them off, leaving them by the roadside.

"Hawk couldn't have made these last three miles any quicker than I can afoot," he thought, as he sped along.

Some time later a tired, dusty, hatless boy staggered up to the door of the only doctor the little town could boast of and told his story in sobbing gasps.

The physician was so accustomed to the emergencies of a western practice that he immediately rushed to his medicine case, ordered his horse saddled, and in five minutes he was ready to start.

Nor was faithful Hawk forgotten. A light wagon soon rolled out of town carrying two men, a keg of water, and such medicines as the one livery stable could furnish.

"You were just in time, my son," said the doctor a few days later. "One hour more and I couldn't have saved your mother."

THE LOST SKATES

One afternoon Jimmie was sitting on the front porch, thinking about his lost skates. He was thinking about them because down the street, near the corner, a little boy was skating back and forth. Watching this boy had made Jimmie think about his own skates.

The boy at the corner went slowly and uncertainly up and down. He seemed to be just learning to skate. Occasionally he tumbled, but most of the time he got along quite well.

As he came close, Jimmie was surprised to see that the boy's skates looked quite new.

"They are very much like mine," thought Jimmie. Just then the boy skated past him.

"They are just like mine," thought Jimmie. Then, when the boy skated past again, Jimmie saw, printed on the straps, the word *Jimmie.*

"Why, they *are* mine!" shouted Jimmie.

He stepped in front of the boy. "Where did you get my skates?" he demanded.

The little boy stared at him with round, frightened eyes. "They're not your skates," he said. "They're mine. The junkman gave them to me."

"I don't care who gave them to you," said Jimmie crossly. "They are mine. What's your name?"

"Stephen."

"Well! See! My name is Jimmie, and here it is, right here, where I printed it myself—*Jimmie.* So they *are* mine!"

The little boy looked worried. "The junkman gave them to

me. He found them in the gutter where they had been thrown away."

"They must have rolled down the walk when I took them off," said Jimmie, recalling that day when he had fallen and hurt his cheek. "Well, anyway, I didn't throw them away. And they are mine. Give them to me!"

The little boy sat down and began to tug obediently at the straps. "I guess you're right," he said. "They must be yours."

Jimmie took the skates and ran home. At his own doorstep he looked back. The boy was still sitting where Jimmie had left him, but now he was leaning over, his head on his arms, crying.

Jimmie had thought he would be perfectly happy to have his skates back again. He had been so sorry to lose them, and he had hunted high and low for them!

But he couldn't help thinking about that little boy. He kept remembering how he had looked, hunched over there on the sidewalk with his head down, crying. Jimmie thought so hard about it that he couldn't enjoy his dinner.

As he was getting ready for bed, he suddenly made up his mind. He slipped his bathrobe over his pajamas and went downstairs into the living room where his mother and daddy were.

"I want to talk to you," said Jimmie.

"Why, what is it, son?" asked his mother.

Then Jimmie told them about the boy who had been skating at the corner that afternoon. He told them how the boy looked—so small and shabby, and how he had put his head down and cried.

"And I think," said Jimmie, at last, "that if you don't mind, Mother, I'll give the skates back to him. He really believed they were his, and somehow it doesn't seem right to take them away, just because the junkman made a mistake and thought they had been thrown away, there in the gutter."

"I think you are right," said his mother. "And I'll tell you something else I think"—and she kissed him—"I think you are a good boy."

And next morning Jimmie and his mother drove over to the little house by the railroad tracks and gave Stephen the wonderful skates to keep for his very own. Stephen was happy—and so was Jimmie!

—J. C. Nolan.

The Discontented Pumpkin

Jack Frost visited Farmer Crane's field one night, and the next morning the gold of the pumpkins shone more brilliantly than ever through their silver coverings.

"It is of no use," said one large pumpkin to another lying beside it. "It is of no use. I was never made to be cut up for pumpkin pie. I feel sure I was put here for something higher."

"Why, what do you mean?" said the other. "You never seemed dissatisfied before. You quite take my breath away. To tell the truth, I do not like the thought of being made for anything but pies. Do tell me of what other use can one be."

"Well, I have always thought that I am not like the other pumpkins in this field, and when Farmer Crane pointed me out the other day as the finest one he had, I heard him say, 'A fine one it would be for a fair.' It was not till then that I really knew for what I was intended."

"I do remember," answered the other. "Yes, I do remember hearing about some pumpkins being taken to a county fair once, but I never heard how they liked it. As for myself, I should be pleased to be made into delicious pies and served on a beautiful plate."

"Why, how can you be satisfied with that thought? But there is Farmer Crane now. He is gathering some of the smaller pumpkins to make pies with, I think."

"Perhaps he knows best what we were made for," answered one to the other.

"What fine pies they will make," said Farmer Crane. "I had better take them now, I think," and they were all quickly added to the golden heap already in the wagon.

How happy they all were—all but one that lay on the top of the large pile.

"How hard it is to be thrown in with these ordinary pumpkins. If I could only slip off by myself. Perhaps there is a place at the bottom of the wagon where I can be alone."

It was a long way from the top of the pile to the bed of the wagon, but it was very little trouble to slip away from the rest. It would take only a second, and then it would be away from the others. But alas, the discontented pumpkin slipped a little too far and soon lay on the frozen ground, a shattered heap.

"Dear me!" said the pumpkins in one breath, "see that fine fellow has slipped off and is broken to pieces. What a feast the cows and pigs will have."

"It is too bad," said one. "He was so anxious to be taken to the fair. It is always better to be contented."

As Cross As a Bear

"You're as cross as a bear," said Bess to Billy.

Uncle Jim whistled. "Bears aren't cross to members of their own family," he said. "Now, I knew a bear once—"

Bess and Billy both ran to him and climbed up on his lap.

"Did you really ever know a bear?" cried Billy, with wide-open eyes.

"Well, not intimately," said Uncle Jim, "but I used to go hunting them when I was up in Canada. One day I was out with a hunting party, and we saw right straight in front of us—what do you suppose?"

"A real bear!" gasped the children in concert.

"Yes, a real mother bear and her little cub. The dogs started after them, and the mother bear began to run, but the little baby bear couldn't run as fast as she did, and the dogs were gaining on him, so what do you suppose the mother bear did? Leave baby bear behind! No sir-ee-ee! She picked the little bear up on her stout nose and tossed him way ahead; then she ran fast and caught up to him and gave him another boost that sent him flying through the air. She kept this up for a mile and a half. Then she was too tired to go any farther, and the dogs surrounded her. She sat up on her haunches, took her baby in her hind paws, and fought the dogs off with her fore paws, and how she did roar!"

"You could hear mother bear miles away. She never forgot her baby, kept guarding him all the time. That's the way the bears stand by each other."

"Billy," said Bess, "you're as good—as good as a bear!"

Then they all laughed together and forgot what they had been cross about.

WORD OF WISDOM

When my appendix was removed, it had burst, and blood poisoning, so they said, in the third and last stage, had set in. There were nine doctors present, and eight said I had to die. The chief surgeon in the hospital turned to President Joseph F. Smith and said, "Mr. Smith, you need not think of such a possibility or probability as that this man shall live. Why, if he should live it would be a miracle, and this is not the day of miracles."

That was the message delivered to me by Joseph F. Smith himself during his last sickness, and he said: "Our doctor friend who said it would be a miracle has passed away. I never saw you looking healthier in my life than you do today, Heber."

I said to the nurse who told me regarding these nine doctors that I did not want to meet any of them, except the one who said and believed that I would pull through. She said, "He is the house doctor; I will call him in."

I asked him why he disagreed with the others, and he smiled (he was a southerner), and he said, "Mistah Grant, ah just took a chance, suh. Ah have felt the pulse, suh, of thousands of patients, being a house doctor, in many, many hospitals, but ah never felt a pulse just like yours, suh. Why, do you know, suh, in all of the tests that I made during an hour and three-quarters that you were under the knife, your heart neveh missed one single, solitary beat, and ah made up my mind that that heart would pull you through."

What kind of heart did I have? I had a heart that had pure blood in it, that was not contaminated by tea, coffee, or liquor.

—President Heber J. Grant.

Antonio's Parakeets

From across the lake, the island of Janitzio looked like a little hill that had just nudged its way out of Lake Patscuaro. From halfway across the lake it looked as if it had been there for a long time. There was a church; one large, beautiful house; and many little, low, flat-topped houses that looked like mushrooms which had sprung up on the beach and were almost tumbling over each other.

On this particular day all the people on the island were preparing to go to market. Canoes made from large logs were pushed down to the beach, and men, women, and children, loaded down with many different kinds of things to sell, were climbing into them. Some had pottery, some had rugs made from grasses, some had vegetables or chickens, and one woman even had a little pig tied up in a gunny sack.

The only person on the island that wasn't busy was Antonio, who just sat on the beach wiggling his toes in the sand. On his lap he held a basket with two little parakeets in it; and while they scolded and scolded, he didn't pay any attention to them at all. He didn't even notice when a big wave washed up on the shore and got his pants wet. Nothing seemed to matter to him until his mother called and said, "Come, Antonio, Señor Romero is waiting."

Then Antonio got up, kicked the sand off his toes, put both arms around the basket and held his little birds, and went and got into the canoe. All the way across the lake he didn't say a word.

When they reached the other side, his mother put her arm around him and said, "You feel very bad about selling your parakeets, do you not, Antonio?"

Antonio didn't want his mother to know how he felt. She could not help it that they did not have enough money. Every morning she got up long before Antonio's eyes were open, and she worked until late every night making doilies to sell in Patscuaro; but these did not bring enough to pay for the little house they lived in and to buy beans and rice too. Of course, Antonio felt very sad about selling his little birds. They were the last thing Papa had given him before he went away. He told him when he left to keep them safe until he came back; but, of course, Mamacita did not know about that. Antonio smiled bravely as he spoke, but Mamacita noticed that a tear would have trickled down his cheek if he had not wiped it away very quickly.

"I do not mind if I have to sell my parakeets if only you will not have to work so hard to make doilies."

Mamacita drew Antonio very close to her for a minute, and then hand in hand they started toward the busiest section of Patscuaro. There they saw all of their neighbors with their wares spread out before them on the sidewalk. Antonio was very glad that he had come. Market day was a holiday to the people in Janitzio. Men and women were dressed in their brightest colors, and all the while they were calling their wares to the passersby, they were laughing and talking with each other. Boys and girls were running to and fro, eating whatever they could buy with their centavos. Some had mangos, some bananas, some tortillas, while others had candy made from goats' milk that they brought in a tiny, round wooden box, and which they ate with a stick broken from the lid.

Soon his mother found a nice spot next to one of her friends. Carefully, she laid her doilies upon a paper while she spread out a clean cloth upon the sidewalk and then placed them upon it so that the people that passed could see all of the different designs she had. Antonio did not stay near his mother. He went about a half block away and sat down in the warm sunshine with his back up against one of the buildings and with his basket of parakeets between his legs. When anyone passed by he would call out, "Want to buy parakeets, Señor? Want to buy parakeets?"

But no one paid any attention to him until the Americano who lived in the one beautiful house in Janitzio stopped by and said, "Hello, Antonio. Why do you want to sell your parakeets? I thought your papa had given them to you and that you wanted to keep them until he came back."

"Oh, yes, Señor, I would like to keep them; but, you see, we do not have enough money since Papa went away, and so I must sell the parakeets to buy beans and rice."

"Oh," said the Americano. "How much do you want for them?"

"You want to buy the parakeets, Señor?"

"Yes, Antonio. I have a little friend I would like to give them to."

"I will sell them to you for one peso, Señor."

"I will give you two pesos, Antonio," said the Americano as he pressed two shiny Mexican dollars into Antonio's hand and took the parakeets away.

Antonio forgot to be happy about the extra money as he watched the Americano pick up the basket and walk away with his own little birds. He could not even eat the cactus candy he had bought. He wished Mamacita would hurry and sell her doilies and that Señor Romero would sell the things he brought so they could go home; but it was not until the rosy light of sunset was blended with the deep blue of the lake that Antonio and his mother climbed into the canoe, and it was almost dark when they walked up the beach toward their house. Even before they got there, they saw a man by their door, but they could not see who it was until he came toward them holding a basket.

"Antonio," he said, "I have brought you a little present."

Antonio could hardly believe his eyes, for the Americano held out to him the basket that held his very own parakeets.

"But, Señor," he said, "I thought you bought these for a little friend."

"And so I did, Antonio, so he could keep them until his father came home."

"But why, Señor, why do you do this for me?"

"Antonio," he said, "your father is in the army—the Mexican army; my son is in the army—the American army. Together they are trying to bring happiness back into the world. Do you not think that we should work together to bring happiness to each other here at home while they are gone? I am lonesome for my son. Would you and your mother like to come and live in the beautiful house on the hill while your father is away? Your mother could clean the house and do the cooking, and she would not have to work so hard making doilies; and you could be my son and carry in the wood; and I would be your father and go for walks with you along the beach and even take you to Patscuaro on market day. We could bring much happiness to each other. Would you like that, Antonio?"

"Oh, yes, Señor, yes, Señor," he said, and then he looked at his mother who was smiling so happily that he knew they would be living in the one beautiful house in Janitzio.

—MARY P. PARRISH.

TRUE TO HIS IDEALS

To Cambridge, Massachusetts, the great American colleges had sent their best men, seventeen hundred in all, to compete at the Harvard Stadium, at the annual meet of the Intercollegiate Association of Amateur Athletics of America in May 1919. Creed Haymond, a Mormon boy studying to become a dentist, was captain of the Pennsylvania team. The night before the meet, Coach Lamson Robertson came to the room. He was in good spirits. In the tryouts Pennsylvania had qualified seventeen men. Cornell, her most feared rival that year, had only ten. As the scoring for the first five places in each event was five, four, three, two, one, naturally the number of men each team had in the finals greatly influenced its chance.

"Creed," Robertson said, "if we do our best tomorrow, we will run away with it."

"We're going to do our best, Robby."

The coach hesitated. "Creed, I'm having the boys take a little sherry wine tonight. I want you to have some—just a little, of course."

"I won't do it, Coach."

"But, Creed, I'm not trying to get you to drink. I know what you Mormons believe. I'm giving you this as a tonic, just to put you all on your mettle."

"It wouldn't do me any good, Robby; I can't take it."

"Remember, Creed, you're the captain of our team and our best point winner. Fourteen thousand students are looking to you personally to win this meet. If you fail us, we'll lose. I ought to know what is good for you."

Creed Haymond believed he had the best coach in the world, and with reason, for since that time Lamson Robertson was chosen head coach of the Olympic teams of 1920, 1924, and 1928. Creed knew too that other coaches felt a little wine to be useful when men have trained muscle and nerve to the snapping point. He also knew that his team needed his best efforts. He intensely wished to give them, but he looked Robertson in the eye and said, "I won't take it, Coach."

Robertson smiled a little, not a broad smile, it is true. On his grim Scots face there was a curious expression. "You're an odd fellow, Creed. You have ideas of your own. You won't take tea at the training table. Well, I'm going to let you do as you please."

He went away and left the captain of his team in a state of extreme anxiety. Supposing, Creed thought, he made a poor showing tomorrow; what could he say to Robertson? He was to go against the fastest man in the world. Nothing less than his best would do. This stubbornness of his might lose the meet for

Penn. His teammates were doing as they were told. They believed in their coach. What right had he to disobey? Only one right, one reason, this thing he had been following and believing all his life, this Word of Wisdom! But what is it anyway, something Joseph Smith thought up, or is it really a revealed message to us from God? He knelt down and earnestly, very earnestly, asked the Lord to give him a testimony as to the source of this revelation which he had believed and obeyed literally. Then he went to bed and slept the sound slumber of healthy youth.

Race Day

Next morning Coach Robertson came into the room and asked anxiously, "How are you feeling, Creed?"

"Fine," the captain answered cheerfully.

"The other fellows are vomiting. I don't know what's the matter with them," he said seriously.

"Maybe it's the tonic you gave them," Creed volunteered.

"Maybe so," Robertson answered shortly.

On that almost perfect day in late May, the Penn team entered the great Harvard Stadium entitled to full measure of confidence. The dope sheets of the coaches and others, where every man was listed and graded from past performance, gave Penn a margin over the best of the other teams. Gathered there was the flower of American athletes. Every man was known. Of the seventeen entrants Pennsylvania had qualified the day before, she counted on seven to win the meet and on others to pile up points.

Two o'clock found twenty thousand spectators in their seats.

As the events got under way, it became plain that something was wrong with the wonderful Penn team. In that beautiful race, the quarter mile, the grinding test of speed and endurance, Pennsylvania's man was figured to take second place and win four precious points. The startled Penn supporters watched the field run away from him; he came in last. In the half-mile event the intercollegiate champion of the year before was Penn's entrant. Coach Robertson's dope sheet gave him first in that event with five points. He finished fifth with one point. Two Pennsylvania men were entered in the pole vault. They were considered the classiest men in America in that picturesque event. They were expected to take first and second places and win nine points. At a height below their own records they tied for third place and won between them five points. The man entered for the high jump, confidently counted on as a point winner, did not place. The one who should have taken third in the low hurdles did not run.

The hundred-yard dash was announced. The six fastest men in the colleges of America took their places. This and the two-hundred yard to be run later were Creed Haymond's races. Penn desperately needed him to win them. Would the jinx that had been pursuing his team get the captain? In the toss-up Haymond had drawn the second lane. At his side in the first lane was Johnson of Michigan, six feet two inches tall.

"Ready!" The six sprinters crouched. Each put his fingers on the ground at the line and his right foot into the hole he had kicked for the start.

"Set!" Every nerve and muscle strained.

The pistol shot—and every man sprang forward into the air and touched earth at a run, that is, all except one, Creed

Haymond. The tall Johnson had used that second lane in the
semifinals and with a greater spread of longer legs had kicked a
hole for his toe an inch or two behind the spot Haymond had
just chosen for his. Under the tremendous thrust Creed gave,
the narrow wedge of earth broke through, and he came down
on his knees behind the line.

Probably most sprinters would have let the others go on.
No coach or crowd would expect a man to get up and make a
pitiful spectacle of himself running behind! But Creed
Haymond got up and ran behind! But man, how he did run!
His brain on fire—the school—the team—Robby—desperate,
but most hopeless at sixty yards, the last in the race—then
seeming to fly—passing the fifth man—the fourth—the
third—the second—only the tall Johnson—ahead and close to
the tape—lips away from teeth—face down in agony—heart
bursting with the strain—sweeping in whirlwind swiftness past
Johnson to victory. The timers caught the flash as he crossed
the tape and called it ten seconds flat—but no man could know
the actual speed of that running.

Through some mistake in arrangement, the semifinals of
the 220 yards were not completed until almost time to close the
meet. With the same bad break that had followed the Penn
team all day, Creed Haymond was placed in the last heat. Five
minutes after winning the one hundred, he was called to start
the final of the 220, the last event of the day. One of the other
men who had run in an earlier heat rushed up to him.

"Tell the starter, Haymond, you demand a rest before running again. You're entitled to it under the rules. I've hardly
caught my breath yet, and I ran in the heat before yours."

Creed went panting to the starter and begged for more

time. Just then the telephone rang, and the starter was ordered to begin the race. Regretfully, he called the men to their marks. Under ordinary conditions Creed would have had no fear for this race. He was probably the fastest man in the world at this distance, but he had already run three races during the afternoon, one the heart-breaking one hundred yards, and only five minutes before, the 220 semifinals!

At a high point in the grandstand Coach Lamson Robertson of Pennsylvania and Coach Tom Keens of Syracuse sat with their stopwatches in hand. The two coaches had chosen this place as the best possible one from which to get the correct time of the race.

With surprise they saw the starter order the breathless men to their marks and, standing behind them, raise his pistol; then the white puff of smoke. This time the Penn captain literally shot from his marks. What a sweet sight as almost arm to arm the runners started down the straight way. Haymond was emerging and definitely taking the lead. Would he have the stamina to hold the pace after the other run? He was sprinting away from the field. Running his race alone, unpressed by competition, the little Penn captain drove himself to the tape in a burst of speed, eight yards ahead of the nearest man. As he crossed it, both coaches, directly above him, snapped their stopwatches; they looked at them and then looked at each other almost with awe. Both watches registered twenty-one seconds flat. Penn had lost the meet. To everybody's amazement, Pennsylvania, out of seventeen entrants, had only one intercollegiate champion, Captain Creed Haymond.

Robertson laid his hand on the shoulder of the captain of his team. There was a touch of sadness in his voice. "Boy," he said, "they're not going to give you your true time. We can't help that, but it may comfort you to know that you just ran the 220 yards in the fastest time it has ever been run by any human being."

CREED'S BOYHOOD

Creed lived in Springfield, Utah, as a boy. He had a twin sister named Elma. One day Joseph J. Cannon visited with the Haymond family. He was years older than the twins. Sitting in the garden under the shade of the fruit trees, Brother Cannon and Creed and Elma made an agreement. They promised that none of them would ever use tea, coffee, tobacco, and liquor unless they all sat down and had them together.

Creed kept his promise. No doubt he would have been true to the Word of Wisdom teachings anyway, because he had faith in God and faith in himself.

He won the race. But more important than this, he won the battle with himself. He was true to himself. He kept the faith with himself and with our Father in Heaven. That was a greater victory than even his record-breaking run of the 220-yard dash.

HONESTY IS THE BEST POLICY

He was a bank errand boy, and in his home he had an invalid mother and a little sister who could not walk. The doctor had been to the home recently and had told John that unless his mother could get into the country where there was plenty of fresh air, she was going to grow worse and perhaps would be gone in the fall. So John had tried to find some way by which he could send the two away, but there seemed none at all, and his heart seemed almost ready to break as day after day his mother grew less and less strong.

One day when John was sweeping under the table in the bank, he found a roll of bills—a big roll with some treasury certificates in the pile. He picked them up and started to go to the office of the president, but he stopped. "Just think what those bills will do," he thought. "They will send Mother and Millie away for the whole summer, and then they will be well. No one knows I have them, and they don't belong to the bank. They were in the waste paper. I'm going to keep them. Finding is keeping, and they are mine." So into his pocket they went, and he finished his sweeping and started for home. But somehow the roll did not feel good. He put them into his inner pocket and then shifted them to his coat pocket. He felt sure that everyone must see them. About an hour after John had gone home, he came back to the bank, knocked for admittance, and went to the office of the president. He threw the bills on the desk, saying, "I found them while I swept," and then with a cry of pain, ran from the bank.

Next morning John was there at work, and after the bank had opened he was called to the president's room. "John," said the president, "I wish you would tell me why you brought those bills back last night. I know why you wanted them, and what they would have done at home. We didn't know you had them. Why did you bring them back?"

Away over the desk leaned John, and looking straight into the eyes of the man, he said, "Sir, as long as I live, I have to live with myself, and I don't want to live with a thief." A few days later the mother and Millie went to the country. But they did not go alone; John went with them for the whole summer, the appreciation of the bank for his nobility.

THE BIG AMERICAN

I saw the big American, elegant in clothes designed for traveling and wearing a peculiarly un-English hat, emerge from Birmingham's busy station in New Street, look around, take a firmer hold on his beautiful leather grip, and then walk briskly up towards the cathedral and the bus station.

At the foot of the hill called Temple Street, he stopped. I stopped too, for I, like the American, had seen the urchin. He was a lad of perhaps thirteen, with the thin, undernourished look of a city sparrow, and hair which badly needed cutting. His thin body was stooping like a flower stem over the enormous suitcase, abjectly tied with dirty string, which he was endeavoring to lug up the hill.

He saw the big American watching him and flushed beneath the dirt on his young, eager face, then he bent himself more earnestly to his task as though to fiercely discount any thought that it might be too much for him.

The big American spoke in a way which suggested that he often carried broken old suitcases tied with dirty string through the more fashionable parts of town, making quite a hobby of it, in fact. He said: "I'm rather good at carrying these things, son. I'm gonna help you. Seems like it's a two-man job." He was superbly offhand.

There was some sort of protest waiting to be born on the

lips of the boy, but it was stillborn. He grinned hugely, as the immaculately gloved hand relieved his of a part of the string, and the battered old suitcase was swung between them.

They walked up Temple Street together. The boy, shy at first, began to respond to the novelty of the situation.

"You're one of those Yanks, aren't you, sir?" he said.

"Guess I am."

"Yes, I thought so."

The big American smiled. He caught the implication.

Once they stopped to change hands, then the tan shoes stamped "New York" were in step again beside the boots with broken backs, whose only stamp was that of aching poverty. Amused glances followed them as they bore their strange burden toward the cathedral. The policeman on point duty gravely saluted them as they passed, but they never saw him. It seemed as if suddenly theirs was a man-sized conversation and, together with the large suitcase, needed all their attention. The boy's face was animated, and he laughed. The big American's eyes laughed too, although he maintained a becoming gravity, and they came to the top of the hill.

I saw the boy draw a torn shirt sleeve across his perspiring face.

"This is where I get my bus, mister. Thank you for coming with me."

"That's all right, son. You know I appreciate it a whole lot, your helping me up the hill with this suitcase. It is sure a weight!"

A pair of perplexed English eyes searched those of the big American for some trace of good-natured teasing but found none.

"I didn't help you, sir! You helped me."

"Listen, son, didn't you walk up that hill beside me?"

"Yes—of course . . ."

"And didn't you hold one-half of the string?"

"Why . . . yes . . ."

"Well, then—what am I telling you? And when anyone is kind enough to help me up a hill like this one with a grip of this size, I guess I like to show my appreciation some way!"

The boy really did try to impress this unusual American with his innate English logic. It was quite simple really. The suitcase was his, the obligation his alone. The big American was enjoying himself immensely. He insisted upon the appreciation—it clinked into the boy's pocket—and the boy became speechless.

He went away, and a moment before he turned the corner, he looked back to wave to the big American. His young face was flushed with an uncertain delight; and if his eyes were perplexed, his smile was warm and friendly.

The big American saw me and smiled. "I guess there goes another Englishman who is trying to understand these Yanks . . . It was fun—and I guess he needed it."

And some time later, here in the once-orphaned British Mission, we toasted that "big American:" "our beloved president, Hugh B. Brown. May God bless him and restore him to our shores."

—EDITH RUSSELL.

PUT TO THE TEST

The following letter was received by the father of a young Salt Lake City soldier who was serving in the United States armed forces during World War II:

"I had a most unusual experience the other day, Dad. The colonel from area headquarters was here making an inspection of our post. Our commandant called my buddy, also from Salt Lake, and me in about noon and asked us to serve the dinner at the guest officers' table. He said he had been watching us and liked the way we did things. He especially liked our clean-cut appearance and would appreciate having us do this particular job for him.

"Well, we did it, all right! I confess we were a little bit nervous with so many brass buttons around. But we managed to get everything in the right place at the right time, and we didn't spill any soup, either. We sighed with relief when it was over, winked at each other, and turned to leave. But believe it or not, Dad, that colonel got up from the table and stopped us before we were out of the room.

"'Couldn't help but notice you fellows while I ate,' he said. 'I was so pleased that I spoke to your commander about you. He tells me that you are from Salt Lake City. By any chance do you happen to be Mormons?'

"Both of us straightened up a little bit more, I think, as we proudly said, 'Yes, we are, sir!'

"'I thought so,' he mused. 'But tell me, what do you believe anyway?'

"Here was the sixty-four-dollar question—bang—right out of the clear sky! Inwardly I shook, and my brain groped for a reply. Unconsciously, I know I uttered a little prayer, for truly I needed help.

"And then the words came. Even I was surprised to hear them, so clear and distinct. 'We believe in God, the Eternal Father, and in his Son, Jesus Christ, and in the Holy Ghost.'

"I went right on, Dad, and thanks to my Heavenly Father and my Primary teacher, who so patiently helped me years ago, I was able to repeat every word of those Articles of Faith.

"The colonel just stood and looked at me. I thought he seemed deeply impressed, but I didn't know what to expect. Then he stepped forward and put his hand on my shoulder. When he spoke, I knew that he meant every word.

"'Young man,' he said, 'if you live up to those beliefs, you needn't be afraid to go anywhere.'"

A BOY WHO DID MORE THAN WAS REQUIRED

Though the Bok family was not poor upon arriving in the United States, business proved to be very unsuccessful for the father of Edward. Gradually conditions grew worse and worse. The depth of humiliation seemed to appear when Edward and his brother found no kindling wood or coal in the bin on several mornings. The boys decided to go out in the evening with a basket and pick up what wood and coal they could find on neighboring lots, around the stores, and along the railroad. The mother insisted that this was not necessary, although deep in her heart she knew that the necessity was upon them.

"But, Mother," said Edward, "this is America, where one can do anything if it is honest. So long as we don't steal the wood or the coal, why shouldn't we get it?"

Turning away, the mother could say nothing. Her pride was hurt, but she could suggest no better plan.

Edward continued to do little jobs like this for a while, but he saw that they were adding very little to the family income. He decided that it was time for him to do more; young as he was, he must begin some sort of wage earning. But how and where could a small boy earn money?

He tried and he tried and was getting very much discouraged. One afternoon as he was walking along the street, his attention was attracted to the window of a bakery shop. The owner was placing buns and pies and tarts on display in the windows. Having placed the articles in as attractive a position as he could, he came out on the sidewalk to look at the arrangement. Edward was gazing wistfully at the window. The baker first went to the edge of the pavement, then to the right of the window, then to the left, viewing his display from all angles with pride.

"Look pretty good, don't they?" said the baker, addressing the little boy.

"They would," answered the Dutch immigrant boy, "if your window were clean."

"That's so, too," mused the baker. "Perhaps you would like to clean it for me."

"Yes, I would," was the boy's prompt reply.

It was then and there that Edward got his first job. The boy put so much energy into the task of cleaning the large window that the baker immediately arranged with him to clean it every

Tuesday and Friday afternoon after school. The salary was fifty cents a week.

One day, after he had finished the window cleaning, and while the baker was busy in the rear of the bakery, a customer came in. She waited for a minute and was about to go without being waited on when Edward ventured to ask if he might do something for her. She stated that she wanted a loaf of bread and a pie. Edward immediately wrapped these up for her. Another customer came in, and Edward sold her some current buns. As the package was being handed to the first customer, the baker was just about to enter the front part of the bakery. But seeing that Edward seemed to be satisfying the customers, he stopped just outside the door and quietly watched his little window washer. He saw how quickly and pleasantly he served the customers, and how the customers were not only satisfied but surprised and amused at the little fellow's efficiency. He thought to himself: "I believe that boy can sell more to some of those people than I can. Why, if they come in to buy a loaf of bread, he sells them the bread, but while doing it he tells them all about the buns, and the tarts, and the pies, and, first thing you know, he's sold two or three things instead of one!"

Having observed Edward for several minutes, the baker entered the front part of the bakery. He complimented the boy and offered him an extra dollar a week if he would come in afternoons and sell goods. Edward hesitated.

"I will do it," said Edward, "if you will let me carry home each evening some of the unsold rolls and buns. They get stale during the night, and they are of little use to you anyhow."

The baker agreed. Thus Edward received his first promotion. He was raised from a window washer at fifty cents a week to salesman and window washer at a dollar and a half a week.

From these small beginnings Edward Bok rose, step by step, until he became one of the best-known editors in America. His attitude toward work and toward making the most of every opportunity seems never to have changed greatly from what it was in his early days of gathering coal and of window washing.

A THRILLING EXPERIENCE

The night crept coolly and quietly up the mountainside until it completely enveloped Shield's Pass, bringing with it a feeling of loneliness and anxiety to Guy Durrant, who had arrived at that particular location just a few hours before. There were in his surroundings only two things which seemed familiar: one was the camp in front of which he was now kindling a fire, the other was the bleating of sheep which came to him faintly from a distance. The last gave him some concern since it indicated that the sheep were not entirely satisfied with their new bedding grounds and might decide to wander off in search of another.

"Wish I could've brought 'em closer to camp so I could watch 'em better," he muttered aloud while piling dry limbs upon the fire, causing it to send showers of sparks into the air as it blazed and crackled in cheerful defiance of the deepening shadows.

Everything was strangely quiet as he went about the preparation of his supper. Guy was only fourteen, and while he had spent several summers in the mountains with his father's sheep, he had rarely been left so entirely alone as at present. He regretted having allowed the camp tender to take a night off. It is quite certain he never would have agreed to such an arrangement had he known what he knew now: there were bear tracks around the spring, which was located about ten yards to the rear of the camp.

He ate his supper of fried potatoes, mutton chops, hot biscuits, butter and honey, without either satisfaction or relish. There was no denying the fact that the weird shadows cast by the trees and underbrush encircling the camp were beginning to unnerve him. He wished he had not left Barker, the dog, out there with the sheep. He even wished the sheep would continue their restless bleating, since anything which sounded familiar served to relieve the tenseness he felt. But as the night wore on, even they quieted down, leaving him nothing for companionship except the stillness and darkness of the night and his own disturbed thoughts and distorted imaginings. Realizing that he could not change his present situation, he determined to make the best of it. Removing his clothes, he crept into bed, hoping to lose himself in sleep until morning when, no doubt, all his fears and fantasies would disappear. But it wasn't as easy to go to sleep as it was to go to bed, and Guy lay shifting restlessly about until midnight before a feeling of drowsiness finally overcame him.

How long he slept before being awakened, he could not say, but suddenly he became aware of a noise as of something pushing its way toward the tent. At first he wondered if he were dreaming, but as the sound came steadily forward, he began to realize how terribly real it was. There could be little doubt as to the identity of the animal which made the wallowing, crushing sounds that, with each second, came more distinctly to his ears. If the thing were hungry, as no doubt it was, the fresh meat and honey he had in camp were almost sure to attract its attention if, indeed, it had not already done so; and if it were to rummage around in camp with him lying in bed, almost anything might happen. In desperation he reached for the large rifle tucked away under his pillow—then stopped. It would be the worst kind of folly to try shooting the animal in the dark. He would probably only succeed in wounding it, and certainly he could not hope to escape a wounded bear.

He could now hear it crowding through the willows leading to the spring, then after an interval it came pushing its way slowly up the bank and—yes, it was making directly for the tent. Guy sprang to his knees, praying fervently: "Father, help me! Help me to know what to do!" Immediately there came to him almost as clearly as though someone had spoken, "Frighten it away before it enters the camp." Leaping out of bed, he seized the rifle and, pushing its muzzle through the tent flaps, fired once, twice, three times in rapid succession. For a moment after the noise of the explosions had died away there was silence, then he heard the animal wheel and gallop precipitously away.

He did not return to bed, but as it was already growing light, he dressed himself and sat in the tent door watching "the dawn come up like thunder" in the east and gradually diffuse itself westward over the sky and landscape. When it was quite light, he went down to the spring and saw that which he had expected to see—fresh bear tracks.

Upon reaching the flock that morning, he found it badly scattered. Barker came up to him whining wistfully, then looked away down the mountainside. Following his gaze, Guy saw where two yearlings had been killed, one lying with its side ripped completely open, from the other an entire hind quarter was missing. These were unmistakable signs of bear. Guy regretted the loss of the two sheep but felt very thankful that nothing of a more serious nature had occurred.

—SILAS L. CHENEY.

TO WHOM SHALL WE GIVE THANKS?

It was a warm summer day, but because Bobby's new birthday ball was such a beautiful bouncer, he could not wait until the cool of the evening to play with it. He tossed and bounced it until he was tired. He sat down in the shade of a tree to rest. Then he felt so thirsty that he hurried to the water tap for a drink. He felt so grateful for that good, refreshing drink that he just couldn't help saying right out loud, "Thank you, old Tap, for a good drink of water."

"Don't thank me," replied the old water tap. "The next time you pass Canyon Reservoir, thank him. He gives me the water which I give to you."

Not many days later Bobby rode in the car with his daddy past the canyon reservoir. It seemed about ready to burst, it was so full of drinks of water.

"Oh, thank you, Canyon Reservoir," Bobby remembered to say, "for the good water you give us."

"Ha, ha," laughed the Reservoir. "I'm not the one to thank. Go find Snowbank high up on the mountain. He is the fellow who gives the water to me."

"I'll never be able to climb to the mountaintop to say thanks to Snowbank," sighed Bobby.

But Bobby climbed up to the mountain one day and said, "Thank you," to Snowbank for the water. And Snowbank said, "Don't thank me; thank Sun, for it is Sun that changed the snow into drops of water."

And when Bobby went to say, "Thank you," to Sun, what do you think Sun said to him?

"Thank the One who made me. Do you know whom to thank then for a drink of water?"

"Oh, yes," quickly replied the little boy, "it's our Father in Heaven who gives me the water to drink." And Bobby thanked our Father in Heaven.

> Thanks to our Father, let us sing,
> For he gives us everything.

—SELECTED.

WEE BEE BABY BEAR AND THE LITTLE FOXES

Papa and Mama Bear and Wee Bee Baby Bear finished eating their porridge. It was very good porridge, and they ate every spoonful of it.

Then Papa Bear sat down in his big fat armchair, put his spectacles on his nose so he could see through them just right, and started to read the newspaper.

"Why, listen to this, Mama," he said, "Mr. and Mrs. Reddy

Fox announce the arrival of a new family: two baby girls and two baby boys, born yesterday, and all are doing fine."

"Well, well," said Mama Bear, as she dried the last dish carefully and put it in the cupboard. "Well, well," she said again as she shook the crumbs from the red tablecloth outside so the little birds of the woods could pick them up for their dinner.

"Let me go see Baby Foxes, please, please," cried Wee Bee Baby Bear, clapping her furry little black paws and hopping joyously about.

"Yes, you shall go see them," Mama Bear said, "but first I must make a present for the new babies. You remember the cute little nightgown Mrs. Reddy brought Baby Bee, don't you, Papa? The yellow one with purple huckleberries painted on it?"

"Yes, indeed," answered Papa Bear, "a very nice nightie and a good reminder too, for every morning when Baby Bee gets up, and I see those huckleberries, I remember to get my pail and trot over to the patch and get some for dinner."

"I will make the baby foxes some nice, warm mittens," Mama Bear said, "because even if it is warm now, they will need them later on. Foxes have such a strange way of staying awake all winter and running about in the snow hunting for food instead of going to bed and sleeping the cold months away as we do."

"Yes, I just can't understand some people's foolish notions," said Papa Bear, scratching his head. "Well, I must go get the berries for dinner, or Growly Grizzley will beat me to them."

"Please may I go, Papa Bear?" cried Wee Bee Baby Bear, and before Papa Bear could answer, she had her little pink dinner pail to put her berries in and was tying her little blue sunbonnet under her chin.

Mama Bear put on a clean apron and sat down in her soft, middle-sized chair with her basket of yarn and knitting needles, ready to start on the mittens when they left.

Papa Bear and Wee Bee Baby Bear stopped just a moment to sharpen their claws on the trunk of a big old pine tree and to sniff the fresh morning air, then hurried to the berry patch and picked and ate and ate and picked until all their buckets and tummies were full of ripe, juicy huckleberries.

Next day when Mama Bear had the mittens all finished, she took Baby Bee through the woods to Reddy Fox's home.

Mrs. Reddy was very glad to see her visitors and gave Mama Bear her biggest, softest chair with a flowered cushion on it.

Mama Bear gave her the little parcels tied in pink and blue ribbons. Mrs. Reddy untied them, carefully saving all the ribbons, and held up two pairs of soft, little pink mittens for the girls and two pairs of soft blue mittens for the boys and said, "Oh, thank you, thank you very much. They are so lovely, and my children will get so much good out of them next winter."

Then Mama Bear and Mrs. Reddy talked and talked about all the things friendly ladies do talk about, and Wee Bee sat very still and kept looking at the baby foxes, then at Mother Bear and then at Mrs. Reddy. She wanted to hold those cuddly little babies more than anything she could think of, but she was afraid to ask if she might. So while the ladies talked and talked, she just sat and wanted and wanted and wanted to hold those babies.

Old Mr. Sun hid his face behind the mountains, and the purple shadows crept farther and farther down over the pine forest. Then Mama Bear looked out and said, "Oh, good gracious, I didn't know it was so late. I must hurry home this minute and get supper. What will Papa Bear say?"

They put on their bonnets and hurried through the woods, but all the way Baby Bear was thinking. "I wanted to hold a baby, and I didn't get to. I never have held a baby, and I want to so much."

She felt so very sad that when she went to bed she was still thinking about it.

Next morning she had an idea. She was very careful to keep her little red dress clean and not spill jam on it as she sometimes did after breakfast. She put her sunbonnet on and went out to pick flowers.

"Don't go too far," Mama Bear called, but Wee Bee hardly heard her because she was thinking that if she picked a beautiful bouquet of flowers and gave it to Mrs. Reddy Fox, perhaps she would let her hold one of the babies, very carefully, for just a minute.

When she had picked all the flowers she could hold, she ran as fast as she could through the forest until she came to Reddy Fox's home. Then she became rather frightened because it was the first time she had ever gone visiting without asking Mama Bear's or Papa Bear's consent.

She knocked timidly on the door. There was no answer, but her heart almost stopped, for from the bedroom came alarming sounds. All four baby foxes were screaming their loudest. She knocked on the door as hard as she could. Still there was no answer; so she opened the door and went in. Mr. and Mrs. Reddy were nowhere in sight, and how their children were crying! "There, there now. Not so much noise," said Wee Bee, trying to sound exactly like Grandma Bear when she and her cousins were too noisy. She felt quite grown up now that she was alone with the full care of the babies. Very carefully she picked up the first baby and sat down in Mrs. Reddy's rocking chair. She rocked and patted the baby softly with her furry little paw and sang, "Rock-a-bye-Baby," and in just no time that baby was happy and sound asleep, even before the teardrops had dried on his fuzzy little cheeks. She laid him down and took the next one and did the same until she had the last baby fast asleep. But he was so cuddly and sweet, she just rocked and sang and rocked until all at once she heard Mama Bear just outside the door saying, "Oh, dear, I've run most all the way here. I've lost Wee Bee, and I'm so frightened. Have you seen her?"

And Mrs. Reddy, who was almost to the house answered, "No, I haven't. I had to help Mr. Reddy catch something for dinner and did not expect to be gone so long. I'm worried about leaving the children alone all this time. Come in and rest. You are out of breath."

They were at the door before Wee Bee could move. She was very frightened because she thought perhaps Mrs. Reddy would be cross because she had come into her house when she was not home. But when Mrs. Reddy saw how well she had taken care of the babies, she gave her a big piece of comb honey and told her she would send for her to tend the babies when she needed help again.

—GENEVA H. WILLIAMS.

PERSEVERANCE

Heber J. Grant firmly believed the motto, "He can who thinks he can." His whole life consisted of a series of episodes in which he proved to himself, and to others, that he could do what he made up his mind to do. He performed no brilliant, sudden miracles, but he showed people what work, tenacity, and perseverance could do.

As a boy he was never much of a student, because he used to have very severe headaches. These were caused by his eyes, and they made him indifferent to school. In writing, particularly, he was backward. One time he discovered that his classmates were laughing at his writing. So he resolved to excel them all. Then he began to write, and headache or not, he never quit practicing until his vow was fulfilled to the letter, and he became one of the best penmen in the state. Any of you who have seen the signature of President Heber J. Grant can see what his tenacity did for him.

On another occasion he was taunted because he couldn't play baseball. He practiced from that day on until he became good enough to play on the Red Stockings team. His team won the territorial championship.

Moreover, when he was a young boy, he once told Bishop Woolley that as soon as he grew up he would build a house for his mother. The bishop laughed. From that time on Heber planned to fulfill that dream. When he was twenty-one he built the home, and the first guest who came to the house at President Grant's invitation was Bishop Woolley.

No wonder President Heber J. Grant was a firm believer in the well-known statement: "That which we persist in doing becomes easier to do—not that the nature of the thing has changed, but that our ability to do so has increased."

TWINK

Twink sat polishing the runners on his new sled. It really wasn't a very good sled, but to Twink it was the best sled in the world, and he was happy. His eyes sparkled, and his lips were whistling a cheerful little tune. The strange part about it was Twink didn't have so much to be happy about as a great many children. He lived in a little three-room house that was very much in need of paint. His sweater was darned and re-darned at the elbows. His shoes had been halfsoled twice already and were almost ready for another half sole. He didn't have a mother at home very much of the time, with whom he could talk and chat. His mother worked in an overall factory, and so she left the house before Twink went to school in the morning and didn't get home until long after Twink came home in the afternoon. Still, he was happy, and it seemed that everybody loved Twink and liked to have him around.

Suddenly Twink stopped whistling and listened. Then he ran to the window and looked out. Sure enough, Mr. Lee's car, that is, what you could see of his car, stopped in front of Twink's house. You see, the gang, Twink's gang, was going coasting, so Mr. Lee's car was almost hidden by sleds and boys.

Twink picked up his sled, shut the drafts on the stove so the fire wouldn't go out before his mother got home, and ran toward the car. Mr. Lee helped Twink tie his sled on the bumper, then they both squoze in the front seat and away they all went.

They couldn't drive very fast because the roads were slippery. Then too a great deal of the time they were going up hill. The place where Mr. Lee was taking the boys coasting was up on the foothills, where there was a steep hill that was well packed with snow. Finally, however, they arrived. Out of the car the boys scrambled, yelling and exclaiming, "Boy, this is the best yet! Can't we go whooping down that hill!" Then each one hurriedly untied his sled from the car and before you could say, "Jack Robinson!" down the hill they went, whooping and calling and laughing as the cold snow flew into their faces. When they arrived at the bottom, up they jumped from their sleds and after puffing and panting up the hill, down they went again, lickity-split.

But they had not been coasting very long when suddenly Twink went flying in the air; then he lit in the snow, rolled for a few minutes, and lay very still, while his sled turned over and landed at the foot of the hill. Mr. Lee and the boys hurried toward Twink, calling, "Are you hurt, Twink? Are you badly hurt?"

For a moment Twink didn't answer. His shoulder hurt, and it seemed his head was whirling 'round and 'round. "I'll just lie here a moment," thought Twink, "and get my breath." Then he heard Mr. Lee calling, "Are you hurt, Twink? Are you hurt?"

"I must answer them," thought Twink. "I wouldn't worry Mr. Lee for the world. He was swell to bring us up here." So Twink mustered up a smile and, sitting up in the snow, said just as Mr. Lee reached him, "Naw, I'm not hurt; I just had sort of a jolt. I'm fine. Say, I look just like a snowman, don't I?"

"You certainly do look like a snowman, young man," said Mr. Lee. "Here, let me brush you off. Sure you're not hurt?"

"Naw," said Twink, though his shoulder still pained. "I feel fine. Think I'll go see how my sled looks."

When Twink saw his sled, for a minute Mr. Lee thought Twink was going to cry, but only for a minute. Twink thought he was going to cry too. There lay his sled, ruined. One runner was bent and twisted; the other runner was broken in two; one of the top boards was splintered and the steering stick was gone. It was the only sled Twink had ever had, and he had waited and waited for it. He knew his mother had skimped to get it for him, and he'd only had it since Christmas. But somehow Twink managed not to cry. Instead, he said, "Well, I surely wrecked that, didn't I?" and then he started to pick up the pieces.

All the boys felt sorry for Twink. They offered to let him take turns on their sleds. For a little while Twink did, but every time he took a ride one of the other boys had to wait, and he hated to have the other fellows wait. His shoulder hurt too, for he had bruised it pretty badly, but Twink made up his mind he wasn't going to spoil the fun for others because his good time had been ruined. At first he whistled all the merry tunes he knew, then he heard someone say it was getting cold, so he decided to scout around and see if he could find some wood to make a bonfire. He walked a little way, and under a huge stone ledge, protected from wind and snow, he found a lot of little sticks and a good-sized log. He piled the little sticks together in wigwam fashion; then he went back to Mr. Lee and borrowed a match. He told Mr. Lee that when he meowed three times like a cat that would be a sign there was a good bonfire going, and all the boys could come over and get warm. It wasn't long before Mr. Lee heard the signal. Immediately the boys hurried to the bonfire. My, it felt good! They warmed their backs and their hands and their toes while Mr. Lee told them about a huge black bear he once killed on that very mountainside. Then the fire burned low, and it began to get dark, so they all piled into the car and sang funny songs as they rode home.

Twink was the first one to get out of the car. He untied the pieces of his sled from the bumper and, saying goodnight, went into the house. No one really knew how discouraged and unhappy Twink felt. He wanted to cry but knew if he did that it would only make his mother feel bad too, so he went into the house whistling as though nothing had happened.

But Mr. Lee knew how Twink felt about his broken sled, so when Twink left the car, Mr. Lee said, "How many of you boys can keep a secret?"

"I can!"

"We all can," came the replies.

"Yes," said Mr. Lee, "you're a bunch of fine fellows. I think I can trust every one of you, so I'm going to tell you about Twink."

"Twink hasn't had it as nice as most of you fellows. When he was just a little boy, his father died and left his mother to care for him and his grandmother.

"When Twink was a little fellow, he was always laughing and cheerful, and his big blue eyes twinkled with fun. At first his father and mother called him Twinkle, and then as he grew older, they called him Twink.

"Some boys, if they had broken their new sleds, would have spoiled the party with their groaning and grumbling, but not Twink. Instead he thought of something nice to do for the rest of us. So I was wondering if we couldn't think of something nice to do for him."

For a moment the boys were silent, then Larry exclaimed, "Why couldn't we all put in a quarter and buy Twink a new sled?"

"That's exactly what I was thinking," said Mr. Lee. "What do you other boys think about it?"

Mr. Lee really needn't have asked, for all the boys' faces were happy and bright, and they were all excitedly discussing what kind of sled would be the nicest.

Each boy liked a different kind of sled. Allen, Mr. Lee's son, suddenly exclaimed, "Say, Dad, couldn't you get us one wholesale?"

"Of course I could," replied Mr. Lee. "Shall I do it, boys?"

"Yes," they all answered.

Mr. Lee drove on while the boys kept talking excitedly. When he stopped in front of Dee Hartley's place, he said, "You know, boys, I was wondering if it wouldn't be more fun if we kept this a secret. You know, not tell anyone we're going to buy it and not even tell Twink where it came from!"

"That would be fun!" exclaimed Max Arnold. "Let's not tell anyone."

"Do you think you boys could keep it a secret?" asked Mr. Lee.

"Of course we could," they answered, a little indignant at Mr. Lee for asking such a question.

"All right then," said Mr. Lee, "you boys all come to my house tomorrow at seven in the evening, and I'll see that the sled is there."

The next evening all the boys arrived at Mr. Lee's. They put their money into a little dish on the table and then fell to examining the sled Mr. Lee had bought. It was a dandy sled. The boys were all tickled with it. Then one of them said, "Let's write a card to put on it."

"Very well," said Mr. Lee, "but what shall we say?"

Since no one could decide, Mr. Lee passed them each a card and a pencil and said, "Each one of you write something, then we'll choose the best."

Finally all the cards were finished. One said, "To a swell fellow." Another said, "To a good sport." A third one read, "To a boy who is always cheerful." Still another said, "To the best fellow in our gang."

When that one was read, someone said, "Oh, that won't do. That one would let him know who sent it."

"Well," said Mr. Lee, "we all know now what we would like to say to Twink, so let's not send any of the cards. Let's just put the sled in his doorway with a typewritten card that says, 'For Twink,' then he'll never guess who sent it, and our secret will always be a secret."

The boys thought Mr. Lee's card was best, so after attaching the card to the sled, they all piled into Mr. Lee's car and took the sled to Twink's.

And Twink, though he tried to guess, and came pretty close to guessing, never knew who left the sled which he found on his porch one winter night, for not one of the boys ever told.

—THELMA J. HARRISON.

ABD-EL-KADIR

G o, my son, I consign thee to God," said the mother of Abd-el-Kadir, after giving him forty pieces of silver and making him promise never to tell a lie. "We may not meet again until the day of judgment."

The boy left home to seek his fortune, but in a few days the party with which he traveled was attacked by robbers.

"What money have you with you?" asked one.

"Forty dinars are sewed up in my garment," replied Abd-el-Kadir, but the robber only laughed.

"What money have you really with you?" inquired another, sternly, and the youth repeated his former answer; but no attention was paid to his statement, which was not believed on account of its frankness.

"Come here, boy," called the chief who had noticed the men talking with the young traveler. "What money have you in your possession?"

"I have told two of your men already, that I have forty dinars sewed up in my clothes, but they do not believe me."

"Rip his garments open," commanded the chief of the robbers. And soon the silver was found.

"And how came you to tell this?" he was asked.

"Because I would not be false to my mother, to whom I promised never to tell a lie."

"Boy," said the leader, "are you so mindful of your duty to your mother, although so young, and am I insensible, at my mature age, of the duty I owe to God? Give me your hand, that I may swear repentance upon it."

He did so, and his followers were greatly impressed. "You

have been our leader in guilt," said his lieutenant. "Be mine at least in the path of virtue." And he took the boy's hand as the chief had done. One by one all the rest of the band did the same.

ONE NICKEL'S AS GOOD AS ANOTHER

Tina danced down her grandmother's front walk. In her yellow dress she looked like a splash of sunshine between the tall, dark cedars. On her glossy brown curls a new yellow ribbon poised like a yellow butterfly. Her chubby fist closed tightly on a handkerchief and two nickels. Grandmother had given her the nickels and helped her tie them in the corner of her "handky."

"Don't you lose them, dearie." How kind and sweet Grandma's eyes were. She was always doing acts of thoughtfulness. Tina threw her arms about her neck and kissed her hard on the cheek.

"Thank you, Grandma, thank you. I won't lose them." And she turned with a cheerful little skip, waving her hand that held the handkerchief.

Think how rich she was! *Two* nickels at the same time. Even one nickel would buy a candy bar, or two oranges, even three bananas if the bananas were soft. Tina liked good things to eat, especially if they were sweet things. She could get five all-day suckers for a nickel. With effort she pushed that thought from her mind.

There was a doll at Schabel's store for ten cents. Two nickels made just ten cents! To be sure it was a tiny doll, but that was the very kind she wanted. It was just big enough, and she'd sew it such pretty things from scraps of silk. It would be lovely! Tina sighed happily.

When she got home, Tina ran into the kitchen, climbed on a chair, and threw her handkerchief, money and all, upon the topmost shelf. "It'll never get lost there," she thought as she jumped down and ran to wash for supper.

The next morning Tina's father was going to town, and he had promised that she might go along.

"Did anyone see my two nickels?" she called, for she had forgotten where she had placed them.

"Here are two I found in the front hall." Her mother held up a handkerchief. "Are these yours?"

"Yes." Tina grabbed them and flew out of the front door to meet her father, who had driven out the car.

She and her father talked as they rode along, so Tina did not think much about the nickels. When she got out of the car, she looked closely at the handkerchief. It was not hers. There was lace on the edge of it. The nickels were not hers either, because there was no buffalo with his head down and his back up as there had been on hers. No, these nickels were not hers. She pushed them uneasily into her pocket. She went into the store and looked at the doll. If she could only find her father, she would trade these nickels for a dime, but she didn't think that was right either.

After having waited on other customers, Mr. Schabel asked her what she wanted. She pointed to the doll. Once it was in her hand, she just couldn't let the dolly go.

"That will be ten cents," said Mr. Schabel patiently.

Tina turned red, grabbed the handkerchief from her pocket, and threw it down quickly on the counter as if it burned her. Then she turned to run because she did not want even the handkerchief that did not belong to her. The dolly seemed smaller than it had looked in the case.

As soon as she saw her mother's face, she knew something was wrong and that she was part of it.

"Why did you take Lucy's nickels and say they were yours?"

"I thought they were mine until I looked at them."

"Then you brought them home again?"

"No. I—I bought a doll with them." Tina's throat hurt, and she couldn't look up into her mother's eyes. "One nickel's as good as another."

"But where are your nickels? Lucy went to school crying because you had taken the money she had put by her books to take to school for the Junior Red Cross."

"I'm sorry, Mother."

"You'll have to be more than sorry. Unless you find your nickels before noon, you'll have to take your doll back to the store and get Lucy's money for her."

The very thought of taking the doll back to the store made Tina ill. She tried and tried to remember where she had put her nickels. The harder she thought, the worse the pain became in her stomach.

Raisins sometimes helped such a pain. Tina stood on a chair and reached for the top cupboard shelf. She tipped the raisin package. Her own handkerchief, nickels and all, tumbled right into her upturned face.

"Here are my nickels, Mother," she shouted, just saving herself from falling.

"Of all the places to put a handkerchief. In the raisin package!"

"I think maybe it was just by it," Tina explained humbly.

"I have a little box I'll give to you to put your precious things in. I want you to learn to keep your things where you can find them and never to take other people's things, even by mistake. We'll put your nickels here for Lucy."

"Yes, Mother."

"And one nickel isn't the same as another."

"Of course not, when one's lost!"

"No, it's more than that. When a thing belongs to another person, you have no right to use it. That's why it matters."

"Oh, I know now, Mother."

"Then run and sew for your dolly."

Tina was making a lovely bed for her doll, and her nickels were on the hall table waiting for her sister, Lucy, when she came home for lunch. Tina could hear her mother singing in the kitchen and that always made her very happy.

—Condensed from the story by Kathleen B. Nelson.

Who Got the Parrot?

There was a little old woman who lived in a small house. On the front porch of the house hung a big red cage in which there was a green and yellow parrot.

One day Alice, Betty, and Catherine passed the house, and the old woman said to them, "Girls, wouldn't you like to have a parrot? I've had this one for many years, and I'm tired of his chatter."

"Give me the parrot!" cried Alice.

"I want the parrot!" shouted Betty.

"I too would like to have the parrot!" said Catherine.

"Well, well, well," laughed the old woman. "I have only one parrot, and all three of you want it. Let's sit down and think what to do." So they all sat down on the front porch and thought.

After a time the old woman said, "Each of you may have the parrot for one week, and while you have him, teach him new words to say." She pointed to Alice and said, "You teach him to say, 'Good morning,' and you, Betty, teach him to say, 'Good afternoon.' Catherine, you teach him to say, 'Good night.' When each one has had the parrot one week, bring him back to me, and I shall decide which of you may keep him for your very own. Here, Alice, you may have him first." All the girls supposed that whoever taught the parrot the best would be the one to keep him.

Alice hung the parrot's cage in the parlor when she got home. Every day she sat beside the cage to teach the bird to say, "Good morning." But he was slow to learn, and Alice neglected her regular work. Whenever her mother called her, Alice would answer, "Not yet, wait awhile," and she would continue to talk to the parrot. But before the week was up the bird learned to say, "Good morning," and Alice was happy.

Then Betty took the bird and hung it in the attic where she could be alone with it all day long. Whenever her mother called, Betty answered, "Don't bother me," and before the week was over she had taught the parrot to say very nicely, "Good afternoon."

When Catherine took the parrot to her home, she hung its

cage in the kitchen so that she could talk to the bird while she washed the dishes and swept the floor. Often she would sit down beside the cage and talk to the funny green bird, but whenever her grandmother called, she answered, "Coming, Grandma!"

At last the three weeks had ended, and the girls brought the parrot back to the little old woman. They put the cage on a table, and then all sat down to await the decision. The parrot looked at each of the girls, jumped to the bottom of the cage and cried, "Good morning! Good afternoon! Good night!"

"Oh, dear," said the little old woman, "how can I tell who should have the parrot?" And then she smiled a sly smile which wrinkled up her eyes. Suddenly she called, "Alice, Alice, Alice!" in just the way she thought her mother had called Alice for her help. The old woman had no sooner called when the parrot opened his mouth and shrieked, "Not yet, wait awhile."

"Now who do you suppose he heard say that?" exclaimed the old woman. Alice knew.

Then the old woman called, "Betty, Betty, Betty!" And the parrot answered, "Don't bother me, don't bother me," in a harsh voice.

But when the old woman called, "Catherine, Catherine," the bird said softly, just like Catherine's voice, "Coming, Grandma."

"Isn't he the smartest bird you ever saw?" cried Alice. "May I have him, please?"

But the bird answered instead, "Not yet, wait awhile."

"You'll come home with me, won't you, pretty parrot?" pleaded Betty.

"Don't bother me," said the parrot very harshly.

"I'd like to take the dear thing home with me," said Catherine.

The little old woman smiled, and the parrot flapped his wings and said sweetly, so it seemed to Catherine, "Coming, Grandma!"

"You see, girls," said the little old woman, "the parrot had made up his mind, and he answered you in the very words he heard you speak. So, Catherine, he must be yours."

"Haw, haw, haw," laughed the parrot. And he flapped his wings gaily as Catherine carried him away in his big red cage.

—USED BY PERMISSION OF THE *SUNSHINE MAGAZINE.*

AN ADOPTED MOTHER

Arthur was a very tenderhearted little boy. There were tears in his eyes when he came into the kitchen one morning, carrying in his arms a big brown hen which had been run over by a hay wagon and killed.

"What will become of Brownie's little chickens, Mama?" he asked. "They are out under a currant bush, all peeping for their mother."

Mrs. Allan went out in the garden with Arthur to look at the poor little chickens. There were thirteen of the yellow, fluffy little things, only three days old.

"They mustn't die," said Arthur. "I'll take care of them myself."

He brought a basket and put all the little chickens into it; then he carried them off to an empty oat bin in the barn, where there was plenty of room for them to run about. The next morning when Mrs. Allan went out to the barn to tell Arthur to hunt for some eggs, she stopped at the oat bin to look at the motherless little chickens. There in one corner of the bin hung a big feather duster, and gathered under it were all the little chickens!

"I thought the duster could be a mother to them, Mama," said Arthur.

So Mrs. Allan let the duster hang in the bin, and the thirteen little chickens gathered under it until they were old enough to roost on a bar.

—FLORENCE HALLOWELL HOYT, IN *YOUTH'S COMPANION*.

DAWN BOY

Setting Sun, wrinkled and tired, sad and old, sat before the door of his tepee. It was nighttime. The stars twinkled; the moon shed silver-pink beams on a darkened earth; a bird called sleepily; and an owl sent forth its weird screech; from out of the distance came the wail of a coyote. But Setting Sun neither saw nor heard, so deeply was he wrapped in his thoughts.

He thought, "No sons have I. No sons! Seven sons were sent to me by the Great Spirit—brave sons they were, handsome as the turkey bird, straight as the water reed, agile as the rainbow fish, fleet as the tawny deer. Good sons they were—gentle like the doe, industrious like the squirrel, courageous as the she cat protecting her young."

As Setting Sun thought, he sighed, but his thoughts went on, "Seven sons has the Great Spirit given me; seven sons have been killed in battle; seven great warriors have gone to the Happy Hunting Grounds.

"Seven sons have I trained that they might be good chiefs; seven sons have I trained so that any one of them would be a fit guide for my people when I, Setting Sun, should die; but now they are all gone, even as are all the stalwart young braves of the tribe, for this year there have been many wars. Only the old men are left. If I should pass to the Happy Hunting Grounds, there is no one with wisdom to guide my people; there is no one to read the signs in the heavens; there is no one wise in the secret of herbs. Only the young boys are left. From these youths, I, Setting Sun, must choose one—one who will be a just, wise chief, though very young; one who will guide my people wisely and well. But whom shall I choose? Whom shall I bring to my tepee to train in the ways of a chief?"

For a long time Setting Sun sat thinking, thinking, trying to decide which boy.

The stars grew pale. The moon disappeared behind a mountain peak. A cool breeze began to creep through Setting Sun's blankets and chill his old bones. Finally, stiff and weary, he arose and went into his tepee. He was very tired but his mind was at rest, for he had made his decision. He had decided that he, Setting Sun, would not choose the boy to become chief of his people. He would hold contests, and the boy would show himself.

Next day all the tribe knew of Setting Sun's decision. All the boys were excited and happy. Each boy was thrilled with the idea that perhaps he would become chief of the tribesmen.

For a fortnight contests were to be held—contests in running, in fishing, and in hunting. Setting Sun would find who could shoot the surest arrow, who could endure longest in the war dance, and who was the swiftest runner. It was also said that by these contests Setting Sun would know who was fair and just, who was honest and good, for Setting Sun was old and very wise.

So the contests began. All the young boys assembled with their bows and arrows for hunting and with their spears for fishing. Each was resolved in his heart that he would be the one Setting Sun would take to his tepee. Mothers and sisters and little brothers came, all hopeful and confident that the one they loved would outshine the others.

Of them all, one stood forth from the others; one surpassed in all the feats. That one was Dawn Boy, son of Singing Arrow, who was a great warrior and friend of Setting Sun.

In the races, Dawn Boy was always the fleetest; in the war dance, Dawn Boy endured the longest; in the shooting contest, not one of his arrows missed the mark. When Setting Sun sent them out to hunt, Dawn Boy was the first to return. With a deer slung over his shoulders and a turkey bird hanging on his belt, he came into camp. When to the river they went to fish, Dawn Boy speared the greatest number in the shortest time. Always joy and strength seemed to radiate from him.

"But," thought Setting Sun, "everything has been easy for Dawn Boy. Nothing has been difficult. Not yet do I know if Dawn Boy is fit to become chief. I must find one more task. I must find something that is difficult for Dawn Boy, something he does not enjoy doing."

So to each of the boys was given one more task. Each one was to make a belt for Setting Sun. The belt was to be made of beads; it was to be beautiful and original in design. One day was given in which the boys should learn the art of beading. Then the contest would begin. In three more suns, the belt was to be finished.

So each boy set forth to make a belt. None complained. It was a test given by Setting Sun, wise chief and beloved. It was a final test to find who was worthy to be taught in the way of wisdom.

Diligently they worked. The first day passed, and the contest began. Some progressed rapidly; some more slowly; Dawn Boy, not at all. Though he tried repeatedly, no design could he make that was really beautiful.

Dawn Boy's mother watched sympathetically, but she could not help. Setting Sun watched too. He watched when he did not seem to be watching.

"At last," thought Setting Sun, "I have found something that is not easy for Dawn Boy—something in which he does not excel. About the belt I do not care. I wish only to see how he acts in time of trouble. I wish only to see if he behaves in a manner fitting a chief."

For half a day Dawn Boy worked. Three designs he started. Three designs lay unfinished. Dawn Boy knew that none of them was good. Finally he arose, and saying no word, disappeared into the nearby woods.

"He's a quitter," thought Setting Sun. "If it's hard for him to do, he's a quitter. A good chief is never a quitter. However, I think I shall follow him and see what he does."

Silently, so that not even a twig crackled, Setting Sun followed Dawn Boy.

On Dawn Boy went, farther into the woods until he came to the winding river. Then he stopped, looked around him to see that he was alone, and finding himself alone, stretched his arms toward heaven, and looking up, said, "Great Spirit, Ruler of the sun, the moon, and stars, to you I, Dawn Boy, come for assistance. Help me, Great Spirit, to fashion a design for the belt of Setting Sun. Help me, Great Spirit, to work with speed that I may make up the time I have lost. As thou hast helped me before, Great Spirit, I pray thee to help me again, that I might dwell in the tepee of Setting Sun, that I might learn to be wise and good as befits a chief." Then turning, Dawn Boy went back to the others.

Setting Sun remained hidden until Dawn Boy was well on his way; then he too went back to camp.

Once again Dawn Boy set to work. Once again it seemed he could make no design. But then a strange thing happened. Crawling up a small twig lying near Dawn Boy's foot was a caterpillar worm. Dawn Boy reached for the twig to move it lest he step on the worm and crush it, but as he raised the stick, he saw that on the worm's back were many colors. He saw that on its back was a pattern, intricate of design, beautiful in color.

Joy flooded into Dawn Boy's face. The Great Spirit, who designed the heavens and the earth, the birds and the animals, had heard his prayer; the Great Spirit had sent one of his own designs to place on the belt of Setting Sun.

Intently Dawn Boy studied the design. Yes, it was the loveliest design he had ever seen. The pattern was repeated over and over again in sections on the worm's back.

Quickly Dawn Boy chose colors from his bowl of beads that corresponded to the colors on the worm's back; then diligently he worked. Occasionally, when it looked as though the worm would crawl from the twig and away, Dawn Boy placed another twig for the worm to crawl on, lest the little creature disappear before he was able to finish the pattern.

At length Dawn Boy finished the first square of his design. He paused to admire it. Identical it was to that on the worm's back. The pale blue, the deep blue, the black, the white, the orange, and yellow looked just as beautiful on the bead belt as they did on the worm's back. But not for long did Dawn Boy stop to admire, for he was far behind the others. Back to work he went to repeat the pattern over and over again, just as the Great Spirit had done.

Finally all the belts were finished—all, that is, except Dawn Boy's. Undaunted, he worked on. Not yet had the third sun set. He must finish his task. At last, just as the great, golden sun slipped from view, Dawn Boy finished. He took his belt to the place where Setting Sun and the others were waiting. He hung his belt over the display rod that Setting Sun had prepared. He heard murmurs of admiration as the tribesmen viewed the beautiful belt he had made.

Setting Sun, however, did not look at the belt. He arose and, with an upraised arm, silenced the group. Then he began speaking.

"Seven sons has the Mighty One given me—seven sons, stalwart and handsome, courageous and good. And now, to me he has given an eighth son to dwell in my tepee. He has given me a son like unto the seven; he has given me Dawn Boy, offspring of Singing Arrow. Fleet he is like the deer; strong like the pine tree; quick like the winging bird; sure like the arrow. But it is not for these reasons I take him in my tepee. A beautiful belt he has made for me, choice among all others. But it is not for this reason I take him to train in ways of wisdom.

"I take him because of his mighty faith—faith in the power, the goodness, the helpfulness of the Great Spirit. Because of this faith I know that when you, my people, are in trouble— that when he, your chief-to-be, has difficulties—to the Great Spirit he will appeal for help and guidance. Because of his great faith, I, Setting Sun, have faith in him—faith that when I am gone, he will be a good and mighty chieftain for my people."

So saying, Setting Sun led Dawn Boy into his tepee.

A great cheer arose among the people—a cheer for Setting Sun, the old chief—good and wise, brave and true—a cheer for Dawn Boy, the young brave who, they knew, would follow in the footsteps of Setting Sun.

—Thelma Harrison.

When Fun Begins

The children's house is not on the top of the hill, and it is not at the bottom. It is halfway up the hill so that when the children go down, they come to the lake; and when they go up, they come to a big tree.

One day the children came out to play.

"Let's go up the hill to the big tree," said Judy.

"No, let's go down the hill to the lake," said David.

"No—no," said Judy.

"Yes—yes," said David.

And everybody waited, and nobody could go anywhere because they could not agree.

When all the five children want to do the same thing, then

that means they agree. Sometimes they can agree, and sometimes they want to do different things, and they cannot agree.

Then Daddy came out to play too.

"Where are we going?" he asked the children.

"Up the hill to the big tree," said Judy.

"Down the hill to the lake," said David.

"We can't go anywhere unless we agree," said Daddy.

So he sat down on the porch and waited. And nobody had any fun.

Then Michael thought of something.

"Let's climb up the hill to the tree and then run fast down the hill to the lake," he said.

"That's a good idea," said Daddy, and he asked Judy, "Do you agree?"

"Yes," said Judy.

"David, do you agree?" asked Daddy.

"Yes," said David.

"Does everyone agree?" asked Daddy.

"Yes!" all the children shouted together.

So they all climbed up the hill to the big tree, and it was fun!

Then they ran down the hill to the lake. On the lake was the rowboat, and the children got in. Three of the children sat at the back, and they were the boys. Two of the children sat in front, and they were the girls. In the middle sat Daddy, and he rowed the boat. If he rowed up the lake, they would go to the woods. If he rowed down the lake, they would come to the falls.

"Which way shall we go?" asked Daddy.

"Up the lake," said the girls.

"Down the lake," said the boys.

"If I do both at the same time," said Daddy, "we'll just go 'round and 'round. Which way shall I go first?"

"Up!" said the girls.

"Down!" said the boys.

And again they could not agree, and so Daddy rowed the boat 'round and 'round in a circle, and they went nowhere at all, and nobody had any fun.

"But we want to go to the woods," said Barbara.

"We want to go to the falls," said Michael.

"You'll have to agree," said Daddy, and he just kept going 'round and 'round.

The girls looked at the boys, and the boys looked at the girls. And Daddy waited and waited, and the boat kept going 'round and 'round while they waited, and still nobody had any fun! Then Peter thought of something.

"Let's let the wind tell us which way to go first," he said.

"That's a good idea," said Judy.

"Do you agree?" Daddy asked the girls.

"Yes!" they said.

"Do you agree?" Daddy asked the boys.

"Yes!" they said.

"Then look at the clouds," Daddy said, "and see which way the wind blows."

They all looked up at the sky. It was blue, and there were little soft white clouds hurrying across it, and they were all hurrying up the lake to the woods.

"What does the wind say?" Daddy asked.

"It says, 'To the woods,'" Barbara said.

"To the woods," they all agreed.

"Now we can begin our fun," Daddy said. "First we will go to the woods, and then we will go to the falls."

And so they did, and it was fun!

—Pearl S. Buck, from *Stories for Little Children*,
collected by David Lloyd; used by permission.

Danny and Tim Help the New Boy

One morning as Danny and Tim were going to school, Danny said, "I'll race you to the playground."

Away they ran as fast as they could go. Danny got to the playground just a little ahead of Tim. But the boys forgot about the race when they saw a new boy standing there.

"Hello," said Danny.

"What's your name?" said Tim.

The new boy only smiled.

Then Jack came along. "Ho, ho," he laughed. "Where did you get the girl's hat?" (The new boy had on a beret.)

"Look at the girl's hat! Look at the girl's hat!" called Jack.

The new boy said nothing.

Jack ran and pulled off the boy's hat and threw it on the ground.

How surprised Jack was when the new boy slapped him.

"Boo hoo," cried Jack as he ran after the boy.

"It serves you right," said Tim.

"That boy didn't do anything to you. If you hit him again, I'll punch you myself."

Just then Danny's teacher came along. "May we take the new boy to the office?" asked Danny.

"Good morning. What's your name?" Miss White asked the new boy.

The boy smiled and handed her a letter.

Miss White read the letter. Then she said, "Angelo's mother is sick so he has come to live with his aunt. He's in the first grade. Maybe he will be in our room."

"I hope so," said Danny.

"I hope so too," said Tim.

"Please take him to the office so that the principal can register him," said Miss White.

A few minutes later Danny and Tim brought Angelo into their room. "Miss Lee said he should come in here," they said as they handed Miss White the card.

"Good!" said Miss White. She gave Angelo a desk between Danny's and Tim's. "These boys will help you, Angelo, until you get used to our school."

Then Danny and Tim showed Angelo where to hang his coat. They got him some crayons and a pencil. They picked out the best books for him to look at. They played with him at recess and explained about crossing the street where the policeman stands. They were so busy helping Angelo that it was time to go home before they realized it.

"I wish you could come over to my house and play with us," said Danny.

"I'll have to ask my aunt," said Angelo.

"May Angelo come to my house to play?" asked Danny when Angelo's aunt came to the door.

"Where do you live?" she asked.

"On the next street," said Danny.

"Then he may go," his aunt said. "Angelo has no one to play with here. He misses his brothers and sisters. Don't get lost coming home, Angelo."

"We'll show him the way," said Tim.

What a fine time the boys had in Danny's back yard! Danny and Tim brought out their trucks and cars and airplanes. The boys played with them until Danny's mother said, "It is nearly time for supper. You had better take Angelo home so that his aunt will not worry."

Angelo gave the little red truck one last push.

"Come over again tomorrow night and play with it," said Danny.

Then Danny and Tim took Angelo home.

That night when Danny was getting ready for bed his mother said, "What did you do to be a good American citizen today?"

"Oh, my! I was so busy with Angelo that I forgot all about it," said Danny.

"Don't you think that was being a good citizen?" asked his mother.

"How?" asked Danny.

"You were kind and helpful and made Angelo happy."

"That was fun," said Danny. "I like Angelo."

"It usually is fun when you are kind and helpful, but it is important for American citizens to be that way. Angelo needed friends at the new school. I am glad that you and Tim helped him."

"Isn't it strange that Angelo can't talk much?" asked Danny.

"No," said his mother. "Probably his parents do not speak

English. Maybe Angelo can do something else better than you can."

"Oh, yes. You should see his pictures," said Danny. "He can draw better than anyone else in our room."

As Danny went to sleep, he thought, "It's really great fun being a good citizen. I think I'll ask Angelo if he doesn't want to be a good American citizen.

—ELIZABETH R. KELLEY, FROM
THE GRADE TEACHER; USED BY PERMISSION.

THE CAMPING TRIP

There never had been a better day for a camping trip. At least that was what the "Three Biscuiteers" thought as they started out for Cottonwood Canyon. The chums, Grant, Ronald, and Jerry, had started out by calling themselves the Three Musketeers; but since they were equipped with biscuits, or at least generous amounts of food on their outings, rather than muskets, the name had quickly been changed.

They had decided to go up Cottonwood Canyon today because Mr. Lee, Ronald's father, could take them part way in the car and call for them again in the evening. That would mean that they could hike a long way up one of the smaller ravines and visit the ice cave, which they had been wanting to explore for a long time.

"I hope we have enough of everything," said Jerry, as they climbed out of the car.

"From the size of those packs it looks as if you had enough provisions for a week instead of just one day," said Mr. Lee, laughing. "Are you sure that you want to go back tonight?"

"Goodness, yes," Ronald answered quickly. "This is only enough for a couple of meals. You get awfully hungry in the canyon, you know."

"That's right," his father agreed. "Well, take good care of yourselves and meet me about sundown."

The boys waved good-bye and started off up the narrow trail that led through the ravine. Everything was nicer, even than they thought it would be. The birds were singing in the pine trees overhead and every once in a while a squirrel or chipmunk would run across the path and into the shadows on the other side. At times, when they came close to the little stream that ran down the ravine, they would stop and have long drinks of the sparkling cold water.

By noon they were more than ready to stop, for the long hike in the mountain air had made them ravenously hungry. They built a campfire, fried bacon and potatoes, and roasted hot dogs. They finished off with cookies, fruit, and hardtack candy.

"Right now I can't think of anything I'd rather do than lie here in this shade," said Grant, as he stretched out on the soft pine needles.

"I can," said Ronald. "I'd like to be sailing across a lake with just enough breeze so that I could sit still and just watch her go."

"I'd rather have a bicycle," said Jerry, "and then I could go all over town in just half the time it takes me to go any place now; and maybe I could get some errands to do and earn some money besides." Jerry hardly realized that he was speaking out loud a dream that had been in his mind for a long time.

"We're sure a lazy crowd," laughed Grant. "Come on, let's

stir up a little ambition and get going or we won't see that cave today."

"Hadn't we better stay long enough to put out our camp-fire?" Jerry suggested as the other two started out.

"It will be all right until we come back," Grant replied, "and by that time it will likely have died down by itself anyway. Come on, we haven't any time to waste."

Jerry was still rather reluctant to go, but the other two were already starting up the trail, so he followed along. They reached the cave after a brisk climb and explored it thoroughly with the aid of their flashlights. They found it almost as cold as its name, however, and even with the sweaters they had brought along, the boys were glad to get out in the sunshine once more.

"Look at that trail over the ravine," said Grant, after they had sunned themselves on the rocks in front of the cave for a while. "Let's go back that way. It might be shorter, and anyway we might just as well try something different."

"Sure," Ronald agreed at once, "that would be fun. Maybe we'll run into some deer, or something."

They were about to start out without further discussion when Jerry said, "But what about the campfire? We were going to take care of it on the way back, you know."

"Aw, shucks," said Ronald. "A little fire like that couldn't do any harm. It probably went out long ago."

"All big fires were little ones first," Jerry persisted. "We've had an awfully dry summer, you know, and a forest fire could start rather easily."

"Well, you can go back if you want to," said Grant, "but I still think that it's just a waste of time. We came up here for some fun, and I'm going to get all I can. How about you? Want to come with me or go along with Jerry and help tend his little campfire?"

"I'll go along with you," said Ronald quickly. "So long, Jerry. We'll meet you down the road."

Jerry was too much annoyed to say good-bye; he stalked off down the trail while they started their climb over the ravine. Maybe he was dumb, he thought, to miss the fun of going another way, but he had heard too much about the dangers of forest fires to be able to go on home with a clear conscience without knowing that the campfire was properly taken care of.

When he reached the place where they had eaten their lunch, he found only a few live embers and thought that Grant and Ronald would probably have laughed at him all the more had they seen how little need there really was for going back. He threw loose dirt on the fire and was just trampling out the last of it when he looked up to see Mr. Matthews, who ran a drugstore downtown, coming toward him up the trail.

"Hello there, young fellow," Mr. Matthews called. "I'm glad to see you obeying the rule of the forest and taking proper care of your campfire. Are you all alone?"

"I am at present," Jerry replied. "A couple of other boys were with me, but they went down another way."

"I see, and you came this way to take care of your campfire. Was that it?"

"Something like that," Jerry admitted.

"I like that," said Mr. Matthews, coming over to help Jerry. "You know, I've been looking for just such a boy as you, someone who could be depended upon without being watched all the time. How would you like to come and work for me a few hours a day?"

"I'd like it fine," Jerry replied, his eyes shining at the prospect.

"Then come over and see me tomorrow, and we'll settle the details."

Jerry thanked him and said good-bye, and then hurried off down the trail so that he wouldn't miss the boys and Mr. Lee at the road. He began to whistle a bright tune. A job! Maybe that would mean that he could get a bicycle at last. Oh, boy! Was he glad that he had come back to take care of that campfire!

—Mabel S. Harmer.

The Gold Basket

It was only a fruit dish of white china with gilt bands around it, but little Vie admired it very much and called it "Mamma's gold basket."

One afternoon Aunt Emily came to make a call, and Mama brought in the basket filled with nice Florida oranges. After everybody had eaten an orange, and Aunt Emily had gone, sister Anna set the basket on the kitchen table, and that was the way the trouble began.

Little Vie went out there alone to play with the cat. She chased her around and around the room till kitty, growing tired of the sport, jumped into a chair, and got up on the table.

"Come down! Come down!" said little Vie. "You must not smell those oranges with your nose. Come down!"

But kitty did not come; she was trying to decide whether the beautiful yellow balls were good to eat. Then Vie caught her by the tail and pulled her backward. She did not do it roughly, but somehow that gold basket got in the way. Perhaps kitty's paw touched it, perhaps it was Vie's arm; but, at any rate, the basket was overturned. Down it fell, broken in pieces upon the floor!

Vie stared in surprise at the dreadful ruin and then stared at the oranges rolling helter-skelter under the stove.

"Who did that? How did it fall?" thought she.

But, the next moment, it came over her that she was herself the one to blame.

Little Vie's forehead was wrinkled, her eyes were full of tears.

"I'll go tell Mamma I did it, and I'm sorry. No, I'll tell her kitty did it—I guess kitty did do it. Naughty kitty!"

The little girl moved one foot, and then she stood still again. The clock ticked very loud—you know how a clock does tick sometimes.

"No, I won't tell Mamma anything; I won't go into the parlor at all. I'll go out in the yard, and then Mamma will think kitty broke the basket, for kitty will be in here all alone."

Vie took three steps toward the outside door, and then she stood still again, and the clock ticked worse than ever. It seemed as if the clock was watching to see Vie make up her mind.

"Tick, tock—if you go and leave the kitty in here alone, it will be the same as a lie—tick, tock—same as a lie." It wasn't that the clock actually said that, but it sounded just like the clock.

"Will it be the same as a lie, a true lie?" said the child. "I will not tell a lie," said Vie, turning her back to the outside door and putting her foot down hard. "I will not tell a lie." And with that she ran into the parlor. She ran every step of the way as fast as she could run and sobbed out, "Oh, Mamma, it wasn't the kitty; it was I! But I didn't mean to at all!"

And her mamma kissed her and said she knew it was an accident.

Whitewashing a Yellow Streak

Blue smoke curled upward in the early morning air. Hot dogs sizzled and sputtered at the end of sizzling willows, presided over by a trio of boys.

Blink, the acknowledged leader of the three, regarded the bursting brown skins with deep satisfaction.

"Better take them off," he counseled, and then, as the two Jenkins boys hastened to do his bidding, he continued, "Mother says she can't imagine even savages liking this kind of stuff for breakfast," and he laughed shortly as he raked some charred potatoes from the coals.

"Let them blow off a little of their steam, and they won't singe the hair of our tongues," he explained as he broke them apart with the sharp end of a dirty stick.

"Funny that women don't know any more than they do." Spud Jenkins cut a huge crescent in a bun, sent out an exploring tongue for any stray crumbs that had settled on the outside of his mouth. "Or men either. My dad says no power on earth could get him up at five o'clock in the morning to come out to a dirty old canal bank to eat dirty food."

Blink rescued a fallen hot dog from the ground, carefully wiped off the offending dust and ashes on his shirt sleeve. "Dirt," he announced, "is good for people. Everybody has got to eat a little dirt, else the old earth will think he's its enemy, and it won't raise anything for him when he grows up."

Spud's younger brother, Spain, nodded approvingly.

The site of their campground was the bank of a big canal that wound around the foot of a small hill. At the top the hill flattened out into a tableland on which stood the trim white house and outbuildings of Mr. Browning, the superintendent of the gas company.

The boys had just finished their last potato when the sound of a motor from the Browning yard caught their attention.

"I wonder where the Brownings are going this early in the morning." It was Spain who spoke.

"The whole shebang are going up to Yellowstone for their vacation," answered Blink. "I happen to know because I heard Mr. Browning tell Dad last night."

The boys watched Mr. Browning drive the big car to the front of the house, stow bags and bedding in the trunk at the back, tuck the rugs around his wife and daughters, and finally open the dog kennel, out of which bounded a huge German police hound. A few moments later the car disappeared down the driveway on the opposite side of the hill.

Breakfast over, the three boys looked about for further worlds to conquer.

"Now that there's no one around, let's go to the top of the hill and roll rocks down," suggested Spud. "They'll make a great splash when they hit the canal."

Blink was skeptical. "You can't make a splash with rocks no bigger than we play jacks with, and I'll bet you that's all we'll find when we get up there."

But since nothing more exciting offered itself, the boys trailed up the hillside.

"Didn't I tell you we wouldn't find anything here?" demanded Blink.

Rebuked, the two Jenkins boys settled down till proper inspiration should come to their leader.

Blink looked about speculatively.

"I wish that dog was here. We'd tie his legs and roll him down," Spud contributed.

"Yah, give him a nice bath." Blink scratched his head. Spud's remark had given him food for thought. "Three horse hairs in water for nine days will change into a snake. Wonder what dog hair would change into? Let's go over to the kennel and see if old Cap has left any of his there."

They crawled under the wire fence and poked into the solidly-built kennel, but not one stray hair was visible. Discouraged, they were about to leave when Blink's face lighted suddenly.

"How about rolling the kennel down? I'll bet that would make a splash."

His two companions looked aghast. "We wouldn't dare!"

Blink's chest came out. "Wouldn't dare, huh? Say, there's nothing I wouldn't dare."

Admiration wiped out the fear on the faces of Spud and Spain.

"Well, I dare you to do it, then," they challenged.

Blink kicked at the kennel. "Can't do it alone. You'll have to help me."

Together they tugged and lifted. With a stick Spain propped the wires of the fence apart where they were already sagging. Blink and Spud pushed the kennel through. Once they were all safely beyond the fence, Blink gave the box-like structure a quick push, and away it went careening down the hillside toward the canal.

The boys waited breathlessly for the splash, but an old willow stump brought the kennel up sharply on the very edge of the stream.

At that same instant the fire siren shrieked shrilly in the town below, and without a backward glance the boys were off to new fields of excitement.

"Four o'clock in the morning is early rising for a twelve-year-old boy," said Mrs. Snyder when she found Blink nodding over his supper. He was more than willing to go to bed as soon as the meal was over.

He slid out of his clothes, flung them over a nearby chair, and flopped into his porch bed. He had scarcely rolled himself up into the ball position he always assumed for sleeping and screwed his pillow into an instrument of torture for any but his own head when the sound of voices disturbed him. Dad and Mr. Sims talking again!

"I tell you, Snyder, there's a yellow streak in anyone who deliberately destroys property." Their voices trailed away into nothingness. Blink was asleep.

It must have been hours later that he woke with a strangled gasp. *Something with a yellow streak trying to destroy him!* He had been dreaming of rolling down the hillside when he felt a furry presence slither across his throat. He sat up quickly, threw the covers back with sudden violence. A convulsed motion of the blanket convinced him that there was no dream about this. Whatever had gone over him was still there under the bedding.

With eyes glued to the wriggling covers, he pushed himself cautiously out of bed and felt along the wall with trembling fingers till he encountered the electric light button.

Suddenly the porch was suffused with light. Relief swept Blink in a great tide. Though his knees still felt weak, he reached out for a broom that stood nearby and began to unpeel the covers. First went the sheet, then the blanket, and then the spread. There was huddled Jenkinses' old tomcat! A loosened square of wire netting on the screen door made his mode of entrance plain.

An uncontrolled fit of laughter seized Blink. "Think of being scared plumb to death of Spud's old tomcat!"

He chased his visitor out with harsh guttural sounds and crept back into bed, but for some reason sleep had forsaken him. He lay for a long time living over the horror of that first moment of waking. It was that fool thing that Mr. Sims had said to Dad that had made the encounter with the tomcat so terrible—that thing about the yellow streak.

He sought about in his mind for the full statement. Just what was it that made people have a yellow streak? Presently the whole sentence came back. "There's a yellow streak in people who willfully destroy property," that was it.

Now that he had recalled it, he couldn't get the thing out of his mind. Like a strain of music it repeated itself again and again, and all the while a slow conviction was growing that he was that kind of person. Hadn't he deliberately taken Mr. Browning's dog kennel and rolled it down the hill, probably smashed it so that old Cap would have to have another house? Whatever had possessed him to do it? What would Dad think if he knew it? What would Mr. Browning think and do? The more he thought about it, the more ill he felt. By morning his guilt would be blazoned to the world. Something must be done about it at once.

"I'd a lot rather be scared by a tomcat than feel like I do now," he thought.

Again he got out of bed. This time he did not turn on the light. He found his clothes, hurried into them, and crept out the door. He scrambled through the raspberry bushes that divided his place from Spud's.

He picked up two soft clods of dirt, then stationed himself directly below the upstairs window of the Jenkins house. He aimed carefully, and as he flung the clod he let out three short yelps—the distress signal the boys always used.

He waited. All was quiet as before.

"Bet they wouldn't be sleeping like that if their old tomcat had been sawing away at their throats like he did mine," Blink muttered, and threw the second clod.

This brought Spud to the window. His voice was heavy with sleep. "What is the matter with you? Can't you let a fellow sleep in peace?"

By this time a second head appeared at the window.

"Come on down as quick as you can, you fellows," Blink whispered harshly. "We've got some work to do, and we've got to do it mighty quick."

Two shadowy figures presently emerged from the window and descended the porch posts.

In a few breathless sentences Blink convinced Spud and Spain that the safety and peace of all three depended upon getting the Browning dog kennel back before daylight.

"There's a yellow streak in people who willfully destroy property of others," he told them solemnly.

It was no easy task to lug the kennel up the steep incline. The night air was chilly, but all three were perspiring violently.

"Gee whizz, I don't see what made us do it," Spain grumbled.

"Quit your talking and push," advised Spud when the kennel slipped back.

"Good thing it isn't broken anywhere." Blink was surveying it cautiously in the moonlight, now that they had it back once more in its accustomed place. "This has sure taught me a lesson," he added as they started back to finish a disturbed night's rest.

The late morning sun splotched Blink's sleeping porch as he opened sleepy eyes to his mother.

"You really will have to get up," she said. "I've called you a half dozen times already. Your father needs you to help him whitewash those chicken coops. The ceilings are a fright, all streaked with yellow."

Blink sat up and rubbed his eyes. "Ah heck," he yawned deeply, "that's what I've been doing most of the night. That's what makes me so sleepy—whitewashing my yellow streak."

—STELLA P. RICH.

FOR THE GLORY OF ARDWYN

Margaret dressed herself with special care one bright spring morning and hurried down to the breakfast table. Usually she waited to be called at least once, but today a very great event was taking place, and late sleeping was entirely out of the question.

"Is my dress all right, Mother?" she asked eagerly as she sat down at the table.

"Your dress looks lovely, my dear," answered her mother. "But I thought it was your voice that you were being judged on today and not your clothes."

"So it is, Mother," answered Margaret with a laugh, "only I wanted to look just as nice as possible. It always seems to me that looks do count, although they really shouldn't, I suppose."

"Who else is trying out for the solo part today?" asked Mrs. Griffiths.

"There are only two others, Megan Rees and Gwenyth Evans. I am not at all afraid but what I can win over Megan, but the other girl has a beautiful voice, and I have heard that she has practiced day and night for this contest."

"Who is this Gwenyth Evans?" inquired Mrs. Griffiths. "I don't believe that I have met her, have I?"

"No, Mother, you probably haven't. She lives in another part of town and goes to a different school than I do. In fact, she is the daughter of a very poor coal miner, I understand."

"Poor little thing," replied her mother. "I suppose that a trip to the great national eisteddfod would mean a great deal to her. If she were not competing against you, I might almost be tempted to wish that she would win."

"Oh, she'll get to go anyway," answered Margaret lightly. "Her voice is so good that she is sure to get a place in the chorus even if she doesn't win the solo part. And don't you dare wish for someone else to win over your own daughter!" and with a playful shake and a kiss, Margaret ran upstairs to put on her wraps.

Margaret was not the only one excited over the contest today, for the great national eisteddfod is one of the biggest events of the year in the lives of the Welsh people. Contestants come from all over the country to find out who has the best choir, who can play the various instruments best, and who can write the finest poetry. It is an honor, indeed, to be allowed to take part.

Margaret was gifted with a very natural, sweet voice, and she had worked for a long time in an effort to win a solo part with the children's chorus this year. She had attended the eisteddfod last year as a listener, but she knew that it would be far more thrilling to go as a participant.

The hall where the contest was to be held was filled with bright-eyed, rosy-cheeked children when Margaret arrived. She was greeted enthusiastically by a number of friends, for she was a great favorite with her schoolmates. Many of them took time to whisper their hopes for her success in the contest, and Margaret smiled happily back at them.

First, the group numbers to be sung without solo parts were practiced carefully, and then the Spring Song, which included the coveted solo part, was sung three different times in order to give each of the girls a trial.

Margaret was not at all nervous, and when she had finished, she was confident that, whether she won or not, at least she had done her very best. When the tryouts were over, it seemed that everyone waited almost breathlessly for the director's decision. It also seemed that he was taking an unnecessarily long time to make up his mind.

Finally he said, "About thirty of you will be included in the chorus, and I shall read those names before you leave today. After much consideration I have decided to award the solo part to Miss Gwenyth Evans."

Margaret was stunned for a minute, but she quickly controlled the tears that wanted very much to fall from her eyes and went over to Gwenyth with the heartiest congratulations that she could manage to say.

Gwenyth frankly made no effort to conquer her tears but managed to smile her thanks to Margaret for her good wishes.

Margaret was very much disappointed, of course, at the outcome of the contest, but she entered into rehearsals with the chorus with all the enthusiasm of which she was capable and determined to do her best there anyway.

Her mother bought her some pretty new clothes to wear to the city and an especially lovely white dress to wear at eisteddfod when her chorus should sing.

Practices were being held nearly every evening now, for Mr. Llewellyn, the director was determined to bring honor to the town of Ardwyn if hard work could do it.

One evening about two weeks before they were to leave for eisteddfod, Gwenyth Evans was absent and the director asked Margaret to take her place in the Spring Song. After the practice was over he asked her to remain for a few minutes, and when the other children had left, he said, "Well, Miss Margaret, it appears that you are to sing the solo after all."

For the moment Margaret felt only surprise. She had almost forgotten that to sing the solo had been her greatest ambition. When she could collect her thoughts, she asked in a shaking voice, "But why, Mr. Llewellyn? What is the matter with Gwenyth?"

"It seems that Gwenyth cannot afford to go," he said regretfully. "As you may know, her father works in the coal mines, and the work has been shut down indefinitely. Our organization here could manage to pay her fare, but her mother says that it will be impossible for her to get the necessary clothes in order to appear at the concert. I am genuinely sorry because Gwenyth has an unusual voice, and I believe that we would have had a very good chance to win with her. However, my dear," he concluded with a smile, "you do very well yourself, and we will try all the harder to win, won't we?"

"We certainly will," promised Margaret, as she left for her home.

Try as she would that evening, Margaret could not feel the thrill of happiness that she believed she ought to feel over the change in her fortunes. She could not help thinking of poor little Gwenyth Evens who had worked so hard to attain the same honor and then had lost out through no fault of her own.

The words of the director, "Gwenyth has an unusual voice, and I believe that we would have had a very good chance to win with her," kept going through her mind. Margaret felt that there would not be a great deal of happiness in the contest for her, after all, if they lost because she was singing the part instead of another.

She had not said anything to her mother about the change in plans on her return home in the evening because she was still so confused in her own mind about it that somehow she felt she did not want the congratulations of the family just yet.

The next morning Margaret and her mother lingered at the

breakfast table after the rest of the family had gone out. Presently she said very seriously, "Mother, would you think it very ungrateful of me if I gave the new white dress to someone else?"

"Why, Margaret!" exclaimed her mother in surprise. "What on earth do you want to give your dress away for? Don't you like it?"

"I love it, Mother, but—" and then she poured out the whole story of how Gwenyth was unable to sing because she didn't have a suitable dress and how Mr. Llewellyn had offered her the part instead but was sure that Gwenyth could do better.

"And do you want to give up your beautiful dress and your chance to sing because of a girl whom you scarcely know?" asked her mother seriously.

Margaret nodded her head. She was too close to tears to speak.

Mrs. Griffiths came over and put her arms around Margaret. "That is my own brave, unselfish girl," she exclaimed. "We will do just as you wish."

The day of the great eisteddfod finally drew near. Margaret and her parents traveled by train to the big city and after much difficulty managed to obtain lodging in the crowded hotels. The first two days were given over to competition between the choruses composed of older people and the instrumental numbers. Margaret sat in the audience and felt quite sure that she was listening to the most beautiful music on earth, which perhaps she was. Certainly no other people are so famed for their singing as the Welsh are.

The next day the children's choruses appeared. There were a great many of them, and Margaret was as nervous as if she had the entire responsibility for the success of their particular chorus upon her own shoulders. Gwenyth, on the other hand, was calm and starry-eyed. She looked beautiful in the new dress, and even when Margaret saw her march in to the place of honor in the center of the chorus, she was not sorry for what she had done.

The Ardwyn chorus was called at last, and the children sang as they had never sung before. When the judges' decision had finally been given, and Margaret knew for a certainty that their chorus had been declared the finest children's chorus in all Wales, she rushed forward and threw her arms about Gwenyth.

Mr. Llewellyn came up just then and taking a hand of each little girl in his own, he said, "My children, I don't know which of you to thank the most for our success this day, but I am happier than I can say at the outcome."

"Why, it was Gwenyth, of course," laughed Margaret. "She did the singing."

"But I couldn't have done it, if it hadn't been for you," said Gwenyth with tears of gratitude in her eyes.

"Suppose we say that we all helped and that it was for the glory of Ardwyn, and let it go at that," suggested Mr. Llewellyn with a smile. And both little girls were only too happy to agree.

—MABEL S. HARMER.

THE SNOWBALL FIGHT

Oh, look!" cried Jacky, hopping out of bed and running to the window, "look! It's snowing."

Ricky ran to the window. "How white everything is!" he said.

Sure enough! During the night all the world had turned white. Everything was covered with snow. How excited and happy the boys were! They could hardly wait to go outdoors. Jacky hurried so fast to get dressed that he even tried to put his shoes on the wrong feet! Then Mother gave them a big breakfast, and they were ready to go outdoors to play.

"Let's make a snowman," suggested Ricky.

"That will be loads of fun," agreed Jacky.

First the boys made a little round ball of snow. Then they started to roll it. How fast the snowball grew! It grew bigger and bigger, until at last the boys couldn't push the ball any farther.

"There," said Jacky. "I guess that's big enough."

"Now we'll have to make another snowball for the top," said Ricky.

"But we don't want such a big one this time."

The boys didn't roll their new snowball far, but it grew so fast that when Ricky tried to lift it, it wouldn't even move.

"Oh," sighed Ricky, "how heavy it is!" He pushed and pushed, but still it would not move.

"I'll help too," said Jacky. How hard the boys worked. At last they lifted the second snowball right on top of the other one.

"Whew! I'm glad that's done," said Ricky.

"So am I," answered Jacky. "Now all we have to do is to make the head."

That didn't take the boys long because they had to make only a small snowball for the head.

"There," said Jacky, looking at the snowman proudly. "He's all finished."

"No, he isn't," answered Ricky. "He has to have a face. Whoever heard of a snowman without a face?"

"I know what we can use for the face," cried Jacky excitedly, and off he ran toward the house. In a few minutes he was back with four big lumps of shiny black coal.

"These two pieces are for the eyes. This one is for the nose, and this long piece is just right for the mouth," said Jacky as he stuck the lumps of coal into place.

"Now he looks like a real snowman," said Ricky.

"It was fun making him," said Jacky. "Let's make another one."

"No, let's have a snowball fight. That's lots of fun too," suggested Ricky.

So the boys made great piles of snowballs.

"I think I've got enough snowballs," decided Jacky at last.

"I have too," agreed Ricky. "Let's start our fight now."

He picked up one of his snowballs. "Ready," he called.

"Oh! Wait a minute," cried Jacky. "I just remembered. Daddy told us not to throw snowballs at anyone. He said that sometimes snowballs are hard and people get hurt."

"Pooh! You're afraid," answered Ricky. "That's what's the matter with you."

"I am not," said Jacky. "I'll show you!" and he grabbed a snowball and threw it straight toward Ricky.

"That didn't hurt a bit," laughed Ricky. "Come on now. Let's start our fight. Ready! Fire!"

Soon the air was filled with snowballs. What fun the boys

had! The snowballs hit their arms and legs and snowsuits, but they didn't hurt a bit.

"I guess Daddy never had a snowball fight," decided Jacky. "Snowballs are soft. They can't hurt anyone."

But just then what do you think happened? Along came a great big snowball straight for Jacky's face. Faster and faster it came!

"Ouch! Ouch!" cried Jacky. "Oh, how that snowball hurt!" Jacky rubbed his face hard to make it stop hurting. He tried hard not to cry.

How frightened Ricky was when he saw what had happened. "I didn't know the snowball would hit your face."

"I know you didn't," answered Jacky, "but it hurts just the same."

"I guess Daddy was right, after all," decided Ricky. "If that snowball had hit your eye, it would have been even worse. I don't want to have a snowball fight any more."

"Neither do I," agreed Jacky, still rubbing his face.

Just then Ricky had a fine idea. "I know what we can do. We can throw snowballs at our snowman," he said. "That will be lots more fun than throwing them at each other."

"And we can't hurt him even if we do hit his face," laughed Jacky.

—Marjorie M. Williams, from
The Grade Teacher; used by permission.

"Do What You Can"

There was once a farmer who had a large cornfield. He plowed and harrowed it and planted the corn and weeded it with great care. He depended on his field for the chief support of his family. He had worked hard, but when he saw the crop begin to wither and droop for want of rain, he began to have fears for it. He felt very sad and went over every day to look at his corn to see if there was any hope of rain.

One day he stood looking at the sky. Two little raindrops up in the clouds over his head saw him, and one said to the other: "Look at that farmer; I feel sorry for him. He has taken such pains with his field of corn, and now it is drying up; I wish I could do him some good."

"Yes," said the other, "but you are only a little raindrop; what can you do? You can't even wet one hillock."

"Well," said the first, "to be sure I can't do much, but I can cheer the farmer a little at any rate, and I am resolved to do my best; I'll try. I'll go to the field to show my goodwill, if I can do no more. Here I go."

The first raindrop had no sooner started for the field than the second one said: "Well, if you are going, I believe I will go too; here I come." Down went the raindrops—one came pat on the farmer's nose, and one fell on a stalk of corn.

"Dear me," said the farmer, putting his finger to his nose, "what's that? A raindrop! Where did that come from? I do believe we shall have a shower."

By this time a great many raindrops had come together to hear what their companions were talking about. When they saw them going to cheer the farmer and water the corn, one said: "If you are going on such an errand, I'll go too," and down he came. "And I," said another, "and I," and so on, till a whole shower came. So the corn was watered and it grew and

ripened—all because the first little raindrop determined to do
what it could.

—SELECTED.

WHEN THE GRASS GREW

Everyone in the neighborhood knew and liked George, that
is, everyone but Lucy, and George had no way of telling
how she felt, for he was almost too embarrassed to look in her
direction. Lucy seemed so little, dainty and pretty, while he felt
long legged, awkward, and plain. Of course, he was not much
different from other boys of fourteen, when legs and arms are
forever in the way and feet are larger than at any other time of
life, but George didn't know this.

What he did know was that, more than anyone else, he
wanted Lucy to like him. Lucy lived with her grandparents, and
they, as most of the neighbors, were extraordinarily fond of
George. They had admired his tender devotion to his mother,
his helpfulness to younger children and kindness to persons in
need. Grandmother Woodruff often spoke of George's excep-
tional qualities, but to her pretty fourteen-year-old grand-
daughter, George Smith was a bothersome tease who dipped
the ends of her long brown braids in his inkwell or chased her
until she almost spilled the yeast she carried in a pail from
Scarce's Bakery to her grandmother's home, every time her
grandmother was going to mix bread.

When George was reprimanded by his mother for torment-
ing Lucy, he explained, "But Mother, that's the only way I can
make her even notice me. Most of the boys have fine clothes,

fancy horses, and time to play around and do the nice things that the girls like. All I can do to make Lucy as much as look at me is to torment her." His mother said no more.

She had no way of knowing that behind George's good disposition, pleasant manner, and smiling face was an aching heart. She did not see him squirm and turn and toss on his straw mattress. No one could see him lie wide-eyed, with hands locked tensely behind his head, as he gazed into the blackness of the night and considered his small chance of ever taking any place of social acceptance among the young people of the ward. He had neither money nor time to spend in that direction.

True, they *did* live in the best part of the city. The Smith home was in the vicinity of the Temple Block where, at that time, most of Salt Lake's wealthiest families lived, but George's family was not wealthy. Their limited income had to be divided into too many parts to dress, feed, and educate his father's many children. If only his father had had fewer children there would be more for each. George checked this thought and his face flushed, for he would not have given up one of his brothers or sisters for all the riches in the world. But my, how he did wish that his family were able to afford some of the extras that seemed to impress young people. If only they owned a fine, large house with a black and gold iron fence in front and a beautiful green lawn from the gate to the house, then he could have lawn parties with a fiddler and Japanese lanterns . . . a party like the one Rex Brown had last summer. . . . He had seen the party that hot summer evening even though he hadn't been invited. He remembered walking down the opposite side of the street where, hidden by the shadows, he could watch his friends dancing on the lawn, among them Lucy. Why hadn't *he* been invited? In his mind George lined up all his faults and all of his good points to compare them, but actually there could be no comparison. He was being as perfect as he knew how to be. He was doing his duty in every respect. Compliments were always pouring upon him from the older people of the ward. And, while the young people laughed at his jokes, enjoyed talking and working with him, they never invited him to their social affairs. Why? Why did they leave him out?

Suddenly he knew several possible reasons: his trousers were too short; he looked funny; he had no fancy buggy and their horses were a work team; their house, though big, airy, and clean, lacked the fine, rose-patterned Brussels carpets, the ornate hanging lamps, and the stiff, red plush furniture like those in the homes of some of his neighbors. And one other thing, the Smiths had no lawn; so of course he could never have a lawn party. Between their front fence and the house was nothing but earth, which became a broad stretch of ankle-deep dust or sticky mud, according to the season. On either side of the path jutted a row of skeleton peach trees, useless, ugly things except that the dwarf peaches might be made into jam for winter use.

George was beginning to realize why he was not accepted by the partying group, but there was little he could do about it except worry . . . and worry he did, for most of the night.

The following morning, as he dressed to go to his work in Z. C. M. I.'s overall factory, where during school vacation he earned two dollars a week by punching out thousands and thousands of buttonholes. His mother noticed that he looked tired and pale and asked if he were ill.

"No, I am well, thank you, Mother," he said, "but I *would*

like a good talk with you tonight." All day as he fed the overalls to the machine, he planned exactly the words he was going to say to his mother that evening. She had helped and advised him always. At her knee he had been taught to ask his Heavenly Father for the blessings he most desired. She would not fail him now. When night came, and the dishes were finished and put away, and the little children tucked into bed, George and his mother sat down in the big, clean kitchen to talk over his problem.

George patted his mother's arm affectionately and then began very seriously, "Mother dear, I don't want you to feel that I am complaining, for I am not, but I must have help and advice. I realize that while Father is still on a mission, I have to be the man of the house. I, being the eldest son, expect to carry the responsibilities. I am glad that I am well and able to work and help you with your overwhelming duties. I am glad that I can milk the cow and curry the horse. I am only too happy to cut the wood and carry the coal and the water. I really want to do all these things, but by working all day, doing chores all evening, going to my meetings, and discharging all of my numerous deacon duties, I have absolutely no time left to devote to myself and to make myself in any way attractive. I should like to learn to dance well and properly, and I should like to have the time to joke and play and fool around with the young people after meetings and not always feel that I should rush home to get busy. I do so long for a more attractive home so that we would not seem like poor people in comparison to some of our neighbors and other ward members."

At this point George's mother interrupted, "Did you say 'poor,' my son? Why, we are some of the richest people in the world! Think of your inheritance. Remember your ancestors; few people are so fortunate; *you* have the noble blood of John Alden and Priscilla in your veins. You also are a descendant of our great Church leaders; you have a good and noble father who, instead of being here to buy you the worldly treasures you desire and that you say your friends enjoy, is giving *himself* and all his time that he may preach to the people of the world that they too may know of the gospel and enjoy its boundless blessings. Who could have greater things to be proud of? Never, never say 'poor,' my boy. You are rich! Very, very rich in the priceless things . . . the things that really count."

"I know, Mother," George interrupted, fearing that he had hurt her feelings, "I know too, as you have taught us, that the beautiful cleanliness and order of our home means more than costly finery, but not everyone else knows this. Haven't you noticed that I am left out of all the big parties? Even Lucy doesn't notice me now that I'm too old to tease her. She seems to be interested in Sam and John."

Mrs. Smith took George's face between her two hands, kissed his forehead, and said, "To me you are the finest, the handsomest, the most wonderful son in the world. Of course I understand, dear, and I'll think about it. Together we'll see what can be done to change things."

The following day seemed doubly long to George, but again the next night, when all the occupants of the big, two-storied house had settled and everything was quiet, George and his mother went outside and sat on the front steps to continue their conversation. The moon shone so brightly that every ugly stone jutting up in the front yard seemed visible. George's mother began, "My son, I have thought of you all day, and I believe I have an idea. Our home is large, clean, and comfortable; it compares favorably with the other houses in this neighborhood. It's our front yard that makes our place seem so unattractive. If we could possibly plant grass in this big front yard; have our path bordered with smooth, round, whitewashed cobblestones; cover the walk with good, sifted gravel; then mend and paint the fence, our place would look as good as many in the ward."

George's eyes shone in anticipation. "You're right, Mother! I can see that you're absolutely right." He spoke excitedly, "Is it possible, do you really think we might fix the place up right away?" Then in a low, hesitant voice he added, "You know I have so little spare time."

"I have considered that too," his mother explained. "Your father won't be back for about fifteen months, so we will have this fall and all next summer to get it done before he comes. My plan is to let the entire family in on the idea. We will make the lawn a project, a surprise for Father. The plan to surprise him will interest each child, and all of them will want to cooperate. You will not have to work alone."

"That's a grand idea," said George, and his mother saw his smile as the moonlight fell upon his face. "I can just see how much better our place will look fixed up like that."

The two of them talked and planned for hours. George went to bed feeling greatly relieved. He slept peacefully and soundly. The next day was Sunday. After Sunday School and Sunday dinner were over, Mother, Aunt Josephine, and George gathered all of the children of the two families in the big square parlor. Then George's mother presented the plan, explaining that it was to be "a wonderful surprise for Father when he gets home in a little over a year from now." All were delighted with the exciting plan. Each asked, "What can I do?" or, "What is my job?" Assignments were made. To some of the older children was assigned the job of cutting down the peach trees that ran the length of the lot, plowing and digging up the hard ground, and spading fertilizer into the soil. The middle-sized children were to carry off the big stones turned up by the plow and haul them away. The little ones were to go up to the old City Creek roadbed and select from the thousands of cobblestones the smooth, clean, round boulders of regular size that would make a neat border for the front path. Mother explained that if they placed these in piles, the older children would call for them every time old Major, the horse, was hitched up for some other job. Mother warned that it would take a long time to do all they planned, for it was a big task. Their house was set back about seventy-five feet from the street and had very wide frontage. But the children were undaunted and enthusiastically fell in with the plan.

Arrangements were made for the gravel, for mountain soil, and even for ways and means for the children to earn the extra money to buy the lawn seed. Every dime of their regular income had many, many uses.

To George, that Sunday was a day never to be forgotten. The plan had sounded promising. In his mind he carried a picture of a neat, white picket fence with a large, smooth-swinging front gate, and from it two nice, uniform rows of whitewashed cobblestones running to the steps, with lawn extending wide on either side. It was a pleasant, enticing picture. He often thought of the apple tree near the house and had pictured himself spreading a heavy, wool comforter on the grass for his friends to sit on while they laughed and talked with him. He smiled every time this thought flashed through his mind. By next summer the home would look like some of the rich homes in the neighborhood. Perhaps Lucy would be one of the crowd who would come to sit on the quilt in the shade of the tree. Thus he dreamed night and day, as the work began.

There were only a few weeks of fine weather remaining in which to get the work started before George must leave for the Brigham Young Academy in Provo. Every evening for the rest of the summer he hurried home from Z. C. M. I.'s factory, rushed through the chores and got to work preparing the ground, that is, every evening when he didn't have deacon duties to perform. Those children who were old enough to stay up and work after supper worked with him, and his mother sat on the steps and sewed carpet rags, for she too had a plan. There was to be a new rag carpet in the parlor and dining room for Father's home-coming surprise, and to complete it she must take advantage of every minute.

One evening while George and his brothers and sisters were industriously working on the lawn, Lucy rode by in a fine car- riage drawn by a handsome team of prancing, black horses. One of the neighbor boys was driving, and as he passed, he called tauntingly, "Hello, George, don't you ever quit working?"

George's face burned. If he had not been so determined to keep his hurt to himself, he would have gone inside and wept; but his mother, immediately sensing his hurt, spoke saying, "George, did you know that Claire fell into the creek today while gathering the stones for the path?" She described the inci- dent, and as they laughed at the description of the dripping, frightened child, Lucy and her unkind, show-off companion were momentarily forgotten. George had not needed to be reminded that he had time for nothing but work. The task was big, and the job progressed very slowly as there was so little time after chores were finished each evening.

George had never failed to do more than his part as a deacon, and in those days deacons swept and scrubbed the church, washed the windows, cleaned and filled the coal oil lamps, built the fires, and cut and carried the wood and the coal to warm the meeting-house. These tasks took at least two evenings out of every week, so almost before preparation for the lawn was well started, the summer was gone, and it was time for George to get into the big "white top" and drive with a number of other students to the Brigham Young Academy.

Even while at school, he constantly visualized the growing lawn. He saw his home becoming more lovely all the time. He was very sure that he must better his situation, for over and over his wise teacher, Karl G. Maeser, kept repeating, in sincere but broken English, "Don't be a scrub." George couldn't afford to be a scrub; he was convinced that he was one of God's blessed children. In his veins flowed the best blood of all the land. He would, he *must* make something of himself! He applied himself diligently. He read the best books. He was a faithful choir member and learned to sing and enjoy good music. He improved his dancing. Bit by bit he sensed that his lankiness and seeming awkwardness was passing. He wasn't quite as uncomfortable when girls were in the group nowadays, but he still wondered how he would feel when he next saw Lucy, which, strangely enough, happened the very day he came back to Salt Lake after finishing that term of school.

Lucy happened to be passing his home stacked to her chin

in bundles, when George walked out of his gate. With new poise he politely lifted his hat and asked to help with her bundles. He walked with her the short distance to her grandparents' home, and just as he handed back her packages at the gate, several of them fell to the ground and tore open. Embarrassed, he gathered the contents for her and carried them inside the house. As he was leaving the porch of the big house, he heard Lucy say to her grandmother, "George has become quite a fine young gentleman." Pride and inexpressible joy almost burst George's heart. At last he was reaching his goal . . . he was really becoming somebody. Her words lingered, and he needed nothing more to spur him to the limit of his strength. Now, when their lawn grew, and when the house looked more like he wanted it to look, he would feel free to invite Lucy to come over.

He quickly applied his energy to the cultivation of the new lawn. Throughout the summer the entire family worked tirelessly to complete the undertaking and to get the grass growing well before their father returned. There were no sprinkling hoses then, so small irrigating ditches had to be hoed and carefully tended in order that the fine lawn seed would be moistened but not be washed out by too much water. George always supervised the watering, as he couldn't take a chance on the others doing it alone. Soon the seeds were sending their first green spears through the ground. The entire family shared his delight in the remarkable change that was beginning to show.

Then, in a sudden thunder shower came tragedy. Torrents of rain fell upon the soft earth and washed out the young grass. Deep gullies were cut in the loose soil, and within a few minutes the family's work of months was destroyed. The ground must now be resurfaced. More seed must be bought, and the only possible money with which to purchase seed was that which George had earned by doing small jobs at school during the winter. These precious savings *were* to have bought a fall suit, to wear first when he met his father at the train.

Should he give up the idea of the lawn and get the suit as planned? True, all of the family would be disappointed if the lawn were not finished, but he so needed a suit and had planned for it many, many months; besides, who could tell whether there might be another thunder shower? For two days George, his mother, and some of the children considered the problem. Finally it was George who insisted that the seed be purchased so that the lawn might be replanted. This time it grew to a thick stand before so much as a drop of rain fell. It looked beautiful! George thought of it all day and hurried home from work to see how much better it looked every night.

The summer was passing and the time for his father's return was growing near. George had never looked nor been so happy. His old coat had been neatly sponged, pressed and darned, and the remaining suit money had bought new trousers and a stiff, white straw hat. He was ready for the glorious long-anticipated day when his father would return and look with inexpressible pride upon his greatly improved home and growing family.

But Brother Smith unfortunately arrived too late Saturday evening to see the lawn. George was almost afraid to go to sleep that night for fear all of them might not waken to be with their father when he first saw the lawn. But early, early Sunday morning the children dressed and walked with Brother Smith to the front door. As he caught his first view of their beautiful yard, his eyes twinkled. He looked proudly upon his eldest son and said, "My, we Smiths are *fine folk,* aren't we, George?" George experienced a joy never before known. He knew then that if his father felt that way, other people would feel that way too. He was not at all surprised when after Sunday School, Lucy and her grandparents walked home with them. Upon Brother and Sister Smith's invitation the three of them came in and sat with them under the apple tree . . . the older people in chairs and the young folk on the quilt, just exactly as George had dreamed a thousand times that they would . . . while George's mother served heaping dishes of lemon ice cream and sponge cake.

It was while daintily eating refreshments that Lucy said, "George, your family has the most beautiful front yard in the entire ward. I should like to sit under this tree whenever you will let me."

George didn't do what he wanted to do, jump straight up and down . . . but his heart did!

•   •   •

Right here Aunt Emily smiled.* She leaned back in her chair and began to slowly rock to and fro. The children who had just heard this story looked at her and guessed from her smile that she knew a part of the story that they didn't know, so Martie and Nancy exclaimed almost together, "Tell us what you are smiling about."

Aunt Emily answered, "You will smile too, when I tell you that this very real, normal boy is your grandfather and the

---

* "Aunt Emily" is Emily Smith Stewart, daughter of President George Albert Smith; Martie and Nancy are children of Edith Smith Elliott, also a daughter of President Smith.

Church's dearly beloved president, George Albert Smith . . . and the lovely little girl Lucy was his wife, who really never cared for the fancy boys at all. From the time she was a tiny girl she recognized George's greatness; she saw the genuine kindness and goodness in his heart and loved him dearly to the very, very last day of her life."

—Vilate Raile.

How My Life Was Preserved

You children have been so patient and good. You have waited a long time to have me tell you the story that I have promised you. I believe I will tell you three stories—three short ones of very important events in my life. Each of them was an occasion when I feel certain the Lord blessed me and spared my life. I would like you to hear me tell the experiences myself. I want to impress on you that the Lord will take care of you in times of danger, if you will give him the opportunity.

The first story I am going to tell you is an experience I had in the mission field. I was just a young man when I went on my mission to the Southern States. Your grandmother and I both labored in Tennessee. Most of the time she stayed at the mission home while I went out into the country sections. On this particular occasion I was traveling with President J. Golden Kimball. We were in a wooded, rural area. During the day we had held meetings with the people in the neighborhood who were very friendly and very receptive to our message. One of the local Saints had invited us to accept the hospitality of his home for the night. It was a humble home, built of split logs. It consisted of two rooms and a small log lean-to. There were six missionaries in the group, so it strained the capacity of the little house to be there.

About midnight we were awakened with a terrible shouting and yelling from the outside. Foul language greeted our ears as we sat up in bed to acquaint ourselves with the circumstances. It was a bright moonlight night and we could see many people on the outside. President Kimball jumped up and started to dress. The men pounded on the door and used filthy language, ordering the Mormons to come out, that they were going to shoot them. President Kimball asked me if I wasn't going to get up and dress and I told him, no, I was going to stay in bed, that I was sure the Lord would take care of us.

In just a few seconds the room was filled with shots. Apparently the mob had divided itself into four groups and were shooting into the corners of the house. Splinters were flying over our heads in every direction. There were a few moments of quiet, then another volley of shots was fired and more splinters flew. I felt absolutely no terror. I was very calm as I lay there, experiencing one of the most horrible events of my life, but I was sure that as long as I was preaching the word of God and following his teachings that the Lord would protect me, and he did.

Apparently the mob became discouraged and left. The next morning when we opened the door there was a huge bundle of heavy hickory sticks such as the mob used to beat missionaries in the South.

•   •   •

The scene of my second story is also laid in the Southern States during my first mission there. Late one evening in a pitch-dark night, Elder Stout and I were traveling along a high precipice. Our little walk was narrow; on one side was the wall of the mountain, on the other side, the deep, deep river. We had no light, and there were no stars and no moon to guide us. We had been traveling all day, and we knew that we would have hospitality extended to us if we could reach the McKelvin home, which was on the other side of a high valley. We had to cross this little mountain in order to reach the home of Mr. McKelvin. Our mode of travel of necessity was very halting. We walked almost with a shuffle, feeling each foot of ground as we advanced, with one hand extended toward the wall of the mountain. Elder Stout was ahead of me, and as I walked along I felt the hard surface of the trail under my feet. In doing so I left the wall of the mountain which had acted as a guide and a steadying force.

After I had taken a few steps away I felt impressed to stop immediately, that something was wrong. I called to Elder Stout and he answered me. The direction from which his voice came indicated I was on the wrong trail, so I backed up until I reached the wall of the mountain and again proceeded forward. He was just a few steps in front of me, and as I reached him we came to a fence piling. In the dark we carefully explored it with our hands and feet to see whether it would be safe to climb over. We decided it would be secure and made the effort.

While I was on the top of this big pile of logs, my little suitcase popped open and the contents were scattered around. In the dark I felt around for them and was quite convinced I had recovered practically everything. We arrived safely at our destination about eleven o'clock at night. I soon discovered I had lost my comb and brush, and the next morning we returned to the scene of my accident. I recovered my property, and while there my curiosity was stimulated and aroused to see what had happened the night before when I had lost my way in the dark. As missionaries we wore hobnails in the bottom of our shoes to make them last longer, so that I could easily follow our tracks in the soft dirt. I retraced my steps to the point where my tracks left the mountainside and discovered that in the darkness I had wandered to the edge of a deep precipice. Just one more step and I would have fallen over into the river and been drowned. I felt very ill when I realized how close I had come to death. I also was very grateful to my Heavenly Father for protecting me. I have always felt that if we are doing the Lord's work and asked him for his help and protection, he will guide and take care of us.

·   ·   ·

My next story is going to be about the Pacific Ocean and the wonderful swim I had in its beautiful blue waters off the shores of California. I was considered a very good swimmer and thoroughly enjoyed the sport. This particular day the tide was very high and very swift. As I left the shore and swam out into the ocean, I dived through the big breakers as they would crest and spray over me. My objective was the large swells beyond the breakers, where I could lie on my back and ride the big swells up and down. While engaging in this interesting sport, one very huge wave crested and broke before I could right myself following the dive through the previous one. The second one caught me and threw me to the floor of the ocean. I could feel myself being dragged out by the undertow. At this particular time many waves came in rapid succession, and I was not able to right myself before I had to dive from one into another. I realized that my strength was rapidly leaving me, that it was going to be necessary for me to find some means of help.

As I rode to the crest of one huge wave, I saw the under-pilings of a pier close at hand, and I thought if with superhuman effort I could reach the security of the pilings that I would be able to save my life. I silently asked my Heavenly Father to give me the strength to reach my objective. As I was washed into arm's length of the pier, I reached out and put my arms around one of the posts. They were covered with sharp, dark blue barnacles, and as I wound my arms and legs around its security, they cut my chest, legs, and thighs. I hung on as long as I could stand the pain and watched for a big friendly swell to come my way that I might throw myself on it and travel closer to shore.

Each time with a prayer in my heart, I would make the effort, traveling from one pile to another with the aid of the rolling swell. Slowly but surely and with great difficulty, I made my way to the shore where the water was shallow enough for me to walk to the beach. When I reached the safety of the warm sand, I fell exhausted. I was so weak and so nearly drowned I was unable to walk home until I had rested for some time. Lying on the sand with its warmth and security, I thought of the harrowing experience that I had just endured, and my heart was filled with gratitude and humility that the Lord had again spared my life.

—PRESIDENT GEORGE ALBERT SMITH.

I will incline mine ear to a parable:
I will open my dark saying upon the harp.

—Psalm 49:4.

Four Wise Men from the West

Rabbit-skin-leggings lifted his hot face to the cooling mountain rain. Great was the honor given to him this day. Of the four Wise Men chosen by his people to seek the white man's Book of Heaven in the faraway paleface nation, he was the youngest, unscarred, untried. If he should fail!

As he stood silently on Blue Mountain Crag, his heart prayed: "For the sacred journey, Great Spirit, let my sight be the eagle's, my strength the bear's, my feet tireless as the antelope's." Then with jaw set, upraised hands clenched in fierce supplication, he prayed: "Let my people never say, 'We were unwise to send young Rabbit-skin-leggings.'"

From the crag a cloud of mist spread out to dim the valley of the Salmon River below. It shut him off and set him apart as he wished to be, alone with his thoughts sacred to the day. Again he heard the head chief's mellow voice: "You, Rabbit-skin-leggings, are young like the morning. Many moons, many moccasins will wear out before the long trail is ended, but you will not fail. Son of the Oak, you will bring us the Book of Heaven. The stars will be your good medicine."

At those words uttered by the great chief in the sunrise council, Rabbit-skin-leggings had felt a strangeness creep over him. The spirit of the laughing boy went out of him, and the fire of a great calling burned his heart. He must get away to think and pray. To the mountains he had come. Up here on the cloud-washed crags the ear of the Great Spirit is ever open to his earth children. His voice in the rocking pines, his touch in the cooling rain give man's troubled mind strength, forbearance.

At last, when the rainstorm had cleared, Rabbit-skin-leggings found his way down the mountain trail in falling darkness. Generally the wild held many voices for this keen-sensed youth, but tonight it had only one—a challenge to be steady as the stars of heaven, for they were his good medicine.

Through the Flathead village of his people he made his way, unconscious of the many dogs that leaped up at his coming. Outside his home lodge his old father sat cross-legged upon a buffalo robe. The rising moon shed a soft light on his wrinkled face. At the footfall of his son the old man raised his head. Such joy shone in his almost sightless eyes! Rabbit-skin-leggings knew that his father was thinking of the great honor this day had bestowed upon his son. Solemnly the youth sat beside the veteran. Neither spoke. But their very silence seemed to say: "Tonight we are *men* together."

Finally the old man's thin lips moved: "I was young like you, my son, when the great redhead chief of the whites came to our people. He it was who told of the white man's Book of Heaven. I would learn more of it, to know with my heart, not just my ears. Many times I have traveled to the great white nation in my dreams. Now I am old. My teeth are worn, my eyes see only what I remember, my legs can travel little more. Before I die, I would hold the white man's Book of Heaven."

There was a quavering in the old man's voice. Quickly he checked it. "You leave in two sleeps, my son?"

"With the Wise Men in two sleeps."

"But the Blackfeet? Know you not the Blackfeet are in warpaint? They watch closely our mountain pass."

"We shall travel noiselessly on foot, say the Wise Men. Move by night and sleep by day."

"Yes, yes, but the Blackfeet have bad hearts. Three sleeps back they scalped fur gatherers who dared catch beaver on their streams. Are your arrows straight and sharp, my son?" There was concern in the old man's voice, but the young man answered evenly:

"I have traded my black pony for a white man's thunderstick. With that I do not fear the Blackfeet."

Old Oak raised his hands to his withered throat. "I hope you can find the redhaired chief of the whites. I gave him my pony. I shared my dried salmon. He will remember that. Do you know where to seek him?"

"At the joining of the Big Muddy with the Father of Waters."

"But his lodge? Can you find his lodge, my son? White people, the travelers say, are numerous as stars in the summer sky."

"We can find his lodge, for the trappers say he is now a great father and friend of the Indian."

"When do the fur gatherers leave with their long horse train for the white nation?"

"In two moons. After their big powwow."

The old man leaned forward. With a knotted hand he caught his son's knee: "If you wait," he whispered, "they could lead you to the redhead's lodge. They could help you through the Blackfoot land."

Rabbit-skin-leggings stared at his aging father. "We are not squaws," he said with dignity. "In two sleeps we go."

"The stars watch over you, my son," whispered the old man, as a light of pride swept his wrinkled face.

At daylight next morning everybody was astir. In lodge,

village, and river valley, all seemed intent on preparing the four Wise Men for the sacred mission to the great white nation.

Rabbit-skin-leggings's mother was cleaning his fine buckskin suit with a paste of white pipe clay brought in from the mountains. His sister was embroidering with dyed porcupine quills a pair of new moccasins for the long journey. His grandmother, aunts, and cousins were making pemmican to go with the dried salmon, bitter roots, and jerked buffalo meat. His little friend Camas Flower was fringing a buckskin bag which was to carry food on the long eastward march.

When the sun reached the high arch of the heavens, Rabbit-skin-leggings hurried to the lodge of the Medicine Man. Here he was to meet the other three Wise Men and go through the rites of purification.

He was glad he arrived first of all. He must never let these great men wait for him. In his small way he could show he was trustworthy.

Up strode Chief Speaking Eagle, the first chosen for the journey because, as the people said, "He is wise and knows the white man's ways."

Then came No-horns-on-his-head, chosen because he was tallest and handsomest of the chiefs.

And last came Chief Min, selected because of his oratory. "Words flow from his mouth as water from the mountain streams," said his friends in recommending him. On seeing the waiting Rabbit-skin-leggings, he said solemnly: "Thy strength be as the honored father's son of the Oak."

Together the four men entered the lodge. After solemn prayers by the Medicine Men and long dancing until all felt dizzy and weak, Rabbit-skin-leggings blindly followed his fellows into the steam room. Cold water, sent sizzling onto hot rocks, had filled the air with a smothering vapor. Soon every pore of his body was steaming water. Even his long black hair was heavy with perspiration. Then a plunge in the cold waters of the Salmon River, more prayers, and the ceremony was over.

But somehow, at the end of it all, he did seem lightened and purified. Returning to his home lodge, his heart lifted to the sun, joyous as a meadowlark's. His eyes were farseeing as the eagle's; his feet, light as the down of the wild duck.

Then came solemn preparation for the farewell council. His hair was soaked in oil. Eagle quills, presented by well-wishing braves, were woven into his long black braids. Vermillion paint, mixed with clays and fish oil, was streaked on his sloping forehead and beardless chin. A pair of buckskin leggings, a handsome hunting shirt, and new robes edged with gleaming shells and curling feathers was draped around his broad young shoulders. A knight preparing to seek not the Holy Grail but something as mysterious and sacred—the white man's Book of Heaven.

With a rush of painted glory, a new day quickened the Salmon River villages into life. Everybody was waiting to see the Wise Men off. With the prayers of the old men and the blessings of the women, the four copper-skinned pilgrims melted into the dawn. Single file they went, Rabbit-skin-leggings at the rear.

Soft as falling leaves their moccasined feet pat-patted along the trail—up, up to the dangerous pass through the snowy mountains! Stealthily under the blanket of night they crept past the Blackfoot lookout. Through the enemy country they slept

by day and moved by night, ever guided eastward by the beaming polar star.

They made no fires lest telltale smoke betray their presence.
They shot no game but ate dried food from their sacks. They
waded shallow creeks and swam deep rivers. The buffalo robe
was their shelter from rain and hail, their protection from the
damp ground when they slept.

Often Rabbit-skin-leggings ached to race through the
woods like a nimble deer, but he must be patient, cautious,
move slowly with the others. They were more wise than he.
Sometimes he acted as lookout and stealthily scouted around
to sight the Blackfoot camps.

After a tedious march across prairie lands, they came at last
to the white man's country. Such queer lodges! Numerous as
the pines in the forest. How could the whites get feed enough
for their horses with people living close together like that?

Early one golden October morning, welcomed by meadow-
larks and whispering autumn leaves, the four Wise Men
solemnly entered St. Louis, Missouri. Single file, up the middle
of the street they marched, their moist black braids gleaming in
the morning sun, their worn moccasins thin as paper from the
long journey. Quite different they looked from the spotless four
who had marched so spiritedly from their home behind the
shining mountains. They were mud-stained, dusty, and weary.

Chief Speaking Eagle, wise in white man's ways, led the
little band. No-horns-on-his-head, the tall handsome chief,
came next. Then came Chief Min, the orator, and last of all,
Rabbit-skin-leggings, son of the Oak.

But where could they find the great redhaired friend and
father of the Indians? Two amazed soldiers, standing by a

blacksmith shop, saw the bewildered look of the four strange Indians, heard their story, and gladly led them to General Clark, the redhaired chief. For many years he had been superintendent of Indian affairs of the West; naturally he was the proper person to receive them. And he was kind to the serious-faced Wise Men who had walked two thousand miles on their strange mission. He quartered them in the soldiers' barracks.

So they were after the white man's Book of Heaven? The general looked puzzled. He ran his fingers through his graying red hair. Rabbit-skin-leggings wondered if he were displeased. The general showed them a big black book that lay on the office table—"The Bible," he called it. In it were many pictures, one of a man, bearded, with a kindly face. Reverently the four chiefs turned the leaves. Then the general sent for Wise White Men to come and explain the book. They talked much and took the Indians to beautiful houses with roofs as high as the tallest pines and with windows that let in rainbow sunlight— churches.

Rabbit-skin-leggings listened much and talked little. With so many wiser tongues speaking, who was he to fill the air with childish nothings?

The curious chiefs were escorted about by soldiers. They were taken to see big ships on the river, schools, theatres, and dances. They were banqueted, fed every kind of strange food, and taken for rides in fine carriages behind glossy horses.

At last they had enough. True, the whites had much to excite their wonder. But for the Indian a bed in the open air, a seat on the ground, a feast of soup and salmon and pemmican—those sufficed his needs. All that they craved from the white men was his Book of Heaven. Given that, they would depart.

General Clark looked disturbed. Again he ran his fingers through his red hair. Again he opened the big book that lay on the table. "The book is not enough," he said. "You should have a Wise White Man along to explain the book. Wait, and I will find someone. With winter soon, it is unwise to travel homeward now."

They accepted his advice simply, and so through the winter months the Wise Men waited. One night Speaking Eagle felt a great dizziness and sank upon his bunk. The next day he did not rise. Then No-horns-on-his-head, Chief Min, and finally Rabbit-skin-leggings became ill too. For days they lay helpless upon their beds. The soldiers, doctors, and even pretty Mrs. Clark herself came to their aid.

Was it cholera? There were other cases on the frontier. Or was the sickness due to the great change from their Indian food and living?

Speaking Eagle, the wise old chief, and the handsome brave, No-horns-on-his-head, never rose again. Each was given a soldier's burial and laid to rest beside the Father of Waters.

Slowly the other two recovered. But for a time Rabbit-skin-leggings felt as helpless as when he had been a papoose on his mother's back. For hours he lay thinking of his old father, the Oak. He was anxious to be on his way back home with the book, but the thought of the long walk made his heart faint.

Finally, with the Cold Month gone, the two homesick chiefs prepared to depart. It was many moons since they had left their quiet home in the Salmon River Valley. As yet General Clark had found no one to accompany them. But at the sight of their sad faces he had not the heart to detain them longer. The steamboat would soon be making its spring trip up the Big Muddy to the Yellowstone, and the chiefs could ride part way on that. Before they left, General Clark handed them a small Testament wrapped in oilskin paper. "Tell your people, soon a white man will come with the big book. A man of God. He will teach you to read, that you may know the book with your heart, not just your ears. A pleasant journey home, my friends!"

A warm handclasp from the redhaired chief and they were off. Up the Missouri River they steamed for many days. When they finally reached the Yellowstone country, Rabbit-skin-leggings was well and strong again. But Chief Min looked with watery eyes toward the ghosts of his mountains in the west.

A cold north wind slapped the thick braids of the Flathead Wise Men as they started their dangerous journey through the Blackfoot country. Night after night they trudged on with the storm beating about them. By day they huddled together without a fire, keeping watch by turns.

One cold morning Chief Min sank in his tracks. "Leave me," he whispered, "but take the Book of Heaven to our people."

"A few more days of travel, brother, a few more sleeps, then warm sunshine in the valley of the Salmon! Kind voices of our people!" encouraged Rabbit-skin-leggings.

But Chief Min would not rouse. Rabbit-skin-leggings tore strips from his buffalo robe and fashioned a harness. With this he tied Chief Min to his back and slowly made his way along the trail. But the raw winds chilled the older chief. A hollow cough racked his thin body. With chattering teeth he begged to be left to die.

At length Rabbit-skin-leggings found himself wearing under the strain. He must build a little fire while they rested to revive their strength. Leaving his friend in a stupor beneath a sheltering bush, he climbed to the top of a nearby hill to view the surrounding country. Blackfoot villages on every hand. A fire here would bring a hundred enemies upon him. He must travel on. At a terrible groan from Chief Min he rushed to his side. Wolves were nearly upon the dying man. Rabbit-skin-leggings drew his gun and fired.

Instantly he realized his danger. That signal might bring the Blackfeet upon him. With a supreme effort, again he shouldered the dying chief and struggled along the trail. He dared not stop. He must not give up. Weaker and weaker he grew. Heavier and heavier was his burden. He was on his knees now—crawling. At last he collapsed in a cold sweat. When his mind had roused from its daze, he whispered: "Brother!"

There was no answer. He peered into the face of his comrade. No need for a fire now. Chief Min of the golden words had ended his journey.

With a desperate courage Rabbit-skin-leggings once again took up his friend upon his back. He climbed a tree. Up there on a horizontal limb he tied the body safe from the jaws of the wolf and deeply shaded from the eyes of the Blackfeet.

Then on the pine carpet at the foot of the sheltering tree, Rabbit-skin-leggings tightened his robe about him, and fell into deep exhausted slumber. He and the Book of Heaven were alone among the Blackfeet. And they had heard the gun.

What happened later that night Rabbit-skin-leggings could scarcely explain. As if something had touched him, he awoke suddenly and leaped to his feet. At the movement a dozen dark forms slunk into the bushes; a dozen pairs of glassy eyes, wolf eyes, gleamed at him in the cold starlight. In prayer he pressed his hand against the little black book. The fire died in the receding eyes, but now Blackfoot warriors towered above him. Closer they came. They were bearing down upon him, the chief with his upraised skull crusher.

"Brothers, see!" cried Rabbit-skin-leggings in the Blackfoot tongue, as he held aloft the little book. "Behold! The great Medicine Book of the Whites. I bring it from their faraway nation. The Book of Heaven. It is here. For Blackfeet! For Flatheads! 'We are brothers,' says the book. In the Happy Hunting Grounds my people and your people will hunt the *wapiti* (elk) together, and there will be plenty for all. I carry the good message to my people. You will help me on!"

For a breathless moment eyes met in challenge. The Blackfoot chief with his upraised skull crusher, young Rabbit-skin-leggings, the Flathead, with his holy book.

Suddenly a white fire burned the heavens—a brilliant star fire that blinded while it mystified. The steadfast stars had broken from their moorings. Across the sky-heaven they coursed as though all the gleams in the Milky Way were falling. Never before had the Great Spirit spoken with sky signals that blinded like the sun. Blackfoot and Flathead fell prostrate on the ground and worshipped!

While the falling stars spoke to the hearts of the Blackfeet, across the valley in the west where the Flathead tribe had assembled for the annual spring buffalo hunt, another heart was lighted by the message from the stars. Rabbit-skin-leggings's father, the Oak, though tottering and nearly blind, had caught the glory of that memorial night.

"My son is come with the Book of Heaven," he whispered to his people. "The stars are his good medicine!" And it was so! Rabbit-skin-leggings alone had returned safely from the four-thousand-mile pilgrimage. He was carrying a precious oilskin package—the book—that told of other Wise Men and of another star that had led to an Infant Chief, Son of the white man's Great Spirit.

True to his promise, General Clark, the redhaired chief, sent white men to teach the meaning of the book to the Flathead people. After the next snow had passed, Jason and Daniel Lee, good white brothers, came with the green grass. Later came Marcus Whitman, Father De Smet, and other missionaries who found in the hearts of these Indians the spirit of peace—true spirit of the white man's Book of Heaven.

As Indian events are reckoned from the "year when the stars fell," so scientists say that in the year 1833 there was a great meteoric shower. To the questioning Flatheads, the starry wonders had been signs from the heavens that the white man's Book of Heaven was true.

—ANN WOODBURY HAFEN.

THE STONE IN THE ROAD

This story happened in a far-off country and a far-off time in the domain of honest Duke Otho, near the little village of Himmelsmerl. One dark night a tall man in a long cloak scooped out a little round hole in the very middle of the much-traveled road at a place called the Dornthau. When it was very deep, he lined the side and bottom with pebbles. From the folds in the cloak, he took something about the size of his fist and placed it in the pebble-lined hole. When this was done, he went to the side of the road and worked at a large stone till it was loosened; it was so heavy he could only stagger with it to the hole which he had dug and let the stone drop so as to cover the hole and then went his way.

Next morning Hans, a sturdy peasant farmer, came that way with his lumbering oxcart. "Oh, the laziness," he cried, "of these people! Here is this big stone right in the middle of the road, and not one of them bethought himself to thrust it aside; it should break the bones of the next body that comes by!" And the sturdy Hans turned around the stone and lumbered away, muttering to himself at the laziness of the people of Himmelsmerl. When he reached home, he told his wife and children that the duke ought to know what kind of folk his people were.

Next a gallant knight, with his bright and waving plume and dangling sword, rollicked along, singing a lively ditty. But his head was too far back for him to notice the stone, and down he fell, with his sword between his legs. His song stopped short as he growled at "those boors and dolt-headed clodhoppers, who leave a rock in the road to break a gentleman's shins."

He went on. Next came a company of merchants with pads, packhorses, and goods, on their way to the fair that was to be held at the duke's great town. When they came to the stone, so narrow was the road, they had to file off on each side, and Berthold cried: "To think the like of that big stone lying there, and every soul to go past all the morning and never stop to take it away! That will be something to tell friend Hans, who is always bewailing the sloth of the Himmelsmerl folk."

And thus it went on for the three weeks that were left of October. Every passenger upbraided his neighbor for leaving the hindrance where he found it.

When three weeks had passed since the tall man in the cloak had put the stone in the road, the duke sent word to his people of Himmelsmerl to meet him on the Dornthau, at the very spot where the rock was, for he had something to tell them. The day had come, and a crowd thronged the road at the appointed spot. Old Hans was there and the merchant Berthold. Said Hans: "I hope my Lord Duke will now know what a lazy set he is duke over."

"It is a shame," answered Berthold.

And now a winding horn was heard, and the people strained necks and eyes toward the castle as a cavalcade came galloping to the Dornthau. The duke rode into the cut, and the people closed in at each end and pressed nearer together on the bank above. Then honest Otho, who had dismounted, began with a half smile to speak.

"My people, you know I am fond of teaching you now and then a lesson in an odd way, and for such a lesson have I called you together this day. It was I who put this stone here, and for three weeks every passerby has left it there and scolded his neighbor for not taking it out of the way."

When he had thus spoken, he stooped down, lifted the stone, and disclosed a round hollow lined with white pebbles and in it a small leather bag. This the duke held aloft, that all the people might see it. Then he read what was written upon it: "For him who lifts the stone!"

He untied it, turned it upside down, and out upon the stone fell, with a beautiful ring, a score of bright gold coins.

Hans looked at Berthold and said: "Humph!"

And Berthold looked back at Hans and said: "Humph!"

And the duke looked round him with a smile and said: "My people, remember the stone in the road."

Better Than That

Joseph was one of Austria's greatest emperors, and many trembled at his frown. The monarchs of other lands paid court to him, and he was the envy of all; but he often grew weary of the cares of state and longed for a more simple life than he could live in his palace. His greatest pleasure at such times was to leave his nobles and wander unattended through the streets of his grand capital so plainly dressed that he might have been one of his poorer subjects. Sometimes he would go for a ramble in the surrounding country, finding in the company of the woodfolk and the rustling of the forest leaves far more delight than in the gorgeous functions at the palace.

One Sunday in autumn, when the trees had donned their richest garb of red and orange, he started out. People he met were dressed in their best, as if bad weather were out of the question. The wind blew up from the rainy quarter, and before long a sharp shower made the emperor raise the hood of his buggy. The citizens now were hurrying to shelter, and he too thought it well to return. He had not driven far upon the homeward road when a soldier accosted him, little guessing to whom he spoke.

"I beg your pardon, sir," he said, "but I thought that perhaps you would give me a lift, as I should not inconvenience you. My uniform is a new one, and I don't want to get it spoiled."

He was a fine, handsome young fellow, with a frank and open face. The emperor was much taken by his appearance and invited him to jump in. In a few minutes they were chatting together as if they had been well acquainted, and the soldier treated his new friend to a glowing account of a pleasant day he had lately spent with an old comrade.

"He gave me a famous dinner, I can tell you," he concluded, and the emperor, much amused, inquired of what this had consisted.

"Guess," cried the soldier, chuckling with delight at the recollection of his feast.

"Cabbage soup, perhaps?" questioned his majesty with an indulgent smile.

"Soup, indeed," the soldier exclaimed with much contempt. "Better than that; you must guess again."

"A calf's head, then?" said the emperor.

"Better than that, even!" was the laughing answer, and the same reply was given when the emperor suggested a big slice of ham.

"Much better than that!" cried the soldier triumphantly. "I had a roast pheasant, and one that I shot myself on his majesty's estate, for my friend is now one of the emperor's gamekeepers. It was delicious, and no mistake."

His companion made no reply, but the soldier chatted away quite at his ease, telling him of the aged parents who were so proud of him, and the dear little Greta who would one day become his wife.

"Where do you live?" inquired his majesty as they neared

the city. "The rain has ceased, but I should like to drive you home."

Much gratified by this further kindness, the soldier thanked him warmly and begged that he would tell his name.

"Ah! It is your turn to guess now," remarked the emperor. "Who do you think I am?"

"Perhaps you also have something to do with the army," hazarded the soldier with a searching look. The emperor nodded.

"You are a private soldier?" was the next guess.

"Better than that," the emperor smilingly returned.

"A lieutenant, then?"

"Better than that!"

"A colonel?" stammered the soldier, beginning to feel alarmed.

"Better than that, I assure you."

"Perhaps, then, you are a general?" the man said timidly, and then in desperation, as the emperor shook his head, he suggested, "A field marshal?"

"Better than that!" said the emperor once more, and the soldier turned pale with terror.

"Then you must be his majesty himself!" he gasped and would have sprung from the buggy if the emperor had not prevented him.

"We will keep to our bargain," he said and insisted on driving him right up to his home. On the way he gave the young man some good advice that he would never forget and ended by saying, with a kindly twinkle in his deep-set eyes: "And be careful in the future not to kill pheasants before first obtaining the owner's permission, or to tell tales of your friends to the first stranger who comes your way."

—LILLIAN GASK.

THE FLIGHT OF FEATHERS

Assuma was an Algonquin chieftain and wise as he was good. For a thousand moons his tribe had prospered under his care. He had restrained the young men when they wished to put on the war paint and go forth to slay, and he gathered the little children around his knees when the fires were bright and warm, that he might fill their minds with thoughts that they would cherish.

The great chieftain had searched the innermost nature of his people and learned that only the good and the true were brave. A world of wickedness about him had shown him the horrible truth that evil ways never failed to leave in their wake a trail of sorrow. He had seen jealousy creep into the hearts of the young, and he had seen pale, dead faces in the night.

On the dark skins that covered the walls of his own abode, Assuma had formed strange signs. There was a cross. When a member of his tribe looked upon it, he remembered his chieftain's words, "You shall help one another." And there was a square. When an Algonquin looked upon it, he remembered the words, "You shall deal justly with one another." And the circle; when they looked upon it, they remembered, "You shall be kind to one another." Finally there was the print of a human hand, which told them to remember the words, "You shall work for the good of all."

It happened one day that Assuma sat at his tepee door, his ear open to the grievances of anyone who might cry for justice. A slender girl approached slowly and dropped to her knees, weeping.

Assuma laid his hand on her head and comforted her, "Why have you come, my daughter?" he asked. "Who has offended you?"

"I have come because I have broken the good circle," the girl confessed.

"How have you broken it, my daughter?"

"I have told that which is not true about one of the maidens of the tribe. Now others are pointing at her, and she is ashamed."

"Why did you do this thing?"

"Because," said the girl, hesitatingly, "her string of shells is prettier than mine!"

"That is bad!" said Assuma. "You have indeed broken the good circle. And you have also broken the cross, because you have harmed instead of helped another. And you have also broken the square, because you have been unjust. And you have also broken the sign of the human hand, because you have worked against the good of all. You must be punished. The evil words that you have spoken must be gathered up, one by one, from the ears of those who have heard them. Thus, only, can justice be done and peace restored.

"At dawn you shall go with me to the top of the high hill yonder. You shall bring with you a large goose. I shall be waiting for you."

The girl went away sadder than when she had come. Then the great chief called one of his runners to him and sent him hastily with a message to all the tribesmen, far and near, bidding them to gather at the council grounds at the foot of the high hill.

The new day dawned, and the sad young girl came at the appointed time to the summit of the high hill, carrying a goose. A great throng was gathering at the foot of the hill. Assuma took the goose and plucked a feather from its wing. He held it up in the air and released it to the wind, which quickly swirled it about, and soon it was lost to sight.

"My daughter," said Assuma, "you shall stand in this spot and pick the feathers from the goose, one by one, and set them adrift upon the wind. When you have plucked them all, come to me at the foot of the hill, where our people have gathered."

All through the day the maiden plucked the feathers and cast them adrift. And when night had come, she crept wearily down the hill.

Assuma met her as she drew near and led her before the gathering. "My children," he said, "you have seen the scattering of an untruth, like the feathers of a goose. Its words have drifted here and there among you on the winds of speech. Lying words are in your hearts, eating like a hungry wolf at the white innocence of another. You alone can find them. They must be found and destroyed that they may do no further harm.

"Tomorrow you shall go into the woods and out upon the plains seeking the feathers this young maiden has plucked from the goose. For each feather that is brought back to me there shall be a reward. When evening comes, we shall gather here again, and you will feast and dance, for the good name of one of us has been brought back to life.

Though the entire tribe searched all day, only seven feathers were found. These Assuma placed in the girl's hand. "Take these," he said, "to the one of whom you spoke evil, and tell her that these seven feathers are all you can give back to her to atone for that which you have taken away."

So was it all done in silence with the light of the evening sun shining golden on the hillside, and peace lit like a silver star above the hearts of men, for a great truth had come to earth.

—USED BY PERMISSION OF THE *SUNSHINE MAGAZINE*.

ROMULUS AND REMUS

Romulus and Remus were twin babies. Their mother died when they were very tiny. No one else loved them enough to care for them, so they were placed in a watertight basket and sent floating down the River Tiber.

The winds took care not to ripple the surface of the water, lest the basket tip. The sun shone on the babies and warmed them as they drifted slowly down the river. It was very much like being rocked in a mother's warm arms.

Although the Tiber could carry them gently on his breast, and the winds could watch over them, and the sun could keep them warm, there was one thing that still troubled the babies. They were hungry and had no milk.

Then the River Tiber called all the little streams which emptied their water into his. They poured into the Tiber until he overflowed his banks, and the basket was carried high on the sand. Then the water drew back and left the babies on dry land.

A mother wolf came prowling beside the river looking for

food. When she saw the basket, she trotted over. Romulus and Remus were crying and putting their fists in their mouths. Somehow they reminded the wolf of her own babies, although her own cubs were covered with fur and could stand on their feet.

She licked the babies with her tongue but never once thought of eating them. She rolled them out of the basket with her paw and pushed them ever so gently over the sand and grass to her cave.

Dragging them inside, she put them in her nest where her little wolves were sleeping. They awoke, as she stretched herself beside them, and crowded around her to get their milk. Romulus and Remus drank too and went to sleep cuddled up close to their strange new mother.

For many weeks they lived in the cave and played with the little wolves, rolling over and over and wrestling with them. They grew strong and could walk long before other babies.

One day they crept to the opening of the cave and saw the blue sky and the sunshine. After that the mother wolf had a hard time keeping them inside. One day when she was away, a shepherd came by and saw the two babies playing on the grass. He carried them home to his wife, who brought them up as her own children.

She taught them to drink milk from cups and made them tunics to wear. They grew to love the shepherd and his wife, but they never forgot their wolf mother and often ran back to the cave to see her and romp in the sunshine with her cubs.

They loved to play beside the river and wade and swim in the warm water or dig in the sand.

"When I am grown," said Romulus, "I shall build a house with wide porches and tall columns of marble beside the Tiber."

Little Remus did not live to grow up. But years after, Romulus built his house on the banks of the Tiber near the cave where the mother wolf had nursed him.

He had many friends who came and built their houses near-by. In time a beautiful city grew up, and Romulus was so strong and wise that the people made him their ruler. That was the beginning of the great city of Rome, which still stands and grows beside the River Tiber.

A Man Who Kept His Promise

David Livingstone was a good man and a great explorer. He loved new places and strange people. Once he went to Africa to do missionary work. Many of the people in that country have very dark skin and live much of the time out-of-doors. They live in tribes as the Indians do and have chiefs for their leaders.

David Livingstone made his way deep into the heart of Africa. Here he found many of these dark-skinned people. He was immediately interested in them and felt sorry for them, for they were being treated cruelly. Many were being sold as slaves. Mr. Livingstone believed that all people were children of our Father in Heaven; so he made up his mind that he would do something to stop this cruelty. He felt that if he could open a way to the west coast, it would help him to accomplish his desire. To do this meant that he must take a long, long journey through the wilderness. It would not be an easy task, and if he didn't have help it would be impossible. He must have the help of his dark-skinned friends, for they knew the way and were used to traveling in that country.

When he tried to get help, one of the chiefs said, "I will get some men to go with you, if you will promise to guide them on their return journey." Livingstone promised, the party was organized, and the journey began. The road was hard, for there were jungles and swamps to get through, large rivers to be crossed, and many other dangers of the jungles to be met. They made their way slowly. Then one day David Livingstone became very sick with a fever. Since there was no place to stop for help, his friends had to carry him on their shoulders the rest of the long, hard way.

After more than six months of exhausting struggle the weary and distressed party reached the ocean, the end of the journey. Here at the coast were food, shelter, medical care, and, above all, a boat just ready to sail for England.

When the captain of the boat saw Livingstone so ill, he urged him to get on the boat and go back to England. Livingstone had not seen nor even heard from his family in nearly two years; he was sick, but he had made a promise to his companions that he would take them back, and he would not break it. He said good-bye to the captain and watched the boat sail away. After he rested for a while he began the hard journey home with his friends of the wilderness, to whom he had made a promise which could not be broken.

We are not surprised to know that when David Livingstone died, his dark-skinned friends carried his body over many weary miles to the east coast of Africa, that he might be buried in his own land from which he had come to them.

Recently a traveler asked a keeper at Westminster Abbey, the place in England where David Livingstone is buried, "Which grave has had the most visitors during the past year?"

"Without a question," replied the keeper, "the grave of David Livingstone." That was the grave of the man who kept his promise even at great cost.

HANS, THE SHEPHERD BOY

Hans was a little shepherd boy. One day he was keeping his sheep near a great wood when a hunter rode up to him.

"How far is it to the nearest village, my boy?" asked the hunter.

"It is six miles, sir," said Hans. "But the road is only a sheep track. You might easily lose your way."

"My boy," said the hunter, "if you will show me the way, I will pay you well."

Hans shook his head. "I cannot leave the sheep, sir," he said. "They would stray into the woods, and the wolves might kill them."

"But if one or two sheep are eaten by the wolves, I will pay you for them. I will give you more than you can earn in a year."

"Sir, I cannot go," said Hans. "These sheep are my master's. If they are lost, I should be to blame."

"If you cannot show me the way, will you get me a guide, and I will take care of your sheep while you are gone."

"No," said Hans. "I cannot do that. The sheep do not know your voice, and—" Then he stopped.

"Can't you trust me?" asked the hunter.

"No," said Hans, "you have tried to make me break my word to my master. How do I know that you would keep your word?"

The hunter laughed. "You are right," said he. "I wish I could trust my servants as your master can trust you. Show me the path. I will try to get to the village alone."

Just then several men rode out of the wood. They shouted for joy.

"Oh, sir!" cried one, "we thought you were lost."

Then Hans learned to his great surprise that the hunter was a prince. He was afraid that the great man would be angry with him. But the prince smiled and spoke in praise of him.

A few days later a servant came from the prince and took Hans to the palace.

"Hans," said the prince, "I want you to leave your sheep to come and work for me. I know you are a boy who will always do your best."

Hans was very happy.

"If my master can find another boy to take my place, then I will come and work for you."

So Hans went back and tended the sheep until his master found another boy. After that he worked many years for the prince.

TOM'S GIFT

Once upon a time in a land far from here there lived the most beautiful queen in the world. She was as good as she was beautiful, and so all her people loved her dearly.

In the good queen's country there lived a little boy named Tom. One morning little Tom heard a number of men talking together in the market place.

"Tomorrow is our dear queen's birthday," said one. "I shall give her a pot of honey, for honey is the sweetest thing in the world."

"I shall give her a cup made of pure gold," said another, "for gold is the richest thing in the world."

"I shall give her a bird in a golden cage. It will sing to her, and everybody knows that music is the most joyous thing in the world," said the third man.

Little Tom walked sadly away. "I love the sweet queen as dearly as anyone else does," he sighed, "yet I alone am too poor to get her a gift for her birthday."

Suddenly his face brightened. "I know what I can do," he thought. "The queen loves the little white flowers that grow in the meadow. I will gather a bunch and give it to her," he whispered. "She would love even one sweet flower."

"Who would love one sweet flower?" asked a voice.

Tom turned around. There stood an old woman, "Granny Jones," everybody called her. She gathered sweet-smelling herbs, dried them, tied them in bunches, and sold them to the doctor for medicine.

"Our beautiful queen would love the flower," answered Tom. "Tomorrow is her birthday, and I am too poor to buy a gift for her, so I came for some flowers, but you see there are none open, not even one."

Granny Jones smiled a peculiar smile, then she said, "I know where a beautiful white flower grows, a perfect one. If you will carry my bundles to town to Dr. Phipps, I will get this beautiful flower for you, and you can take it to the queen."

Tom was delighted to think he was about to get a perfect white flower, so he gladly offered to carry the bundles of herbs to town.

The journey was pleasant, and the bundles of herbs were not heavy. Coming home seemed longer and very lonesome, because it was late, and Tom had no one to talk to. In his pocket was the money Dr. Phipps had given him for the herbs.

As he came near the place where he had left old Granny Jones, there she stood waiting for him, eager to get the money. She had the white flower and gave it to Tom in exchange for the money.

"There, Tom, is your sweet, white flower," said Granny Jones.

Tom could hardly speak for joy, but he managed to thank her for her kindness to him, and clasping the dear, white flower gently in his hand, he hastened home to show his mother and tell her of his journey to town.

Next day Tom stood timidly at one side and watched all the people give their presents to the queen. At last he drew near and handed her his one perfect blossom, saying, "My gift, dear queen, is very small, but my love is very great."

Tears came into the eyes of the beautiful queen. She took the fair flower and whispered, "Thank you, dear little Tom. I like your gift the best of all, for I know, and you know, and everybody knows that love is the best thing in the whole world."

—JENNIE B. HUFFAKER.

THE SILVER SKATES

Hurry up!" shouted Gretchen. "It's almost time to be there." "Yes, yes," replied Hans, "I am coming soon; just wait until I can find my skates."

Soon the two children were scurrying through the streets of a little Dutch town toward the canals. Ice was everywhere that January day, and the daily papers had announced that it was thick enough for the thousands of people who were to look on at the skating contest, an annual event, in which only the children took part.

What a merry scene it was. Every yard of the three-mile run was lighted by crackling fires; banners waved in the breeze, and little booths had been erected where the hungry and thirsty might find hot cakes and warm drinks.

The start for the race in which Gretchen and Hans were to take part lay opposite one of the booths, and the first bell had already rung when they came to the canal.

"Skates on!" rang a loud voice, and a hundred children stooped and fastened on their skates.

How bright and excited they all looked, for was not the prize to be a pair of silver skates, the finest ever seen?

"Three miles and back," rang out the voice of the manager again. "Turn at the blue flag and skate back to the starting point."

"My, what a long distance," said an American who had come many miles to see the famous race of the children.

"Oh, that's nothing for a Dutch girl or boy," said a man standing near. "What would you think of twenty-five miles and back? That's something they like; but they are brought up to it, you know."

"Hark!" Another bell, then the word "Go!" and off started the children, all clad in loose-knitted blouses, baggy trousers, with brightly colored caps upon their heads!

With hearts beating rapidly, Gretchen and Hans began the return trip. Their round faces were red and glowing, and the sparks fairly flew from the irons of their skates. They turned not to the right nor left now, but went straight to the mark, while the other skaters were far in the rear; in fact, most of them had given up the race long ago.

Only a mile separated them from the booth where they had started—a half mile—a few yards—when suddenly with a crash, a fall, and poor, little Gretchen lay with her face to the cold ice.

"Just a yard more and she would have won!" exclaimed the American again, as Hans turned to help his little playmate. Gretchen was a brave child, for had she not behind her a race of brave and hardy people. Although she had stumbled on the hard ice and was badly hurt, not a tear was shed.

"It is yours!" she cried, as she tried to rise. But Hans shook his head. "No, Gretchen," he said, "the silver skates are yours. You were ahead when you fell; I could not have won, anyway," and he helped her forward to the booth where lay the prize in its beautiful red velvet case.

"They are yours, my little man, and bravely won," said the manager to Hans heartily.

Without a word Hans took the silver skates and handed them to Gretchen. Gretchen was so happy she didn't know whether to laugh or cry. As they walked away together, the great crowd set up a shout for Hans, who was so unselfish.

—SELECTED.

I'M GOING TO

Johnny," said his mamma one day, "will you bring me an armful of wood?" "Yes," said Johnny, "I'm going to," but just then he heard Carlo the dog barking at a chipmunk over in the meadows, so he ran off as fast as he could go.

Now this is not the first time that Johnny had said to his mamma, "Yes, I'm going to." He meant to do it; but he never thought of that wood again until about dinner time, when he began to feel hungry.

When he got back, he found that dinner was over, and Papa and Mamma had gone for a ride. He found a piece of bread and butter and sat down on a large rock, with his back against the stump of a tree to eat it.

When it was all gone, Johnny began to think what he should do next. He closed his eyes again as people are apt to do when they think.

Presently he heard a score of voices about him. One was saying, "Wait a bit." Another, "Pretty soon," another, "In a minute," another, "By and by," and still another louder than the rest kept screaming as loud as it could, "Going to, going to, going to," till Johnny thought they were crazy.

"Who in the world are you?" said he in great surprise. "And what are you making such a noise about?"

"We are telling our names," said they. "Didn't you ask us to tell our names?"

"No," said Johnny, "I didn't."

"Oh, what a story," cried they all in one breath.

"Let's shake him for it," said one.

"No, let's carry him miles and miles over the hills and up to a big cave in the mountain." Then he heard ever so many more voices, and it was noisier than ever.

"Where am I?" he said, as soon as he could speak.

"Oh, you're safe at home," said Wait a Bit, for he seemed to be the spokesman, "And they have been expecting you for some time."

"This isn't my home," said Johnny, feeling very miserable and beginning to cry.

"Oh, yes it is," said a chorus of voices. "This is just where such folks belong. There are many of you fellows here, and you won't be lonesome a bit."

They had begun to unwind the web from his eyes now, so he opened them and looked about him. Oh, what a wretched place it was.

Against the side of the cave stood long rows of boys and girls, with very sorry faces, all of them, saying over as fast as they could speak, "Going to, going to," "Wait a bit, wait a bit," "Pretty soon, pretty soon," "In a minute, in a minute," studying the names just as hard as if they were lessons.

There were Delays and Tardys and Put-offs with ever so many more; and in a corner by themselves, and looking more unhappy than all the rest, were the poor little fellows whose names were Too Late.

"Oh, dear, dear! Where am I?" said Johnny in despair. "Please let me out. I want my mamma!"

"No, you don't," said Wait a Bit. "You don't care much about her, and this is where you belong. This is the Kingdom of Procrastination, and yonder comes the king."

"The kingdom of what?" asked Johnny, who had never heard such a long word in all his life before.

But just then he heard a heavy footfall and a great voice that sounded like a roar, saying, "Has he come? Did you get him?"

"Yes, he is here," said Wait a Bit, "and he'd just been saying it a little while before we picked him up."

Johnny looked up and saw a monstrous giant. "Let me have him," said the giant. So he took him up just as if he had been a rag-baby and looked him all over, turning him from side to side and from head to feet. Oh, but Johnny was frightened and expected at every moment to be swallowed.

"Let's see," said the giant. "He always says 'Pretty soon!' No, that isn't it. What is it, my fine fellow, that you always say to your mamma when she asks you to do anything for her? It isn't 'Pretty soon,' nor 'In a minute.' What is it? They all mean about the same thing to be sure and bring everybody to me in the end, but I must know exactly, or I can't put you in the right place."

Johnny hung his head and did not want to tell, but an extra poke of the giant's big finger made him open his mouth and say with shame that he always said, "I'm going to."

"Oh, that's it," said the giant. "Well, then, you stand there."

So he unwound a bit of the web from his fingers—just enough that he could hold the Procrastination's primer—and stood him at the end of a long row of children, who were saying over and over again, just as fast as they could speak, "Going to—going to—going to—going to." Just that and nothing else in the world.

Johnny was tired and hungry by this time and longed to see his mamma, thinking that if he could only get back to her, he would always mind the very moment she told him to do anything.

He made a great many resolutions while he stood there. At last the giant called him to come and say his lesson.

"You shall have a short one today," said he, "and need only say it a thousand times, because it is your first day here. Tomorrow you must say it a million."

Johnny tried to step forward, but the web was still about his feet, so he fell with a bang to the floor.

Just then he opened his eyes to find that he had been asleep and had rolled from the rock to the grass, and that Mamma was calling him, and this time he didn't say, "I'm going to."

THE FRIENDSHIP OF DAMON AND PYTHIAS

Dionysius was a tyrant who ruled the town of Syracuse, in Italy. Whoever made him angry was put to death. The tyrant's wrath fell one day upon a youth named Damon, who had complained of the cruelty of Dionysius, and Damon was condemned to die. He begged first to be allowed to go to see his wife and children, but Dionysius laughed him to scorn.

"Once you get out of my way," he thought, "you will never come back."

Damon said that he had a friend who would answer for his return, and his friend Pythias came forward to offer himself as surety in his friend's place.

The tyrant was astonished that a man should love his friend so dearly, and he gave Damon six hours to go to see his wife and children.

Damon expected to be back within four hours, but when four hours had come he had not come. Five hours, then almost six hours passed, and still there was no sign of him. The happiest man in the prison was Pythias, who actually hoped that Damon would not return, because he was willing and anxious to suffer in his place and spare his friend for the sake of his wife and children. At last the death-day dawned, the very hour grew nigh, and Dionysius came to see his prisoner die.

Quietly and bravely Pythias prepared for his execution. His friend, he said, had had an accident, or perhaps he was ill. At almost the very moment for the execution, however, Damon arrived and embraced his friend. He was tired and travel stained. His horse had been killed, and he had had to get another, but by hard riding he returned just in time to save Pythias from suffering for him. But Pythias did not wish it so. He pleaded with Damon; he pleaded with Dionysius to let him bear the punishment.

Dionysius had never seen such faithfulness before. Here was something beautiful that he did not think existed in the world—friendship that welcomed death if death would help a friend. His heart was stirred within him; he wanted men like these to be his friends. He came up to Damon and Pythias as they were disputing, each eager to give up his life for the other. Dionysius took their hands, set them free, and begged to be allowed to share their friendship.

THE MAGIC MASK

In a far-off country across the seas lived a great and powerful prince. He had hundreds of fine-trained soldiers in his army. With banners flying he would set out to battle against his foes. With the help of his soldiers he was often victorious and ruled with an iron hand over vast strips of country.

His enemies as well as his friends feared him because of his strong determination to have his own way in all things, and unlucky was the man who brought upon himself the thunder and lightning of his wrath.

Yet he won the respect of all by his bravery. The prince was always found in the foremost ranks or in the thickest of the fray. But no one loved him, and as he grew older, he became lonely and unhappy, which made him more stern and severe. His face became seamed with hard, cruel lines, and a deep frown was furrowed on his forehead, and no one ever saw him smile or heard him laugh.

Now it happened that in one of the cities which he had taken from his enemies lived a beautiful princess whom he wished to marry. He had watched her for many months as she went about among those in need, administering to their wants, and he knew she was as good and kind as she was beautiful. Because he always wore his heavy helmet when he rode through the city, the princess had never seen his face.

One day he put on his royal robes and golden crown and set forth to ask the lovely princess to marry him and live in his beautiful castle.

As he entered the hall of the home of the fair Lenore, he caught a glimpse of his reflection in a great mirror that stood against the wall. He sprang back startled, for in his face he saw nothing but what would cause fear and dislike. He tried to smile, but so set were the frowns that it made him look worse than ever. So he quickly gave it up and fled back to his own castle without seeing the princess. Then to him came a happy thought. Sending for the great magician of his court, he said to him: "Make for me a mask of thinnest wax so that it will follow every line of my features, but paint it with your magic paints so that it will look kind and pleasant. Fasten it upon my face so that I shall never take it off, and I will pay you any price you ask."

"This I can do," said the magician, "on one condition only. You must keep your face in the same lines that I shall paint, or the mask will be ruined. One angry frown, one cruel smile will crack the mask and ruin it forever; nor can I replace it. Will you agree to this?"

"Yes," replied the prince, "I agree, but tell me how may I keep the mask from breaking?"

"You must train yourself to think kindly thoughts," said the magician, "and to do this you must do kindly deeds. You must try to make your kingdom happy rather than great. Whenever you are angry, keep absolutely still until the feeling has gone away. Be gracious and courteous to all men."

So the wonderful mask was made, and when it was put on, no one would have guessed it was not the prince's true face.

The lovely princess willingly became his bride, for she could see no fault in his smiling countenance.

As time went on, the magic mask was often in danger of being destroyed, but the prince made a tremendous struggle to overcome his terrible temper and ugly frowns. His subjects marveled at his gentleness and said: "It is the princess who has made him like herself."

The prince, however, was very unhappy. He knew he was deceiving the princess with the magic mask. At last he could bear it no longer, and, sending for the magician, he commanded him to remove it.

"Remember," protested the magician, "I can never make another."

"So be it," cried the prince. "Anything would be better than to continue to deceive one whose love and trust I value so greatly."

The mask was removed, and in fear and anguish the prince sought his reflection in the mirror. To his joy and surprise the ugly lines were gone, the frowns had disappeared, and his face was molded in the exact lines of the magic mask!

And when he came into the presence of his wife and his subjects, they saw only the kindly features of the prince they had learned to honor and love.

HOW LITTLE CEDRIC BECAME A KNIGHT

To be a knight meant that a man must be brave enough to undertake any task, however difficult and dangerous, and also that he must never overlook the smallest courtesy. Small services were quite as important as the greatest one, and gentleness and gallantry as much the measure of a true knight as daring and courage."

A long time ago a little boy named Cedric lived with his parents at the foot of a very high hill on top of which stood a grand old castle. Here lived Sir Rollin Du Bois and his faithful knights. Little Cedric used to watch these knights as they rode down the hillside. He thought the shining armor and helmets, the sleek, prancing horses, and best of all, the noble faces of the knights, the prettiest picture in the world.

One day he saw them come galloping along, and at the same time he saw his pet kitten asleep in the road. Darting forward he snatched it up just in time to save it from the horses' feet.

One of the knights drew up his horse and smiled at Cedric. "My boy," he said, "you are almost brave enough to be a knight some day."

Cedric never forgot those words. He thought of them all day and dreamed about them at night. "If I only might be a knight," he thought.

He told his mother and asked if she thought it would ever come to pass. She told him how knights are always honest and brave, truthful and courteous, and Cedric resolved to be all of those things.

Late in the summer a knight rode up and asked for a drink. When Cedric brought the water, the knight thanked him. "I am glad to be able to serve you," said the boy.

The man replied, "You are as courteous as a knight, my boy."

Several years passed and when Sir Rollin needed a boy at the castle, he chose Cedric. How happy the boy was! He lived there until he grew to manhood, and all loved him because he always spoke the truth, thought of others before himself, and never complained of his coarse food or hard bed.

One day Sir Rollin made him very happy by trusting him with a very important message to the king. It had to be delivered before the next night, so Sir Rollin let him take his own swift horse. In less time than half an hour he galloped off. He rode for a long time. At last he entered a deep forest. The road was very dark and lonesome, but Cedric remembered that he must be brave if he ever expected to be a knight. Suddenly he heard a growl and saw a wild boar coming toward him. He hurled his spear just as the beast was about to spring upon him, and the wild boar rolled over dead.

Just before night he came upon a crowd of boys laughing at an old man. Cedric was indignant. "How dare you laugh at an old man?" he exclaimed. The old man was going to the nearby village, and Cedric put him on his own horse and allowed the old man to ride while he walked by his side.

It was afternoon of the next day before the king's palace came in sight. Cedric gave his letter to a servant to take to the king. In a short time the king sent for him. He told Cedric that among other things Sir Rollin's letter had told him how brave and true and unselfish Cedric had proved to be while in his service. This was a happy moment, but imagine Cedric's delight when the king told him that he had decided to make him a knight.

In time Sir Cedric had a beautiful castle of his own and splendid armor and fine horses. And all the people loved him.

JUST FOR FUN

Make a joyful noise unto the Lord, all ye lands.
Serve the Lord with gladness:
Come before his presence with singing.

                                 —Psalm 100:1–2.

TICK AND TOCK

It was night. It was dark. The moon begged the gray clouds to stand in front of her because she was tired of looking at the dreary earth. The stars danced behind the clouds and refused to let their twinkles peep through. Yes, it was very dark. The little brick house stood on the side of the hill in the darkness. It said to itself, "I am not afraid of the dark. It will soon pass." Inside the little red brick house lived Daddy and Mommy and Betty and Joe.

It was night, and Daddy and Mommy and Betty and Joe were fast asleep—asleep and dreaming too. They had forgotten the dark and were dreaming of the morning when the sun fairies would dance through the darkness and break the spell of night. They smiled in their sleep.

It was night, and all was quiet in the little house—all save the chatter of two little elves, two charming little elves. Now these tiny little elves lived inside the clock that stood on the shelf in the kitchen. It was really a lovely place in which to live, warm and cozy. They had lived there ever since they could remember. Yes, they must have been born there. They had never been outside the clock. They had many relatives, but they had never seen any of them, because, you see, their relatives lived in other clocks, and only two elves could live in one clock at a time. There just wasn't room enough for anyone else. They couldn't remember ever having seen their mother or father—but, of course, they had a mother and a father—somewhere. Now these two little elves had names. You've guessed them already, for sure! The name of one was Tick, and the name of the other was Tock.

Every night Mommy fed Tick and Tock to keep them alive. She opened the clock, put in a key, and wound and wound. This winding made the most delicious meals, everything the heart or stomach of an elf could want. Tick and Tock worked and worked. Their job wasn't hard, but it was exceedingly tiresome. They sat on a teeter-totter, and as it went down Tick ticked to Tock, and as it went up Tock tocked to Tick, all day long and all night long too. So you see, though they had a nice place to live and good meals, there were disadvantages. They finally grew tired of it and wished for something else.

It was night. It was dark. All were asleep in the little red brick house that stood on the side of the hill except Tick and Tock. For a long time they teetered and tottered. Then an idea came into Tock's head and he talked.

"Tick, I'm tired. I'm not going to tock any more."

"But, Tock," ticked Tick, for he was more timid than Tock, "do you think it is wise?"

"Yes, I do. For many years we have worked, and no one in this house has given us a thought. Tonight they didn't even feed us. I'm hungry and tired."

It was true. Mommy had forgotten to wind the clock that night.

Tick ticked, "I'm hungry too."

"Then let's stop."

"But, Tock, I couldn't work without you. If we go to sleep, Betty and Joe will forget to get up, and they will be late for school."

"Do Joe and Betty ever think about us? No. They keep us cooped up in this old clock all the time and scold if we get too tired to work. Now, are you going to sleep?"

"Well, I am tired."

"Of course you are. I can't remember when we last had a rest. Now is our only chance. Not even the moon can see us. We can sleep and sleep, and when we wake up, we'll climb out of this old house and run away and see our folks."

"Oh, Tock, we couldn't run away."

"We'll talk about that after we have a sleep—sleep—"

"Tock!"

"Yes, Tick."

"I'm going to sleep too, Tock."

"Goodnight, Tick."

"Goodnight, Tock."

"Tick."

"Tock."

Tock rolled over with a "tock," and Tick stopped ticking with a "tick," and there they were fast asleep!

It was night. It was dark. All was quiet—truly and honestly quiet—in the little red brick house. Time passed by and smiled. What a long, lovely rest Tick and Tock had! How many hours they slept nobody knew because hours had always been measured by Tick and Tock.

Now in this house, as in your house, everything was done by the clock. Betty and Joe went to school by the clock, and even Mommy cleaned the house by the clock.

The night passed. The dark passed. The moon went down. The stars stopped dancing. The clouds glided away. It was morning! The sun came up. The sunbeam fairies danced in the windows and over the beds. Suddenly the brightest fairy tripped right across Daddy's eyes. Quick as a wink he jumped out of bed with a startled cry, "My land, what time is it? The sun is up. It must be late." He ran to the clock. The hands stood at half-past one which, of course, was the wrong place to stand at this time of the morning. Where were Tick and Tock?

"The clock has stopped!" called Daddy in a most unpleasant temper. "Whatever is the matter with it? The thing is worn out, I guess. Mother, you had better throw it in the junk pile and get a new one. We can't have this happen every morning. I'll lose my job."

Tick and Tock were awake now. Who could sleep in such a commotion? They heard every word Daddy said. Dear! Dear! They didn't want to be thrown in the junk pile. They knew now that if they weren't fed by Mommy every day they would die. They didn't want to die. What could they do? Yes, they had a good sleep, but they were hungry. They were too hungry to even talk. Why didn't Mommy think to feed them? They forgot all about running away. They would rather work than die, and if they didn't work they would surely die and be thrown in the junk pile. Oh dear—oh dear! So much depended on them.

Said Mommy, "I believe I forgot to wind it last night. We'll give it another chance." And with that she walked right over to the clock, put in the key, and turned and turned.

When Tick and Tock saw that breakfast—well, they couldn't resist. They started the teeter-totter with a jerk and sang merrily as they ate. It was the same old song they sang the day before, but jollier, for they had decided they liked their work. So Tock tocked to Tick with a jolly laughing tock, and Tick ticked to Tock with a very merry tick.

"Tick!"

"Tock!"

"Tick!"

"Tock!"
"Tick!"
"Tock!"

—ARTA ROMNEY BALLIF.

A NEW WAR PAINT

One bright summer morning when my mother was churn-
ing butter, all of a sudden she heard the clatter of horses'
hoofs and the whooping of Indians. She left the butter on the
table and, gathering her children in her arms, ran out the back
door to hide in a clump of bushes. You see, Mother was frightened, for she and the children were all alone.

Soon the Indians arrived at the log cabin. They got off their
horses and went into the house. The first thing they spied was
Mother's pretty yellow butter on the table. They thought it was
a new kind of war paint, so they dipped their hands into the
butter and began rubbing it all over their bare chests and arms.
After plastering themselves in such a manner, they danced out
of the house to jump on their horses.

They looked very greasy in the bright sunshine . When they
had disappeared down the dusty road, Mother came back into
the house to find the butter gone. She did not mind much,
however, because she was thankful that she and the children
had not been harmed.

— LOU DICKSON, ADAPTED.

WHY DIDN'T HE THINK?

Tommy Timpkins was as good as most boys and much better than some, but he was more useful and quick with his feet than with his head. Tommy was obedient, yes, but his heels ran ahead of his thinking, so this is what happened to him.

One cloudy Monday morning Mother Timpkins said, "Tommy, my dear son, please do me a favor! Hurry to Tummy Tum Town and buy me a big bag of salt so that our porridge will be salted today. Here are ten pennies to buy a big bag of salt."

So, Tommy Timpkins hurried to Tummy Tum Town and bought a big bag of salt for ten pennies. As Tommy trudged homeward it rained buckets and tubs and barrels of rain. So when Tommy got home, the salt had all melted away, and no porridge was salted that day.

"Oh, Tommy, Tommy," cried Mother Timpkins, "you should have covered the salt with cabbage leaves!"

Then said Tommy very sadly, "To be sure! Why didn't I think?"

One sunny, bright Tuesday morning Mother Timpkins said to Tommy, "My dear son, please do me a favor. Hurry to Tummy Tum Town and buy me a nice, fat rabbit for supper!"

So, Tommy Timpkins hurried to Tummy Tum Town and bought a nice, fat rabbit for ten pennies, and he carefully wrapped the rabbit in cabbage leaves.

As Tommy trudged homeward the day grew sunnier, and the rabbit grew hungrier, so by the time Tommy got home the rabbit had eaten away all the cabbage leaves and ran merrily away, and there was no rabbit stew for supper that day.

"Tommy, oh, Tommy," cried Mother Timpkins, "you should have put the rabbit in a hat!"

Then said Tommy gloomily, "To be sure, Mother! Oh, why didn't I think?"

One very windy Wednesday morning Mother Timpkins said to her son Tommy, "My good son, please do me a favor. Hurry to Tummy Tum Town and buy me two papers of pins, for all my curtains must be pinned up today. Here are ten pennies to buy us two papers of pins."

So, Tommy Timpkins hurried to Tummy Tum Town and bought two papers of pins for ten pennies, and then he very carefully put the papers of pins in the crown of his hat.

But as he trudged homeward the wind grew gustily and blustery—phew ewey, and when Tommy got home, the pins were entirely lost—so they pinned up no curtains that day.

"Oh, Tommy, Tommy!" cried Mother Timpkins. "Why didn't you put the papers of pins in your coat pocket?"

Then said Tommy tearfully, "To be sure! Oh, why didn't I think?"

One very hot Thursday morning Mother Timpkins said to her son: "Blessed boy, please do me a favor. Hurry off to Tummy Tum Town and buy us a pound of fresh butter! We are to have biscuits for supper today. Here are ten pennies to buy us a pound of fresh butter!"

So, away hurried Tommy Timpkins to Tummy Tum Town and bought a pound of fresh butter for ten pennies, and he put the butter in his coat pocket. As he hurried homeward, the day grew hotter and then hotter, and by the time he got home the butter had melted away. (Oh, whee, what a buttery mess!) So they had no beaten biscuits for supper that day.

"Oh, Tommy, Tommy," mourned Mother Timpkins, "you should have put the butter in a basket!"

"Oh, dear!" cried Tommy. "Of course! Why didn't I think?"

One slippery, slidy Friday morning Mother Timpkins said to Tommy, "Dear son, please do me a favor. Hurry off to Tummy Tum Town and buy us a big fat pig, for it will be nice to have bacon for supper tonight. Here are ten pennies to buy us a nice fat pig!"

So, Tommy ran all the way to Tummy Tum Town and bought a big fat pig for ten pennies, and with some trouble he pushed the big pig into the basket.

As Tommy trudged homeward the day grew more slippery and the pig more jiggery, and by the time he got home he had no pig in the basket, so there was no bacon for supper that night.

"Oh, Tommy, Tommy," wept Mother Timpkins, "why didn't you tie a rope around the pig's leg?"

"To be sure," sighed Tommy. "Why didn't I think?"

One bright Saturday morning Mother Timpkins said to Tommy, "My brave son, please do me a favor. Hurry to Tummy Tum Town and hire me a pretty maid, for we are having guests today. Here are ten pennies to hire our pretty maid." (My dears, I think our mothers would be happy if they could hire maids for ten pennies each.)

So, Tommy Timpkins rushed off to Tummy Tum Town and hired a pretty maid for ten pennies, and he carefully tied a rope around the pretty maid's ankle. Then, away he started to run— but—the pretty maid boxed Tommy's ears soundly, and home went Tommy alone. So when he got home, there was no maid to wait upon the guests that afternoon.

"Oh, Tommy, Tommy," said Mother Timpkins, "you should have bowed politely to the pretty maid, saying, 'Good morning to you, fair maiden.'"

"Alas, alas!" moaned Tommy. "Why didn't I think?"

One pleasant Sunday morning Mother Timpkins said to Tommy, "My very dear son, please do me a favor. Hasten to Tummy Tum Town and buy me a red cow, for we must have cream for our strawberries today. Here are ten pennies to buy a red cow!"

So, off went Tommy to Tummy Tum Town and bought a red cow for ten pennies, and he bowed very low to the red cow saying, "Good morning to you, fair maiden!" As he bowed politely, the day grew more pleasant than ever, but that red cow didn't care. She tossed Tommy over the moon . . . ker-swoosh.

And Mother Timpkins had no cream for strawberries that day. And as Tommy went sailing through the air, he said to the moon, "Oh, dear, why didn't I think?"

That's all I need to say of Tommy Timpkins—the little boy who didn't think.

—JOHN MARTIN.

LONG AGO

NELSON
WHITE

Where there is no vision, the people perish.

—Proverbs 29:18.

Jamie Watt and His Grandmother's Teakettle

Jamie Watt, a little Scottish boy, sat by the great open fireplace in his grandmother's kitchen. Above the rosy, glowing flames there hung an old-fashioned teakettle.

Jamie had been whittling a piece of wood and making a cart with wheels, but now he dropped his work in his lap. Something had happened to the teakettle that caught his eye, and he began to watch it closely, for he never let anything strange pass by without finding out the reason for it. The water in the kettle had begun to boil and a little white column soon rose. S-s-s! S-s-s! Piff! Piff! The lid of the teakettle began to rattle. S-s-s! S-s-s! Piff! Piff! Piff! Something lifted the lid right up in the air!

"O Grandma! Grandma!" cried the boy in great excitement. "What is there inside of your teakettle?"

Grandma was busy laying the table for supper. "Nothing, Jamie! There's nothing in there but water," she answered.

S-s-s! S-s-s! Piff! Piff! Piff! Up popped the lid again.

The boy watched it, breathless with interest.

"But, Grandma, there must be something inside the kettle," he insisted. "See! Something keeps lifting the lid!"

"Ho, ho!" laughed his grandmother. "Perhaps it's a brownie or a pixie you're thinking is in the kettle! No, no! It's only the steam that does the lifting! You can see little clouds of it puffing out all around the lid."

Now Jamie wasn't thinking at all that it was a brownie or a pixie that was in the kettle. But he was thinking that he wanted very much to know what this thing called steam was that had so much strength and power. Carefully he leaned over and lifted the lid to look inside. Nothing at all could he see but boiling, bubbling water.

"Grandma," he asked, "where does the steam come from? How did it get into the kettle?"

Grandma was used to his questions; he was always wondering about things.

"Why, dearie," she answered, "steam always rises from water whenever water boils."

The boy stood studying the kettle for a little longer, then he sat down again; and while he was thinking, he began absentmindedly spinning the wheels of the little cart he was making. At last he burst out: "Grandma, if the steam in that kettle is strong enough to lift the lid, why couldn't steam from a great deal more water lift much heavier things? Why—why couldn't it push wheels around?"

"Push wheels around!" Grandma did not even try to answer so absurd a question. Jamie had strange and idle dreams, she thought, and she wished he would spend his time thinking of something more useful than pushing wheels around with steam.

But Jamie never left off wondering about the steam just the same, nor was his wondering so idle and useless as his grandmother supposed.

"That steam has the strength of a giant," he used to say to himself. "If I could only find out how to make use of it, it would not only lift heavy weights, but it would make all kinds of machinery go and do all sorts of work for men."

So Jamie went on studying and working as he grew to be a man. Many times he made experiments with steam engines, and his engines failed to go; but he always learned something new from each failure. Other people thought him foolish and laughed at him.

"Ho, ho! Jamie Watt is going to harness up the clouds that puff out of his granny's teakettle and make them do the work of a giant!" they would jeer. But in spite of all this, Jamie worked right on year after year until at last he did indeed make what no one had thought he could—a steam engine that was a success. And that was the little Scottish boy's great gift to the world.

It was Jamie's engine that made possible the engines that draw trains, push steamboats, turn machinery, and do all the hundred and one useful things that steam engines do today. Men had lived for thousands of years beside that great giant, steam, and yet not one of them ever learned how to harness it and make its mighty power of service to man till one small boy began to think and to question how it lifted the lid of the old teakettle in his grandmother's kitchen.

—OLIVE BEAUPRE MILLER.

WILFRED GRENFELL

When Wilfred Grenfell was a young man, he decided to devote his life to missionary work. He knew that people needed help in bettering their living conditions and their health as much as they needed religion. He went to school at Oxford, England. Later, he studied medicine in the London Hospital. He became interested in helping people who were poor and neglected. He helped to establish hospitals so that sick people could get the proper care. In 1892, when he was twenty-seven years old, he went to the coast of Labrador. This is a very treacherous country. The only way people can go from place to place is by dog team over the ice. Fishing is the chief occupation among the inhabitants along the coast.

In this country—which has been called "The Country God Forgot"—Dr. Grenfell made his home. He established several hospitals and churches. He was very happy in this work. It was said he attended the sick, christened babies, married the young couples, and buried the dead. His was a mission of practical service as well as the teaching of religion.

One day some messengers were sent sixty miles to get Dr. Grenfell on an urgent case of a sick boy. He lost no time in having his things packed for the trip. The dog sleigh was equipped, and with the dog team he started at once. He was proud of his eight dogs. They had often aided him in saving lives.

They stopped at night for a few hours' rest at a village twenty miles from their starting point. The next morning he sent the messengers ahead two hours because their outfit was rather slow. Ten miles of the remaining journey was on an arm of the sea, on salt water ice.

The wind was blowing this "slob ice" solid against the shore. It looked good, although it was very rough. The waves had broken it up, and the wind had packed it solid again. When he was part way over this shortcut, the wind suddenly fell, and he saw that the ice upon which they were traveling was becoming loose. It was too late to turn back, for already they were sinking into it. Dr. Grenfell quickly cut his dogs loose from the sleigh. He slowly worked his way through the soft mush-ice to a large block of solid ice. After working very hard he pulled his dogs on the piece with him. Then he saw it was too small to hold them, so they struggled through the water-logged ice to a larger piece, which was fast drifting out into the open sea. Dr. Grenfell had lost his coat, hat, and gloves. To keep the cold wind out, he cut his high boots and made a jacket to warm his back. He then decided he needed the skins of some of his beloved dogs to keep from freezing. He killed three of his beautiful animals, and in a crude fashion he laced the skins together with bits of the harness. As night came on, Dr. Grenfell said he felt no particular terror. He knew that death was inevitable but thought it best to die struggling.

He knew he had small chance of being seen, because he was drifting farther and farther away from the shore. However, since he was not in the open water yet, he unraveled rope and cut bits of flannel from the harness and stuffed them into his thin shoes. After these precautions were taken against the cold, he cuddled down by his largest dog, wrapped the three skins around him and over his head, and fell asleep.

Before daylight he thought he should have a flag. He had no flagpole and no flag. He patiently worked to cut off the dead dogs' legs and tied them together with rope and harness scraps. As the sun rose, he sacrificed his shirt for the flag. As the sun warmed and thawed the frozen legs, the flagpole became very wobbly. He held it high above his head. His eyes ached as he searched the distant shoreline for some signs of help. The ice block was becoming smaller. Dr. Grenfell was not without humor even in that hour of despair. He had on an old football uniform which he had worn twenty years before at Oxford.

"Five dogs, myself in colored football costume, and a

bloody dogskin cloak, with a gray flannel shirt on a pole of frozen dogs' legs." What a picture!

Suddenly he saw what he thought was an oar. He was afraid it was not real, because he was still in a mass of slob ice. He waved his flag high and strained his snow-blind eyes in the direction of the oar. Finally he saw a hull. Then he saw his rescuers waving their arms and heard their shouts. As the men helped him into the boat, tears of joy ran unheeded down their cheeks.

Even after this frightful experience Dr. Grenfell did not rest until he had the sick boy brought to the hospital. They both recovered, and both loved life as they never had before.

OVERBOARD

During the Spanish-American War, when the cruiser *Boston* was in the battle of Manila, one of the power boys pulled off his overcoat, which fell over the railing into the ocean. He turned to the officer, who was standing near him, and asked if he could jump overboard and get his coat, which was floating on the water.

The officer refused to let the boy jump overboard. Slipping around to the other side of the ship, the lad jumped and swam around to the place where the coat was floating. Then he swam back and climbed aboard.

The officer saw him as he climbed back. He immediately put the lad into the small prison on the ship, and when the battle was over, the lad was tried for disobedience under fire. He was found guilty, but the decision of the court had to be reviewed by Commodore George Dewey, commander of the fleet.

Dewey sent for the boy and asked him in a friendly way why he had risked severe punishment in order to get the coat.

"My mother's picture was in a pocket of the coat, and I just had to have it back," replied the boy.

The great commodore swept the boy into his arms and hugged him. Then he ordered that all charges against the lad be dismissed. "A boy who loves his mother well enough to risk his life for her picture cannot be imprisoned on my ship!" exclaimed Dewey.

—Used by permission of the *Sunshine Magazine.*

Faithful unto Death

Lucius was a young soldier in the army of ancient Rome, and he was so handsome and brave that when he strode along the streets, people would turn to look a second time. This may have been because he was so splendidly clad, for his coat of mail, with the burnished breastplate and shining helmet with its nodding plume, gleamed like gold in the sunshine. But more probably it was because he walked with his head erect and chest out, instead of lounging along as some people do.

The officer, Claudian, who commanded Lucius's legion, was very proud of this fine soldier. He had noticed how obliging Lucius was, for he never needed telling twice to do a thing, and what is more, he did it with such a happy face that the officer promised to promote him.

About this time the day came round when all the garrisons

in different parts of the empire were rearranged. Legions were drafted from one place to another, and every soldier was eager to know just where he would be sent. And Lucius, with the promise of promotion in his mind, was full of hope that he would get a chance of showing his devotion and courage. Where would his legion go? To Gaul? That was his dearest wish.

There was a great war raging in Gaul, and that was why Lucius thought he stood a chance of doing something heroic and great. To his disappointment when the lists were issued, he found that instead of being drafted to go there, or to some of the distant parts of the empire, his legion had been assigned garrison duty in Italy.

As he was returning to his quarters, feeling very depressed, whom should he meet but his officer, Claudian. The young soldier saluted, but the other stopped and said, with a smile, "How fares it with thee? And why art thou so sad of face?"

"Well, sire," replied Lucius, "I have just seen the lists, and I hoped that we were thought brave enough to be sent to the wars."

"Yea, and so hoped I, for I am disappointed even as thou."

"But could we not appeal to the senate, sire, and crave permission to go? I would like to show myself a man."

"No," replied Claudian. "What Caesar wills must be obeyed. And where he sends us, we must prove our loyalty and courage."

There was nothing more to be said, and shortly afterwards the legion found itself in the city of Herculaneum.

That very year—it was A.D. 79—there was a fearful eruption. The volcano suddenly belched forth its fiery lava, and the molten mass swept down upon the city. The alarm was given. Crowds of people fled for their lives along the roads leading to the countryside, while others, stricken with fear, hid in their houses, hoping they might be safe.

Lucius was on guard at one of these gates. It would be another three hours before he went off duty, and as he looked first at the flaming crater of the volcano and then at the people surging past him, he wondered what to do. The ground shook under his feet. Buildings were toppling in ruin about him. Should he flee like the rest or stay there at his post?

Then he recalled swiftly how he had learned to show his devotion and bravery, and the words of his officer came back: "Where Caesar sends us we must prove our loyalty and courage." He could still show the kind of man he was! And so, because he had been set to guard that gate, he remained true to his trust. He was faithful unto death!

Centuries have passed. But a few years ago some very clever men were digging amid the ruins of that buried city. They had unearthed part of the walls, and in an archway they discovered the remains of a Roman sentry. He was still at his post, and the price of his fidelity had been his life. You will remember that Christ said, "He that is faithful in that which is least, is faithful also in much."

He Who Would Command

"He who would command, must first learn how to obey." Perhaps the Duke of Wellington had read that quotation. At any rate, he followed its teaching. As a result, he became one of the world's greatest commanders. It was the Duke of Wellington who beat Napoleon at Waterloo.

As he grew older, Wellington developed more and more in the habit of commanding. He accepted people's obedience as unthinkingly as he accepted his own right to give orders, but a little incident reminded him once more how rare it is to find strict and unquestioning obedience.

He and some of his soldiers were riding through the English countryside when they came to a locked gate. Guarding this gate was a young boy who refused to open it for them.

The soldiers threatened him, but he did not mind their threats. They offered him money, but he refused to receive it. At last one of them came up to him and said in commanding tones:

"My boy, you do not know me, but I am the Duke of Wellington. I am not accustomed to being disobeyed, and now I command you to open the gate that I and my friends may pass through."

The boy lifted his cap and stood uncovered before the man whom all England delighted to honor and then answered firmly: "I am sure the Duke of Wellington would not wish me to disobey orders. I must keep the gate shut; no one can pass through it but by my master's express permission."

The brave old warrior was greatly pleased with this. He took off his own hat and said, "I honor the man or boy who can neither be bribed nor frightened into disobeying orders. With an army of such soldiers, I could conquer, not the French only, but the world." Then, handing the boy a sovereign, he put spurs to his horse and galloped away.

A Boy Who Believed in God

Along, long time ago there lived in a city far away across the sea a father, mother, and their four sons. They were wealthy, for they had gold and silver, houses and property.

This city was the largest in the land. Great kings, like David and Solomon, had lived there nearly five hundred years. A temple, the most beautiful ever built by the Jews, was the pride of the city and the nation.

The name of the city was Jerusalem. The four boys loved Jerusalem as all the Jews did. Why shouldn't the boys be happy there? They had friends, places to go, things to see, and a nice home in which to live.

Their father, however, was not happy. He was a prophet of God and could see that the people were wicked, proud, and selfish; he could see how the people robbed the poor and cheated in their business and forgot to do what the Lord wanted them to do. So this good man, whose name was Lehi, went about telling the people to quit their evil deeds and pray to the Lord.

What do you suppose the people did? They laughed at him and gave no heed to his words. Yes, they even threatened to kill Lehi.

Our Father in Heaven loved Lehi, for he was a good and courageous man. So the Lord spoke to him in a dream, saying: "Blessed art thou Lehi, because of the things which thou hast done; and because thou hast been faithful and declared unto this people the things which I commanded thee, behold, they seek to take away thy life."

The Lord then showed Lehi what was going to happen to

Jerusalem in just a few years. The great king of Babylon, a king with an odd name that is hard to spell—Nebuchadnezzar—had a great army ready to swoop down on little Palestine and destroy the proud city of Jerusalem, temple and all. As a result many of the Jews would be carried away as slaves to Babylon.

The Lord told Lehi to take his family and flee from the city of Jerusalem. So Lehi "left his house, and the land of his inheritance, and his gold, and his silver, and his precious things, and took nothing with him, save it were his family, and provisions, and tents, and departed into the wilderness."

How would you like to pick up all your belongings and leave home for some other land? It would be fun for a while, especially if you were in a car, knew where you were going and could come home to friends, mother's cooking, and a good bed again when you wished.

Lehi's sons were now young men and were saying good-bye forever to their home and city and country. The two eldest boys, Laman and Lemuel, didn't want to leave their home. They complained to their father every day. They were often angry and called their father a foolish man and a dreamer. However, the youngest son, a strong lad named Nephi, and his other brother, Sam, believed in their father, Lehi. They also believed in their Father in Heaven. They had no fear of the wilderness—of danger, adventure, and hardships so long as the Lord would guide them. Their journey proved to be real adventure. On more than one occasion it was Nephi who saved their lives.

As they journeyed into the wilderness, their supply of food gave out, and they had to rely on wild game and animals which they could kill. There were no guns, so their chief hunting weapon was a bow and arrows. One day Nephi broke his steel bow. Moreover, the bows of his brothers, Laman, Lemuel, and Sam had "lost their spring" and were no good to them. There was no food, and they were all faced with starvation.

What did they do in such a serious situation? Nephi wrote, "Laman and Lemuel did begin to murmur exceedingly, because of their sufferings and afflictions in the wilderness; and also my father began to murmur against the Lord his God; yea, and they were all exceedingly sorrowful, even that they did murmur against the Lord."

But not Nephi, who had courage and faith in the Lord! While the rest groaned and grumbled, he made a bow out of wood and an arrow out of a straight stick. He also took a sling and some stones and was ready to hunt animals again.

Before starting out, Nephi asked his father to pray to the Lord to direct him to the place where he could obtain food. So Lehi prayed, and his prayers were answered. Nephi went up into the mountains and slew wild beasts and carried them back to the tents, and his family rejoiced to have food again.

After traveling for a long time, Lehi and his company came to the sea. There they were told to build a ship, and the Lord would guide them across the waters to a choice and rich land where they would be able to live in peace and rear their families in righteousness.

But how were they to cross the ocean? They knew not the way. There were no steamships, for this was over two thousand years before Columbus crossed the ocean. These young Jewish men were not shipbuilders like the Norwegians and the Dutch. They had lived in the hills of Judea. Their fathers had been shepherds who felt at home in the desert. They feared the water.

Laman and Lemuel, the older sons of Lehi, began to murmur again against Nephi, because the Lord had told Nephi to build a ship, and Nephi had already begun to do so. He made tools out of ore which he had melted using some bellows made from animal skins. Nephi had also gathered timbers from which he could construct the ship.

Again, Laman and Lemuel ridiculed Nephi. "He thinketh that he can build a ship; yea, and he also thinketh that he can cross these great waters."

Nephi was no fool, but a strong man of great faith. He built the ship just as he had killed animals for food, because our Father in Heaven helped him. Nephi had a motto, or a guide, in his life which went like this: "I will go and do the things which the Lord hath commanded, for I know that the Lord giveth no commandments unto the children of men, save he shall prepare a way for them that they may accomplish the thing which he commandeth them."

Nephi could face unafraid any danger or difficulty—his angry older brothers, starvation in the wilderness, the task of building a ship, or crossing the mighty deep. Why? Because he had faith in our Father in Heaven.

Nephi led his people to the promised land of America. There he became a great prophet and leader and the first recorder of the events in the Book of Mormon.

—LOWELL BENNION.

AMMON, THE SON OF A KING

An ancient king named Mosiah had several sons who were much beloved by their father and his people. When Mosiah became old and knew that he would soon die, he wished to make one of his sons ruler in his place. All the people in the land also wanted one of Mosiah's sons to become their king.

Most sons would gladly become king. Many a story from olden times tells how brothers have even fought each other to see which would become king. Kings have wealth, power, and honor. They have servants and armies at their command. They live in palaces.

Strange to relate, these sons of Mosiah were different. Each of them in turn, from the eldest to the youngest, refused the kingship with its luxury and power. Other goals beckoned them. They wished to become missionaries and go forth and teach people about the Savior. As younger men, they had done things that were not right. Now they were sorry for their past deeds and were anxious to blot them out with good deeds.

The mission they chose was not an easy one. It would be full of hardships and danger. They were going to the Lamanites, the enemies of the Nephites. Every chance these Lamanites had to murder and steal from the Nephites, they took. For five hundred years Nephites and Lamanites had been enemies. And now Ammon and his brothers gave up the chance to become king over the Nephites to go into the land of the Lamanites to tell them about the Savior.

The Lamanites were not only enemies, but also a wild and ferocious people. They loved riches, gold, silver, and precious

stones. They preferred to steal rather than work for the things
their hearts desired. Instead of praying to Father in heaven,
many of them made idols of images of men and beasts and
bowed down to worship before them. They knew little or nothing about Jesus who was soon to be born in Bethlehem.

Ammon and his brothers were men of faith and courage,
and their hearts were burning with a love for the gospel. They
must go and teach these Lamanites no matter what the cost.
They went, and as they arrived on the border of the land, they
separated. Each went alone to a different place to preach, hoping to see the others some time in the future.

Ammon, the eldest brother, marched straight toward a
group of Lamanites. They bound him, "as was their custom to
bind all Nephites who fell into their hands, and carry them
before the king; and thus it was left to the pleasure of the king
to slay them, or to retain them in captivity, or to cast them into
prison, or . . . out of the land, according to his will and pleasure."

The king over the Lamanites in this part of the country was
named Lamoni. Lamoni liked Ammon and even asked him to
marry one of his daughters; but Ammon said, "No, but let me
be thy servant." His services were accepted, and Ammon went
forth with the Lamanites to herd and water the flocks of the
king.

The first day out, other Lamanites came and scattered the
flocks of the king for the purpose of stealing them. The servants
were afraid. Yes, they wept, for the king had slain other servants
who had lost his flocks. But there was one among them who
was not afraid. That was Ammon, the Nephite.

Strong in body, quick in mind, and full of faith in the

Lord's help, Ammon saw his chance. He took action. With the help of other servants, he encircled the flocks of the king again; and then Ammon went forth to fight quite a large group of Lamanites. He went alone, with a sling and a sword. With his sling, he threw stones at them, killing six. Then, as they rushed upon him with clubs, he killed their leader and wounded others with his sword.

Ammon had no desire to kill or harm men. Yet, as a faithful servant of the king, he had to save the king's flocks from the thieves. Fighting for his rights, he won the respect and gratitude of his fellow servants and even the king himself. Ammon had won his way into the hearts of the Lamanites. They were now ready to listen to this Nephite stranger who was obedient, brave, and strong. He was now in a position to be a real missionary.

—LOWELL BENNION.

SMUT, THE SOLDIER DOG

There was a little boy named Kelly, who had a dog of his very own. The dog's name was Smut because he was so black. When Kelly went to school, Smut always stayed home because Kelly knew that dogs shouldn't go to town or school.

On his way to school one day he patted Smut's black head and said, "Good-bye, Smut, I'll see you after school." Smut barked and barked and wagged his tail. On the way home from school Kelly passed the post office. There he saw a large sign which said, "Uncle Sam needs dogs to help win the war. Have you a dog that could be a soldier?"

"I have a dog," said Kelly, "a very fine dog. Could Smut be a soldier? How could he help win the war? I'll ask Daddy. Daddy will know. Daddy knows most everything."

Kelly hurried home. There was Smut waiting for him. Daddy was mowing the lawn.

"Come here, Smut, we have to talk to Daddy." They ran over to the end of the lawn. Daddy stopped cutting the grass.

"How can dogs help win the war, Daddy?" asked Kelly. "How can they help the soldiers?"

"Well, Kelly," answered his daddy, "dogs cannot be too big. They cannot be too little. They must be just right. Dogs cannot be too old; they cannot be too young. They must be just right if they are to be soldier dogs."

"Oh, Daddy! Is Smut just right? Can Smut be a helper for the soldiers?"

"We will see," said Daddy. "Go get the leash. We will take Smut downtown. We will ask a man if Smut can help the soldiers."

So they took Smut downtown. The man saw Smut and liked him very much. Smut was not too old. He was not too young. He was just right. The man said Smut would have to go to dog school. He would have to learn many things. Smut would have to go on a train far away and stay at the dog school.

"Smut, you can be a soldier dog. You can help the soldiers. You can help win the war," said Kelly as he patted the dog's black head.

Smut barked and barked and wagged his tail.

The next day Kelly and Daddy took Smut to the train. They put him in a big cage, and then they put him in a baggage car.

"Good-bye, Smut," said Kelly. "Be a good dog, and help the soldiers."

Smut barked and barked and wagged his tail. The train went. It took Smut far, far away to a dog school.

Soldier Bill was Smut's teacher. He fed Smut. He gave him meat and dog biscuits. Smut liked Soldier Bill, and Soldier Bill liked Smut.

Smut learned many things. He learned not to bark; he learned not to growl. Soldier dogs had to be very quiet. He learned to jump high. He could jump over a high fence. He learned to listen and tell Soldier Bill he could hear something coming. He did not bark; he did not growl, but he pulled Soldier Bill's trousers. Then Soldier Bill knew something was coming.

After Smut had learned many things at the dog school, Soldier Bill wrote a letter to Kelly. The letter said, "Smut has been a good dog. He can be a helper for the soldiers now."

Soldier Bill and Smut got on a boat. They crossed the ocean and went to the South Seas.

One day Soldier Bill and many other soldiers went for a long march in the jungle. Smut went with them. It was very hot, and the soldiers became very tired. Soldier Bill said, "We will rest. We will go to sleep. Smut, you cannot go to sleep. You must watch."

All the soldiers went to sleep under a tree. Smut stayed awake to watch.

After a while Smut saw something in a tree. It was very long. It was wiggling. It stuck out its tongue.

Smut wanted to bark; he wanted to growl, but he did not. He wanted to tell Soldier Bill that a big snake was in a tree.

Soldier Bill was asleep. All the soldiers were asleep. Smut went over to Soldier Bill and pulled his trousers, he pulled his trousers hard. Soldier Bill awakened. Smut looked up in the tree. He pointed his nose at the snake. He wanted to bark, but he did not. He just wagged his tail.

Soldier Bill told all the soldiers to wake up. He told them to move quickly because a big snake was in the tree. All the soldiers moved quickly. Soldier Bill took his bow and arrow and killed the snake. When Smut saw the dead snake, he wanted to bark and he wanted to growl, but he did not. He just wagged his tail.

Soldier Bill wrote another letter to Kelly. The letter said, "Smut saved our lives. He told us a snake was in the tree. He told us to move."

Soldier Bill finished the letter. Then he put Smut's paw in some ink. He put Smut's paw on the letter to Kelly.

When Smut saw his paw mark on the letter to go to Kelly, he wanted to bark and bark, but he did not. He just wagged his tail.

—Lorna Call Alder.

Wolfgang Mozart's Prayer

Many years ago in the town of Salzburg, Austria, two little children lived near a pleasant river in a cottage surrounded by vines. They both loved music, and when only six years old, Frederica could play well on the harpsichord. But from her little brother such strains of melody would resound through the humble cottage as were never heard before from so young a child. Their father was a teacher of music, and his own children were his best pupils.

There came times so hard that these children had scarcely enough to eat, but they loved each other and were happy in the simple enjoyment that fell to their lot. One pleasant day they said, "Let us take a walk in the woods. How sweetly the birds sing, and the sound of the river as it flows is like music." So they went. As they were sitting in the shade of a tree, the boy said thoughtfully, "Sister, what a beautiful place this would be to pray."

"What shall we pray for?" asked Frederica, wonderingly.

"Why for Papa and Mamma," said her brother. "You see how sad they look. Poor Mamma hardly ever smiles now, and I know it must be because she has not always had enough bread for us. Let us pray to God for help."

"Yes," said Frederica, "we will."

So the two children knelt down and prayed, asking their Heavenly Father to bless their parents and make them a help to them.

"But how can we help Papa and Mamma?" asked Frederica.

"Why, don't you know?" replied Wolfgang. "My soul is full of music, and by and by I shall play before great people, and they will give me plenty of money, and I will give it to our dear Papa and Mamma, and we'll live in a fine house and be happy."

At this a loud laugh astonished the boy, who did not know that anyone was near them. Turning, he saw a fine gentleman who had just come from the woods. The stranger made inquiries, which the little girl answered, telling him: "Wolfgang means to be a great musician; he thinks that he can earn money so that we shall be poor no longer."

"He may do it when he has learned to play well enough," replied the stranger.

"He is only six years old now," said Frederica, "but he can play beautifully and can compose pieces."

"That cannot be," replied the gentleman.

"Come and see us," said the boy, "and I will play for you."

"I will go this evening," answered the stranger.

The children went home and told their story to their parents, who seemed much pleased and astonished.

Soon a loud knock was heard at the door, and on opening it the little family was surprised to see men bringing in baskets of food in variety and abundance. They had an ample feast that evening.

Soon after, while Wolfgang was playing a piece which he had composed, the stranger entered and stood astonished at the wondrous melody. The father recognized in his guest, Francis I, the emperor of Austria.

Not long afterward the family was invited by the emperor to Vienna, where Wolfgang surprised the royal family by his wonderful powers.

At the age of fifteen Wolfgang Mozart was acknowledged by all the great composers as a master. The simple trust in God which he learned in childhood never forsook him.

—Selected.

"Sooner Shall These Mountains Crumble"

One of the most thrilling monuments of all history is a monument to friendship and the peace pact of Chile and Argentina. It clearly shows that war is not more heroic than peace.

On the summit of the great Andes Mountains in South America is the dividing line between Chile and Argentina. The women of the two countries decided that it would be a fine thing to put a great monument to peace on that high joining place. It wasn't long before they had interested their countrymen. The great cannons of the two countries were brought together, melted, and out of the metal great artists molded an immense statue of Christ.

The world was so interested in what they were doing that it soon became famous. "Very well," said Argentina and Chile, "we will have it mean 'Peace to all Nations.'"

On March 13, 1904, it was unveiled. The people who came from far and near for the service were thrilled by the great Christ who watched over the two countries and their friendship.

Some of the priests have built a refuge at its base. In it they care for all those wanderers who find the snow and the wind and the cold too much on this peak of the world.

And so the Christ of the Andes, a symbol of eternal peace, was made from the cannons of war. And nothing in all history is more inspiring than the words engraved at the feet: "Sooner shall these mountains crumble into dust than Chileans and

Argentinians break the peace which at the feet of Christ, the
Redeemer, they have sworn to maintain."

AND WHO IS MY NEIGHBOR?

A certain man went down from Jerusalem to Jericho, and
fell among thieves, which stripped him of his raiment,
and wounded him, and departed, leaving him half dead.

"And by chance there came down a certain priest that way:
and when he saw him, he passed by on the other side.

"And likewise a Levite, when he was at the place, came and
looked on him, and passed by on the other side.

"But a certain Samaritan, as he journeyed, came where he
was: and when he saw him, he had compassion on him,

"And went to him, and bound up his wounds, pouring in
oil and wine, and set him on his own beast, and brought him to
an inn, and took care of him.

"And on the morrow when he departed, he took out two
pence, and gave them to the host, and said unto him, Take care
of him; and whatsoever thou spendest more, when I come
again, I will repay thee.

"Which now of these three, thinkest thou, was neighbour
unto him that fell among the thieves?"

—LUKE 10:30–36.

ABRAHAM LINCOLN KEEPS HIS PROMISE

One day Abraham Lincoln was riding in a stagecoach, as they rode in those days, in company with a Kentucky colonel. After riding a number of miles together, the colonel took a bottle of whiskey out of his pocket and said, "Mr. Lincoln, won't you take a drink with me?"

Mr. Lincoln replied, "No, Colonel, thank you, I never drink whiskey."

They rode along together for a number of miles more, visiting very pleasantly, when the gentleman from Kentucky reached into his pocket and brought out some cigars, saying, "Now, Mr. Lincoln, if you won't take a drink with me, won't you take a smoke with me, for here are some of Kentucky's finest cigars?"

And Mr. Lincoln said, "Now, Colonel, you are such a fine, agreeable man to travel with, maybe I ought to take a smoke with you. But before I do so, let me tell you a little story—an experience I had when a small boy." And this was the story:

"My mother called me to her bed one day when I was about nine years old. She was sick, very sick, and she said to me, 'Abey, the doctor tells me I am not going to get well. I want you to promise me before I go that you will never use whiskey or tobacco as long as you live.' And I promised my mother I never would. And up to this hour, Colonel, I have kept that promise. Now, would you advise me to break that promise to my dear mother and take a smoke with you?"

The colonel put his hand gently on Mr. Lincoln's shoulder and in a voice trembling with emotion said: "No, Mr. Lincoln,

I wouldn't have you do it for the world. It was one of the best promises you ever made. And I would give a thousand dollars today if I had made my mother a promise like that and kept it as you have done."

THE PRODIGAL SON

What man of you, having an hundred sheep, if he lose one of them, doth not leave the ninety and nine in the wilderness, and go after that which is lost, until he find it?

"And when he hath found it, he layeth it on his shoulders, rejoicing.

"And when he cometh home, he calleth together his friends and neighbours, saying unto them, Rejoice with me; for I have found my sheep which was lost.

"I say unto you, that likewise joy shall be in heaven over one sinner that repenteth, more than over ninety and nine just persons, which need no repentance.

"Either what woman having ten pieces of silver, if she lose one piece, doth not light a candle, and sweep the house, and seek diligently till she find it?

"And when she hath found it, she calleth her friends and her neighbours together, saying, Rejoice with me; for I have found the piece which I had lost.

"Likewise, I say unto you, there is joy in the presence of the angels of God over one sinner that repenteth.

"And he said, A certain man had two sons:

"And the younger of them said to his father, Father, give me the portion of goods that falleth to me. And he divided unto them his living.

"And not many days after the younger son gathered all together, and took his journey into a far country, and there wasted his substance with riotous living.

"And when he had spent all, there arose a mighty famine in that land; and he began to be in want.

"And he went and joined himself to a citizen of that country; and he sent him into his fields to feed swine.

"And he would fain have filled his belly with the husks that the swine did eat: and no man gave unto him.

"And when he came to himself, he said, How many hired servants of my father's have bread enough and to spare, and I perish with hunger!

"I will arise and go to my father, and will say unto him, Father, I have sinned against heaven, and before thee,

"And am no more worthy to be called thy son: make me as one of thy hired servants.

"And he arose, and came to his father. But when he was yet a great way off, his father saw him, and had compassion, and ran, and fell on his neck, and kissed him.

"And the son said unto him, Father, I have sinned against heaven, and in thy sight, and am no more worthy to be called thy son.

"But the father said to his servants, Bring forth the best robe, and put it on him; and put a ring on his hand, and shoes on his feet:

"And bring hither the fatted calf, and kill it; and let us eat, and be merry:

"For this my son was dead, and is alive again; he was lost, and is found. And they began to be merry.

"Now his elder son was in the field: and as he came and drew nigh to the house, he heard musick and dancing.

"And he called one of the servants, and asked what these things meant.

"And he said unto him, Thy brother is come; and thy father hath killed the fatted calf, because he hath received him safe and sound.

"And he was angry, and would not go in: therefore came his father out, and intreated him.

"And he answering said to his father, Lo, these many years do I serve thee, neither transgressed I at any time thy commandment: and yet thou never gavest me a kid, that I might make merry with my friends:

"But as soon as this thy son was come, which hath devoured thy living with harlots, thou hast killed for him the fatted calf.

"And he said unto him, Son, thou art ever with me, and all that I have is thine.

"It was meet that we should make merry, and be glad: for this thy brother was dead, and is alive again; and was lost, and is found."

—LUKE 15:4–32.

The earth is the Lord's, and the fulness thereof;
the world, and they that dwell therein.

—Psalm 24:1.

WHAT HAPPENS IN SPRING

Peter got up one morning at the end of winter. The sun came in at his window.

"I want to go to the woods to play today," he said.

"That is a good idea," Mother said. "We will all go."

After breakfast all the children put on their outside playsuits and went to the woods. They had not been there for a week because every day it had rained. Something had happened in the woods while they were away. They found that lots of things had happened.

Peter said, "Oh, look!" He saw something on the ground, and he stopped to see it better. Everybody came to see it. "It's a flower!" Peter said. And it was a tiny white flower.

"It is a spring beauty," Mother said.

"Oh, look!" Michael said. And Michael saw something soft and bright and fuzzy on a little tree.

"I know what that is—a pussy willow," Peter said. And it was a pussy willow!

"Oh, look!" Barbara said. She had found a little nest in a bush. It was not finished yet.

"Let's leave it," Mother said. "A little bird is going to make a house there this spring and lay some eggs."

"Oh, look!" said Judy. And everybody looked, and there was a green frog beside the bush, looking very sleepy.

"He has just awakened from his long winter nap," Mother said.

"Oh, look at what I see!" David said in a big voice.

They all looked and there on a log in the warm sunshine they saw a little gray snake, lying very still.

"The snake has been asleep too," Mother said. "But now it is spring, so he wakes up."

"Shall I throw a stone at him?" David said.

"No, because this little snake doesn't hurt people," Mother said. "He has just come out as we have, to find some sunshine."

All day the children played. When night came they were tired and ready for bed. They had their baths. They put on their pajamas. They brushed their teeth. Daddy and Mother each read them a story, and then they tucked them in bed. Daddy opened the windows. Outside it was dark. But in the dark Peter heard a noise. It was like this:

"Peep—peep—peep—peep!"

It was a little noise, but the children all heard it.

"What's that? What's that?" they all asked.

"Peepers," said Daddy. "They are little frogs. They are down by the lake in the woods."

"Why do they sing at night?" Peter asked.

"So we will remember even at night that spring has come," Daddy said.

—PEARL S. BUCK, FROM *STORIES FOR LITTLE CHILDREN*,
COLLECTED BY DAVID LLOYD.

THE ELEPHANT'S FRIEND

William sat in the grass behind the big circus tent with his arms about Rover's brown body. The dog thumped his thick tail against the ground and looked up into the boy's face.

There were tears in William's eyes, and his hands trembled as he hugged the dog closer to him. This was Rover's last day with the circus. Tomorrow, when the tents and cages and all the other animals moved to the next town, Rover would be left behind.

Mr. Freeman, William's father, who owned the circus, had said so. He said the dog was no longer of any use. He was too old to jump through the paper hoops. He was too old to play with Silver the clown in the sawdust ring. About all he could do was to sit upon the back of Jumbo the elephant and soon he would be too old for that.

A shadow fell across the grass, and William looked up. There stood his father looking down at him. Rover wagged his tail very fast. William quickly brushed away his tears.

Mr. Freeman stood looking at the two of them for some moments. At last he said: "Well, William, you may as well try to forget about the dog, for we have to get rid of him. There's a man coming for him later in the morning. He will take the dog and give him a good home. The man owns a small farm just outside the town, and Rover will be happy there—"

"Oh," cried the boy, getting to his feet. "Let me keep him, Father! Please! We're such good friends, Rover and I!"

Mr. Freeman shook his head. He put an arm around his son's shoulders and said: "No, my boy, Rover will be better off on the farm. A circus is no place for animals that are old and of no use. It costs money to feed them, and they are in the way. Don't feel sad about the dog, my boy. You will soon forget him."

William tried hard not to sob. He said: "I'll never forget him! We've been such good friends! He—he's the friendliest dog I ever knew."

Mr. Freeman shook his head and walked away. He really

was not unkind. He just didn't quite understand how much his son loved the old dog.

William leaned over and patted Rover's head. He said to himself: "I can never forget him! Oh, if only I could make my father change his mind! But I can't think of a way!"

William walked slowly around the tent, and Rover followed him. It was the middle of the morning, and no one was at the circus grounds except the animals and the men and women who took part in the circus.

On the other side of the tent stood Jumbo the elephant. Around his leg was a rope, one end of which was fastened to a stake driven into the earth. Jumbo was very big and strong, and he looked very old and very wise. At sight of Rover his little eyes blinked in a friendly way. He flapped his ears and moved his long trunk this way and that.

Rover trotted up to Jumbo. They had always been good friends during the six years that Jumbo had been with the circus.

The dog now rubbed his nose against one of Jumbo's huge feet. The elephant rubbed his trunk against Rover's head, just behind the ears. Rover always liked that. He wagged his tail.

Then the long trunk wrapped itself around the dog's body, and the next moment Jumbo lifted his friend high in the air. Rover was not afraid, for Jumbo had done it a good many times. Now the trunk bent sideways and placed the dog on the elephant's back. Rover sat there for a few moments, and Jumbo stood quiet, with his trunk hanging toward the ground.

William, watching them, thought: "Jumbo will miss Rover almost as much as I shall! Poor old fellow! If my father would only keep him!"

Just then Rover barked. Jumbo knew what that meant. Up went the long trunk again. It circled the dog's body and very carefully lowered him to the ground. When his feet were on the ground, Rover wriggled and danced with delight, and Jumbo's little eyes blinked rapidly, as if he too were pleased.

While they were standing there, Mr. Freeman came out of the big tent. With him was a tall man with a straw hat. He was the farmer who was to give Rover a home.

Mr. Freeman said to him: "All right, there's the dog. You may as well take him now."

The farmer drew a thin rope from his pocket. He bent over and tied one end to the dog's collar.

"Come along, old fellow," he said and started to walk toward the road.

Rover did not want to go. He whined a little, and his tail dropped until it almost touched the ground. But he followed his new master, glancing backward at William every few seconds.

William watched them until they were out of sight. There was a great lump in his throat, and again tears filled his eyes.

"Don't feel sad, William," said his father. "The dog will be well cared for. Cheer up now."

Mr. Freeman went into the tent. William stood with lowered head. He was sure that he never would see Rover again.

The Chase

A shrill cry came from the elephant. William glanced up and then stepped quickly backward. Jumbo was moving his trunk angrily from side to side. The little eyes were blinking very fast.

Jumbo was very old and very wise; he understood. They had taken his friend away from him, and he did not like it! He began to thump the ground with his huge feet. He screamed again and again. He tugged at his rope. He tugged so hard that the stake moved a little in the ground.

Mr. Freeman came running from the tent. Two men who worked with the circus followed him. They drove the stake deeper into the ground. Then one of them hurried off and returned with a big bag of peanuts, which he scattered on the grass in front of the elephant.

After that Jumbo was more quiet. With his trunk he swept up the peanuts and ate them. But now and then he thumped the ground with his feet.

"He is all right now," said Mr. Freeman. "Come away from him, William."

All the rest of the morning William thought of Rover. Not for a moment could he forget the dog that he loved.

William had been with the circus ever since he was five years old, living now in one place, now in another. He had never known his mother, who had died when he was a baby. Aside from his father, it seemed that his best friend had been Rover. And now the dog was gone! They would never see each other again!

Early that afternoon, when people were beginning to come into the big circus tent to see the show, something happened. William was at the upper end of the circus grounds. He was about to enter one of the small tents in which Silver the clown was painting red circles on his face. Just then a long shrill came to his ears. It sounded like Jumbo's voice when he was angry. Someone shouted hoarsely, "Look out! Look out!"

Then came a loud crash and the sound of breaking wood. One of the men ran past the small tent. As he ran he shouted: "Jumbo's broken loose! And he's mad! He pulled up his stake"

In a moment William was running toward the place where the elephant had been tied. He gave no thought now to Rover, for when an angry elephant breaks loose in a circus, all kinds of trouble may follow. Among cars and cages and tents William ran until he was in the open space before the big circus tent.

The first thing he saw was Jumbo running toward the road. Crowds of people were pushing one another to right and left in order to get out of his way. Everyone seemed to be shouting.

Jumbo was running fast, swaying a little from side to side. The stake, still tied to his rope, was striking the ground and leaping into the air again. The elephant's long trunk was curved out in front of him, and his sharp tusks, gleaming white in the sunlight, looked dangerous.

There was a low fence between the circus grounds and the road. Jumbo crashed into it, and down it went. The elephant was on the road now. William, running at top speed, could see automobiles turning to right and left out of the way.

Jumbo was screaming wildly. His huge feet went thump, thump on the hard earth. Down the road he ran with all his speed. Then suddenly he turned to the right. Up a low bank he pounded and crashed through the bushes at the top. In a moment he was running across a field.

William caught sight of his father, about to climb into an automobile. He was shouting, "We've got to get him before he hurts someone!"

One of the circus men named John was at the wheel of the

car. He answered, "Yes, but Jumbo is mad! How we are ever going to bring him back, I don't know!"

William reached the car just as his father was sitting down. Mr. Freeman opened the door again. He said, "Jump in!"

The car started with a roar and a jerk, throwing William into the seat beside his father. Down the road they went. Other cars followed them.

William could see Jumbo running through a field at the right. The ground was moist and soft, and he left huge tracks behind him.

"Not so fast!" Mr. Freeman called to the driver. "Wait a bit, John! Jumbo doesn't like the soft ground up there. He'll come down on the road again, I think."

It was true. In a few minutes the elephant turned and began to move toward the road. He broke through a fence and slid down a steep bank, reaching the road about twenty yards in front of the car. He seemed tired now and was willing to trot along slowly.

The car followed him at a safe distance.

Once the elephant stopped suddenly and turned around. His trunk was raised in the air. He looked very dangerous then. He looked as if he meant to rush at the car and crush it. John put on the brakes, and the car stopped with a loud screech.

Jumbo stood blinking at it for a few minutes. Then he turned and trotted forward again.

"We shall never be able to lead him back!" cried Mr. Freeman. "He'll kill somebody! I know he will! See where he's going now!"

How Jumbo Found His Friend

Jumbo had reached a path that led off from the road. He stopped for a few seconds in front of a gate across the path. Something seemed to interest him very much. With his trunk he sniffed the ground. He sniffed and sniffed and sniffed. At last he raised his great head and blinked his little eyes in the direction of a farmhouse on a hill at the end of the path. And then—crash! Down went the gate, and Jumbo was trotting up the hill!

John stopped the car. He and Mr. Freeman and William jumped out. Mr. Freeman put both hands beside his mouth and shouted: "Look out up there! Look out for the elephant!"

Then all three of them ran up the hill.

William could see a woman and two children at a window of the house. They looked frightened. Jumbo saw them also. He waved his trunk at them. Then he started around the house. He went halfway around, then he came back and stopped in front of the door.

"Jumbo!" Mr. Freeman shouted. "Jumbo, old fellow!"

The elephant paid no attention. He looked as if he wanted to break the door down and go inside the house.

"Jumbo!" shouted John. "What's the matter?"

The elephant only lowered his head and pushed it against the door.

At that moment William saw a brown shape coming around the house. Although his attention was upon the elephant, yet he knew that brown shape! It was old Rover! This must be the farmhouse where Rover was to make his home.

Jumbo stepped backward and prepared to throw all his great weight against the door.

William suddenly rushed forward. "Jumbo!" he cried. "Don't do it, Jumbo! Here's Rover! Here's Rover! Look Jumbo! Here's old Rover!"

And just then the dog barked.

The elephant was very still for perhaps a second. Then he slowly turned his head to the right.

Rover trotted up to his big friend. He rubbed his head against Jumbo's foot, quite without fear. Down went the elephant's trunk. The end of it touched the dog's head and began to scratch it behind the ears. Rover wagged his tail. Then the trunk circled the dog's body, as it had done that morning, and lifted him high in the air. It placed him on the elephant's back—and there old Rover sat, looking down at William and thumping his tail against Jumbo's thick skin.

Mr. Freeman looked at the driver. "Whew!" he cried, wiping his forehead. "John, what do you think of that?"

"I think we're pretty lucky!" said John. "See Jumbo's eyes? He's not mad now. Yes, we're pretty lucky, Mr. Freeman! Jumbo has found the dog, and that was what he wanted."

John stepped forward and took hold of the rope that still hung from the elephant's leg. He put the stake under his arm. Jumbo's trunk gently felt of the man's coat, and then going into a pocket, it brought out a peanut.

Mr. Freeman suddenly laughed. He looked very different from the way he had looked in the automobile. William watched his father, almost afraid to ask the question that was on his lips.

But this time Mr. Freeman understood. He said: "William, I'd be a mean man if I didn't let you keep Rover after what has just happened! Yes, we'll keep him! I'll see the farmer and tell him so, for you want him, and Jumbo wants him, and—and, yes, now I want him too!"

And so it was a happy procession that started back toward the circus grounds. It would be hard to say who was the happiest—William or Mr. Freeman or Jumbo or old Rover seated upon the elephant's back!

—RUSSELL GORDON CARTER, FROM *THE ELEPHANT'S FRIEND
AND OTHER STORIES*, EDITED BY R. R. BUCKINGHAM;
USED BY PERMISSION OF GINN AND COMPANY.

WHY DAPPLE GRAY CHANGED HER MIND

When they were big enough to open their eyes, Mrs. Dapple Gray told her kittens all about the lovely big house and the milk and bread which they should have when they got big enough to go there for their meals as she did.

Every time the mama cat came back from the house she told the kittens about the lovely romp she had with the baby and how sunny and nice it was there, till they could hardly wait to go and see it all for themselves.

One day the mama cat said, "I have found a nice new house for you in a very large trunk, where some old clothes are kept, and I think we will move in at once."

Then she picked up black kitten and walked right out of the barn with him in her mouth. The mama cat went into the hall upstairs and dropped black kitten in the open trunk there. Then she started for white kitten.

But what do you think! The lady who owned the trunk came out and, seeing it open, shut it with a bang. She did not know that a dear little kitten was in there.

Oh, how frightened mama cat was when she came back with white kitten! She scratched and clawed the trunk and rushed to the lady, who was playing with her baby in another room. "Mee-ow! mee-ow! You have your baby, and I want mine," she cried and rubbed against her dress.

The lady saw the mama cat jump on the trunk and scratch it with her sharp claws. "What can the matter be?" said the lady, and she opened her trunk. There, cuddled up in the clothes, was black kitten sound asleep.

Before the lady could ask mama cat a single question, she had picked up black kitten out of the trunk and started for the old home in the barn.

When she got the three babies back in the hay, Mrs. Dapple Gray Cat told them that the house was a very nice place to go, but that the barn was the best home to bring up little kittens.

— Child's Hour.

Little Brown Music Maker

Listen—a small, brown bird is singing from a bush— "Sweet, sweet, sweet!"

It's the song sparrow. See the brown streaks on his sides and the brown spot on the center of his breast?

He's looking at us. Is he a bird friend of yours? He's an old friend of mine. I've known him all my life. Keep your eyes on him, and I'll tell you his story.

Our little song sparrow is six and one half inches from his beak to his tail. He is cheerful and brave and the best singer of his kind. He has a short, thick beak like a little cone. It is just the bill with which to open seeds. This kind of beak makes him a finch, no matter what else he may be called.

He is a singing finch. Do you like his name? In June we hear him singing love songs, but I have also heard him sing on sunny, winter days. Most of his comrades go south in the fall, for only a few of the song sparrows love ragweed and goosefoot seeds well enough to stay in the north. These brave ones find shelter in the thick evergreens.

Spring is the singing time for little song sparrow. Before the other birds come back, he has his whole world to himself. He fills it with his music, "Sweet, sweet, sweet—lovely the world whatever the weather!" The words just fit his trills.

Sometimes he sings when the sun has gone to bed. Once I heard him singing in the night, "Sweet, sweet—" But this song was never finished. I wondered if an owl had picked him from his perch, or if he had been too sleepy to finish the song he had begun.

The song sparrow loves bushes and little trees. He perches as high as he can sing. The owl cannot bother him by day. If danger comes, the song sparrow dives into the bush below to hide.

Mother song sparrow builds a nest of grass and weeds. She builds it on plants that are close to the ground. She tries to hide her nest, but sometimes an unfriendly bird watches her. When she flies away, this stranger bird comes. It is the cowbird mother. She is the blackbird's cousin, although her feathers are brown. In the song sparrow's nest she lays her spotted eggs.

The song sparrow hatches them out with her own. But what a greedy orphan is her guest. He is large and strong. He snatches food from the mother's beak, and the little sparrows often go hungry.

May brings the spring rains. The cold water sometimes rises several inches high. Often the baby sparrows drown. Then the song sparrow mother builds again. This time she is wiser. Her second nest is several feet above the ground. It is safe from rain and hidden in a thick bush. The cowbird may not find it. Why does she always build her first nest on the ground? No one really knows. It is well that she brings up a second family, and sometimes a third, each year. Her first brood so often meets with misfortune.

The song sparrow is always busy singing or building or feeding her young. In summer she hunts for seeds and caterpillars. She likes the smooth ones. In winter, if she stays north, she lives upon seeds alone.

Summer or winter, her mate knows no idleness. He is never sad. He sings and sings, "Sweet, sweet, sweet—lovely the world whatever the weather!"

—Cormack and Alexander.

THE BLUEBIRD LEARNS
A NEW SONG

B enny Bluebird sat disconsolately on a bare twig in the apple tree, attempting not the tiniest bit of a song. He was feeling decidedly out of sorts, and the longer he sat there thinking of his troubles, the worse he felt.

Perhaps Benny couldn't be blamed for his lack of cheerfulness. In the first place, he had been lured north by a mischievous breeze who had whispered to him that the spring was coming and wanted him to hurry along with the news. And it was not so at all. When he and Mrs. Bluebird arrived at their summer home, they found that it was only February. Winter had still a good many days to reign and several storms and fierce north winds to be let loose from his bag of weather. So the bluebirds found themselves shivering even in the most sheltered places that they could find and going hungry because food was hard to find—and sometimes the winds were so fierce that they could not get out at all but had to remain hidden in a cold barn loft. It was enough to make any bird cross; Benny was sure of that.

On this particular day, the sky was dull and gray—not a single Sunshine Fairy could get through those cold, dark clouds. Patches of snow lay on the frozen ground; Benny's search for food had brought very unsatisfactory results. He wondered what he should do next.

"Well, Benny, why don't you sing?" suddenly called a mocking voice. Benny turned to see the mischievous breeze who was really the cause of his troubles.

"I don't want to sing!" declared Benny crossly. And because

he was angry with the breeze, he said more crossly still, "In fact, I'm not going to sing again until I have a new song. So there!"

"Oh, Benny!" said the breeze. "Please don't be cross! I only meant it for a joke."

"Well, it was a fine joke, I'm sure. Now go away and find me a new song. I'll not sing again until I have one, and that's just what I mean. Go away, I said, Breeze."

"But, Benny, you must listen. I've just come from Mother Nature."

"Oh," said Benny. "I hope she scolded you soundly."

"She did," sighed the breeze. "That's why I'm here now. She said I must help you find a warm place to stay—and I have."

"Have you, really?" The bluebird was interested now.

"Yes, indeed. It's a nice warm attic. You'll like it. Come and see."

"We must get Mrs. Bluebird first," he said; then away they all flew.

The attic was really a very pleasant place, with an open window at one end through which they could enter. A chimney passing up through the other end made a cozy, warm corner, and the bluebirds immediately felt more cheerful.

"Now then," said the breeze, "in this house there are a boy and girl who are kind to Mother Nature's creatures. Let them see that you are here—and see if they don't help you."

Sure enough, the breeze was right. Benny and Mrs. Bluebird had flown in and out of the window only a few times when the children spied them.

"Mother, dear Mother!" they shouted joyously. "The bluebirds are here!"

The mother came out to look. "Why, they surely are," she agreed. "Now it won't be long until spring comes."

"Spring!" echoed Benny. "Breeze, see what you've done! No one will ever believe me after this."

"Oh, yes they will," answered the breeze. "Mother Nature is going to send spring a little earlier this year, and it won't be very long until she comes. But listen—what are they saying now?"

The boy and girl seemed much excited. "Mother, they've gone into our attic; think of it—having happiness birds right inside our house! Aren't we lucky?"

"Yes, we should be happier than ever now," smiled their mother.

"What do they mean, Benny?" asked Mrs. Bluebird.

"I'm sure I don't know," Benny answered. "Do you know, Breeze?"

No, the breeze didn't know either. They sat looking at each other wonderingly. The children had called them "happiness birds." What did they mean?

Presently they stopped thinking about it and flew out to look for food. And this time they were lucky; for the children, Ted and Louise, had set out a box of lunch for them—bits of meat, bread, and cake crumbs. How those hungry bluebirds did eat! They were very grateful to the thoughtful children.

While they were eating, the breeze hovered near them. "Now sing—won't you, Benny? Take back what you said about waiting until you have a new song," he begged.

Benny smiled. He was feeling much better now. "Well, I might," he said. "But I would like to have a new song anyway. I'll tell you what! When I can find out what the boy and girl meant by calling me a happiness bird, I'll make a new song about that."

"Let's start, then," laughed the breeze. "Probably Wisey Owl can tell us. Come on." And away they hurried.

When they told Mr. Owl why they had come to him, he fairly hooted with laughter. "Well, well! To think that you don't know who you are! Hoot!"

"But of course I do!" protested Benny. "I'm Benny Bluebird."

"Hoot! Hoot!" said Mr. Owl again. "But don't you know that to human beings you are a symbol of happiness?"

Benny nearly fell off the twig on which he was perched. "I? The symbol of happiness?"

"Yes, indeed. You're supposed to bring happiness. Wherever you go you're supposed to sing of happiness. Now then—see that you do it!"

Benny sat very still. He could hardly believe such a wonderful thing. Why, happiness is one of the most beautiful and precious things in the world. And he, the bluebird, had been chosen by human beings to be a sign and bringer of happiness!

Presently he spread his blue wings and went soaring toward the sky, singing joyously. The breeze, following after him, caught the song and carried it down toward the earth. And the children heard him and said to each other, "Listen! The bluebird is singing. How happy he is!"

And if they could have heard the words of Benny's new song, it would have been something like this:

"Wonderful! Wonderful! Wonderful! I'm the Happiness Bird, the Happiness Bird! Wherever I go, I'll carry happiness with me, for someone, for someone! I'll never be cross nor

gloomy again—for I am the Happiness Bird! Wonderful!
Wonderful!"

—MARY H. WOOLSEY.

SHELTERING WINGS

It was intensely cold. Heavy sleds creaked continuously as they scraped over the jeweled sounding board of dry, unyielding snow; the signs above the shop doors shrieked and groaned as they swung helplessly to and fro, and the clear, keen air seemed frozen into sharp, little crystalline needles that stabbed every living thing that must be out in it. The streets were almost forsaken in mid-afternoon. Businessmen hurried from shelter to shelter; every dog remained at home; not a bird was seen or heard. The sparrows had been forced to hide themselves in crevices and holes; the doves found protected corners and huddled together as best they could; many birds were frozen to death.

A dozen or more doves were gathered close under the cornice of the piazza of a certain house, trying with little success to keep warm. Some small sparrows, disturbed and driven from the cozy place they had chosen, saw the doves and came flying across the piazza.

"Dear doves," chirped the sparrows, "won't you let us nestle near you? Your bodies look so large and warm."

"But your coats are frosted with cold. We cannot let you come near, for we are almost frozen now," murmured the doves sadly.

"But we are perishing!"

"So are we."

"It looks so warm near your broad wings, gentle doves. Oh, let us come! We are so little and so very, very cold."

"Come," cooed one dove at last, and a trembling little sparrow fluttered close and nestled under the broad wings.

"Come," cooed another dove, and another little sparrow found comfort.

"Come! Come!" echoed another warmhearted bird, and another, until at last more than half the doves were sheltering small, shivering sparrows beneath their own half-frozen wings.

"My sisters, you were very foolish," said the other doves. "You mean well, but why do you risk your own beautiful lives to give life to worthless sparrows?"

"Ah, they are so small and so very, very cold," murmured the doves. "Many of us will perish this cruel night; while we have life let us share its meager warmth with those in bitter need."

Colder and colder grew the day. The sun went down behind the clouds suffused with soft and radiant beauty, but more fiercely and relentlessly swept the wind around the house where the doves and sparrows waited for death.

An hour after sunset a man came up to the house and strode across the piazza. As the door of the house closed heavily behind him, a little child watching from the window saw something jarred from the cornice fall heavily to the piazza floor.

"Oh, Papa!" she cried in surprise. "A poor, frozen dove has fallen on our porch."

When he stepped out to pick up the frozen dove, the father saw the others under the cornice. They were no longer able to move or to utter a cry, so he brought them in and placed them

in a room where they might slowly revive. Soon more than half
the doves could coo gratefully and raise their stiffened wings.
Then out from beneath the wing of each revived dove fluttered
a living sparrow.

"Look, Papa," cried the child, "each dove that has come to
life was folding a poor little sparrow, close to her heart."

They gently raised wings of the doves that could not be
revived. Not one had a sparrow beneath it.

Colder and fiercer grew the wind without; cutting and
more piercing grew the frozen crystalline needles of air; but
each dove that had sheltered a frost-coated sparrow beneath her
own shivering wings lived to rejoice in the glowing, gladsome
sunshine of the days to come.

—SELECTED.

THE THREE LITTLE GOLDFISH

Three little goldfish lived in a beautiful bowl. One was
white and so transparent you could almost see his bones,
one was as gold and gleaming as a sunbeam, and the other was
as black as night. They belonged to a dear little boy who had
named them Wynken, Blynkin, and Nod, from the beautiful
poem his mother read him at bedtime. Every other day Sonny
Boy fed them the tiniest bit of food. It looked like a piece of
tissue paper. When he wanted to give them a piece of cake,
Mother told him it would make their stomachs ache.

One cold winter night Sonny Boy's mother tucked him
deep beneath the covers. The snow outside covered the earth,
and even the moon in the sky seemed to be pale with cold.

Father put coal in the furnace, so they would all sleep warm and sound. When morning came, Mother called her little boy to see the wonderful pictures Jack Frost had painted on the window panes. He clapped his hands with joy. But only for a moment, for when he looked at the goldfish bowl he saw that Wynken, Blynken and Nod were frozen solid in a block of ice. A window had been left open all night, and Jack Frost had sneaked in and frozen their water.

"Mama, dear, they are dead," he sobbed. She tried to cheer him, but there were also tears in her eyes.

Mother picked up the bowl and put it behind the kitchen stove till the ice would melt, and she could throw the dead fish out. Then she went about her work. After a while she was in the bedroom making beds when she heard an excited call, "Mama, Mama, they have come back to life." She hurried into the kitchen. The goldfish were swimming about as though nothing had happened. The ice had slowly thawed in the warm room. Wynken was trying to stand on his head; Blynken flipped a little fin in pleasure; and Nod stared at Sonny Boy.

—Elva Hunt Anderson.

Kindhearted Little Porky

Porky was such a dear little pig. He had soft, pink ears, a wee curly tail, and the best manners of any animal in the farmyard.

But oh! How unhappy everyone made him! He tried so hard to be kind and polite. But the hens pecked at him. The dogs chased him. Even his own family made fun of him. They called him "'Fraid-Cat Porky." The only one in the pen that was kind to him was another small pig named Pinky. She tried to take his part, but she was too little to help much.

Little Brownie who lived in the barn tried to help too. But it was no use. When he saw the pigs eating at the trough, he would push one of the larger pigs over to make room for Porky. But as soon as Porky found the hole, the other pigs would shove him out again. Porky was too polite to push back. Brownie really got cross with him.

Porky was always giving someone the largest apple he found. If he was lying in a nice, cool mudhole, he would move over to make room for one of his family. Then, like as not, he'd be pushed out himself!

One day Brownie found Porky crying.

"Why don't you fight back?" asked Brownie, a bit crossly.

"Sometimes I think I will," answered Porky, "and then I think I might hurt them."

Poor Porky looked so unhappy that Brownie could not help feeling sorry for him.

"Maybe I'd better go off into the woods and live by myself," sniffed Porky.

Brownie thought this might be a good idea, but he was afraid Porky might get lonesome.

It was only half an hour later that the king of the elves flew by. He saw the worry wrinkles on Brownie's forehead. "What is the matter, Brownie?" he said. "You are looking old."

So Brownie told him about Porky. The king put on his thinking cap.

"It's no use to give Porky horns," he said. "He wouldn't use them."

Suddenly an elfish grin spread over his face. Then he laughed right out loud.

"I have it!" he chuckled.

Then he whispered in Brownie's ear. Brownie turned a double somersault. Then he looked sober again.

"But wouldn't Porky be lonesome?" he asked.

The king put on his thinking cap again. Then he leaned over and whispered in Brownie's ear again. This time Brownie turned two double somersaults.

Then the king and Brownie hurried to the barnyard. They saw little Pinky under a big oak tree. Not far away, Porky was piling up the nicest acorns he could find.

"These are for Pinky," he said to Brownie and blushed till he was as pink as Pinky herself.

At that moment a strange thing happened. Each soft little bristle on Porky and Pinky began to grow long and stiff.

Just then the pigs heard the call for supper. Porky and Pinky ran for the trough. They got there first, but up rushed all the other pigs trying to push Porky away, as usual. But what a surprise they got! Each long bristle on Porky's body stood straight out. And they were very sharp!

"Ee—ee-ee—ee!" How those pigs did squeal! They backed away quickly. You can better believe they did not come back till Porky and Pinky had finished supper.

"Why, Porky," said Pinky admiringly, "how brave you are, chasing all those rude pigs away! Why didn't you do it before?"

"I don't know," said Porky honestly. "I don't want to hurt anyone. But when anyone tries to hurt me these days, every bristle on me stands straight out!"

The hens and the dogs soon learned to let Porky and Pinky

alone. All the farmyard folks stopped calling the little pig "'Fraid-cat Porky." His spines were sharper than pine needles. So they addressed him politely as PORK-U-PINE.

Before long Porky and Pinky went out to the woods and built themselves a fine little house. They were so happy there that they returned to the farmyard only once in a while for a visit.

—LAURA JOHNSTON, FROM *THE GRADE TEACHER;*
USED BY PERMISSION.

THE LITTLE SEED

Far down in Mother Earth a tiny seed was sleeping, safely wrapped in a warm, brown jacket. The little seed had been asleep for a long, long time, and now somebody thought it was time for him to wake up. This somebody was an earthworm that lived close by. He had been creeping about and found that all the seeds in the neighborhood had roused themselves, and were pushing their roots down into the earth, and lifting their heads up, up through the soil into the bright sunshine and fresh air.

So when the worm saw this little seed still sleeping, he cried, "Oh, you lazy fellow, wake up! All the seeds are awake and growing, and you have slept long enough."

"But how can I grow or move at all in this tight, brown jacket?" said the seed in a drowsy tone.

"Why, push it off. That's the way the other seeds have done. Just move about a little, and it will come off."

The little seed tried and tried, but the tough jacket wouldn't break; and all the time the worm was telling him how happy the other seeds were, now that they had lifted their heads into the sunshine.

"Oh dear, oh dear!" said the seed. "What shall I do? I can't break this jacket, and I shall never see the beautiful sunshine! Besides I'm so sleepy I just can't keep awake any longer." And he fell asleep again.

"The lazy fellow," thought the earthworm. "But it is strange that the other seeds shed their jackets so easily. Who could have helped them, I wonder?"

The little seed slept soundly for a long while, but at last he awoke and found his jacket soft and wet, instead of hard and dry, and when he moved about, it gave way entirely and dropped off.

Then he felt so warm and happy that he cried, "I really believe I am going to grow after all. Who could have helped me take off my jacket? And who woke me, I wonder? I don't see anybody nearby."

"I awoke you," said a soft, happy voice close by. "I'm a sunbeam and I came down to wake you; and my friends the raindrops moistened your jacket, so that you might find it ready to slip off."

"Oh, thank you," said the seed. "You're all very kind; will you help me grow into a plant too?"

"Yes," said the sunbeam, "I'll come as often as I can to help you, and the raindrops will come too; and then, if you work hard, with our help you will become a beautiful plant, I'm sure."

"But," said the seed, "how did you know that I was sleeping here? Could you see me?"

"No," said the sunbeam, "but the Creator could. He looked

down from his home in heaven, and he saw you far beneath the earth trying so hard to grow, and he called the raindrops to him and said: 'One of my little seedlings is sleeping down there, and he wants to grow. Go down and help him, and tell the sunbeams to follow you and wake the seed, so that he may begin to grow as soon as he will'!"

"How kind he is!" said the seed. "If he had not seen me sleeping here, I should have always been a brown seed, I suppose. Who is this kind Creator?"

"He is your Creator too. He is everyone's Creator and takes care of everybody; nothing could live without him."

"How can I thank him?" asked the seed. "What could I do that would please him very much?"

"Grow into just the best plant that you possibly can," said the sunbeam. "That will please him most of all."

So the seed grew into a beautiful vine that climbed higher and higher towards the heavens, from which the Creator smiled down upon him to reward his labor.

—ANNE E. POUSLAND, FROM *HALF A HUNDRED STORIES FOR LITTLE PEOPLE*, MILTON BRADLEY CO.

THE SQUIRREL FAMILY

Once upon a time there were some frolicsome squirrels who were having a lovely time hopping and jumping from pine tree to pine tree. The mother squirrel didn't have time to play; she had something more to do. She was cleaning house. She worked hard until her hole in the tree was all nice and clean; then she called her children squirrels to come home. Squirrels always go quickly when they are called, and these squirrels went just that way. They ran, hopped, and jumped right into their hole in the tree to hear what the mother had to say.

"My little ones," said Mrs. Bushy Tail, (for that was mother squirrel's name), "it is going to storm, I fear, and we shall all have to get in our winter supply of food. You won't have time to play for some time, but you must gather all the nuts you can. Something tells me winter is coming."

Her little Frisky-Top said, "Well, here I go first of all to get my nuts," and out of the hole he jumped.

But her little Bright-Eyes said, "Oh, I would rather play, and then I'll get my nuts tomorrow."

Well, you should have seen Frisky work. He found such fine, large nuts and oh! so many of them. And Mrs. Bushy Tail too gathered in a great many nuts. But little Bright-Eyes played all day except when he stopped to eat a nut.

That night some great clouds came, and soon it started to snow, and before long everything was white.

Little Frisky-Top said, "How glad I am I have a store of nuts."

"Yes," said Mrs. Bushy Tail, "I too am glad, for now we shall not need to go out in the cold and snow."

Little Bright-Eyes said nothing, but he was thinking hard. How he wished he had obeyed his mother when she told him to gather in his nuts.

The next morning Bright-Eyes jumped out of his hole in the tree; everything was covered with snow. Little Bright-Eyes was hungry, but he didn't have one nut. Oh! how he wished he had minded his mother. No telling how long that snow would last. His mother said, "Bright-Eyes, why don't you eat some of your nuts?" He felt ashamed, but he told his mother the truth of how he had not minded her at all when she told him to gather in his nuts.

"Well," said Mrs. Bushy Tail, "I'll give you some of my nuts."

Frisky-Top said, "I'll give you some of mine, enough to last until you can get some for yourself."

Some time after that, the snow partly melted away, and Bright-Eyes hurried out to get some nuts. After a hard time he found some. And after that, I tell you, Bright-Eyes never played when his mother told him to gather nuts.

WHY THE ROBIN'S BREAST IS RED

Once, long ago, there were no matches. The Red People of the Far North had just one fire. They never let it go out. They all went to this fire to get coals for their homes. If the fire should go out, they would freeze. Then the great white bear, who loves the cold and hates the fire, would have the country to himself. So the Red People left a hunter and his little boy to watch the fire day and night.

One day the hunter became very ill. The little boy had to watch the fire and take care of his sick father besides. For several days and nights he did not sleep. At last the little boy grew very tired and sleepy. One night he could not hold his eyes open any longer. He fell fast asleep. The great white bear was nearby. He was watching for a chance to put out the fire. When he saw the little boy asleep, he ran quickly and jumped on the fire. He stamped it with his wet, snowy feet, then he rolled upon it. He thought he had put the fire out. So he went away happy.

A passing robin saw what the bear was doing. The robin waited until the bear had left. Then he flew down and searched about until he found one bright spark of fire. He fanned and fanned the spark with his wings. The coals caught fire and blazed again. Alas, the flame burned the little robin's breast until it was as red as the fire! But the good bird did not stop. He flew away to every lodge of Red People in the North. Whenever he touched his breast to the ground, a bright fire sprang up. Soon there were many fires burning in the great northland.

The white bear was very angry. He growled fiercely. Then he hid in an ice cave. He knew that now he never could have all the country to himself.

That is why the Red People of the North love the robin. They never tire of telling their children how the bird came to have a red breast.

—ASA PATRICK, FROM *THE GRADE TEACHER;*
USED BY PERMISSION.

INDIAN PAINTBRUSHES

Hundreds of years ago lovely wild flowers that look so much like paintbrushes dipped in red paint began to grow in many parts of North America. The Indians told their children many stories about these flowers. One of these legends is from the old southwest part of the United States, where once there lived Pawhokee, an Indian boy who loved all things beautiful.

This boy grew up into a tall, handsome young chief. The love of beautiful flowers had inspired him to do beautiful things. So one day he tried to paint a picture of the sunset, but his colors were war paints, and his brushes were rough. For days and weeks and months Pawhokee tried to paint the sunset, but in vain. He knew that the Great Spirit painted the flame and the soft hues in the western sky, so he prayed to the Great Spirit to help him.

Then one evening as he sat in front of his wigwam thinking about the Great Spirit and longing to make a picture of the lovely colors in the sky, Pawhokee thought he heard a voice saying, "Behold your paintbrushes." He looked down, and at his feet he saw a lovely plant with a slender stem and a bright blossom like a brush. The blossom was the color of the sunset. He threw off the deerskin from his shoulders, picked up the brush which was dripping with color, and began to paint the picture of the sunset.

But the colors in the sky began changing. So Pawhokee looked about and saw other paintbrushes at his feet, each bearing tints of the sunset glory. He picked up each tint as he needed it and painted as never an Indian had painted before. And when the last gleam of gold and crimson had faded from the sky, Pawhokee's heart sang with joy, for on his deerskin blanket was the picture he longed so to paint—the Great Spirit in the Sunset.

Early the next morning, as the sun was shining over the mountains into Pawhokee's wigwam, he was awakened from a refreshing sleep by shouts of joy. Looking out, he saw a great number of Indian children picking flowers that were springing

up all over the hillside. "Indian paintbrushes! Indian paintbrushes!" shouted the children as they picked their arms full.

And from that day to this, wherever Indian children find
the Indian paintbrushes splashing their color over the fields and
meadows, they remember Pawhokee and the Great Spirit.

—Used by permission of the *Sunshine Magazine.*

Little Daffy-Down-Dilly

"Dear me," said little Daffy-down-dilly, tossing her yellow
head haughtily, "I can't see how you, my dear Miss
Hyacinth, with your delicate colors and sweet perfume, can
bear to have that ugly angleworm crawling around your roots. I
think he is just horrid."

Miss Hyacinth smiled pleasantly and answered, "I don't
believe you're acquainted with little Mr. Angleworm, or you
would not talk so about him."

"No, indeed!" exclaimed Daffy-down-dilly the daffodil. "I
do not know him, and I do not want to know him—the ugly,
slimy, crawly thing!"

"And yet he is one of your best friends," said Miss
Hyacinth.

Just then the angleworm spoke, "You have beautiful blossoms, little Daffy-down-dilly, but you owe their beauty in a
great measure to me."

"To you!" retorted the daffodil. "Why, I never heard of such
impudence! If for a moment you think that a flower with such
beautiful blossoms as mine would have for a friend an ugly
earthworm, you are very much mistaken!"

"All right," answered the worm, "if that is the way you feel about it, I will tell other worms not to come near you. We have always helped you to grow, but we will stay away and see how you will get along without us."

"You do wrong to despise the help of our humble friend," said the hyacinth. "I am sure Miss Tulip and your sister, Miss Narcissus, and all the rest of us are very grateful to Mr. Angleworm for his work."

But Miss Daffodil only tossed her yellow blossoms in disdain.

Days and weeks went by and little by little the earth around the daffodil's roots grew harder and harder. The rain softened the earth so it could pack together closely, and then the hot sun dried it, and there were no little angleworms to crawl through the tightly-packed ground to loosen up the earth. It gradually grew harder and harder until it was almost like a stone.

About this time Miss Daffodil thought she would send out some new rootlets to help nourish her little baby bulbs, for daffodils possess bulb roots, and every young bulb has to grow little roots.

When Miss Daffodil started her new rootlets growing, she was surprised to find they could not get through the tightly-packed earth. Try as she might, she could not force them through the ground. In her trouble she called to Miss Hyacinth. "Oh, dear Miss Hyacinth, what shall I do? I cannot make my roots pierce through the hard ground, and my baby bulbs will surely die."

"Of course, you cannot," answered Miss Hyacinth. "Little Mr. Angleworm kept the earth all nice and loose for you so you could easily send your roots down into the ground. Now you have driven him away, there is nothing for you to do except to beg him to come back—or else die."

Poor little Daffy-down-dillly, upon hearing this, began to weep. "Why does not the earth stay nice and soft without the ugly angleworms?" she cried.

"Mother Nature orders that all the little bugs and worms that crawl shall have some good work to do to help others. Why she does this I do not know," said the little hyacinth, "but I do know that not one of us flowers could get along without the help of the bees and butterflies, the bugs and the worms."

"Does everybody have to depend upon others?" asked Daffodil.

"I know that it is so in flower land," answered little Hyacinth, "and Sir Breeze whispered to me that it was just the same among the sky people."

"Oh, dear," sobbed Daffodil, "what shall I do?"

"Tell Mr. Angleworm you are sorry, and beg him to help you," said sensible little Hyacinth. "It is not pleasant, of course, but it will be more pleasant than starving."

"Do you suppose that he will forgive me?" asked Daffodil humbly.

"Try him and see," replied Hyacinth.

What Miss Daffodil said to Mr. Angleworm I never knew, but the next morning I found any number of little angleworms busily at work loosening the earth around the roots of Miss Daffodil.

THE LITTLE CLOUD

One day Mother Nature dressed her cloud children in their best white dresses and sent them out to play.

"Now, children, try to keep your dainty dresses clean, and stay close together so you won't get lost," said the mother.

Then all the clouds floated out in the blue sky. It was such fun playing that they all forgot to watch the littlest cloud. She was so small that she could not keep up with the others as they floated along, pushed by the gentle breezes.

At first Little Cloud was frightened when she found herself so far behind the others. She could see them way over the hills, but even though she floated as fast as she could, she could not catch up with them. She was a brave little cloud, so she blinked back her raindrop tears as she watched the other clouds disappear out of sight.

After a while she met some golden sunbeams. "Oh, sunbeams, let me play with you. I am so lonesome, and I cannot find my family."

"You funny little cloud," laughed the merry sunbeams. "We never play with clouds. We are making it bright and sunny for those little earth children while they have a picnic."

"I won't spoil their fun," promised Little Cloud.

"Oh, yes, you would," said the sunbeams. "You should hear the things people say if they see a cloud in the sky when they start out for a picnic." Then the sunbeams danced merrily on their way, leaving the sad little cloud alone again.

After awhile Little Cloud saw a beautiful rose garden down on earth. The lovely flowers had their sweet faces turned toward the sky so that Little Cloud could see them plainly. As she watched them, their lovely heads began to droop.

Just then a bird flew past Little Cloud. "Why don't you do something about it?" called the bird.

"What is the matter?" asked Little Cloud.

"Those poor roses are dying because they are so thirsty. Why don't you send down some raindrops so they will not die?" asked the bird.

"My raindrops are so few they could not help much," replied Little Cloud.

Just then the breezes came by. "Oh, Breezes, please find the other cloud children and bring them here so we can save the beautiful roses."

So the breezes hurried over the hills until they found the other clouds playing hide-and-seek. "Come quickly," called the breezes. "Little Cloud needs you to help her save the rose garden. The roses are dying because they are so thirsty."

"Where is Little Cloud, and where are the roses?" asked the clouds in a chorus.

"Get on our backs, and we will carry you to them," said the kind little breezes. So the clouds climbed on the backs of the strong little breezes, and away they all flew through the blue, blue sky.

When they found Little Cloud, she was weeping because she thought the other clouds would never come to help save the beautiful flowers. Her raindrop tears had made it a little cooler in the garden, and the roses began to raise their pretty heads. Then all the cloud children sent down a gentle rain to earth, and soon all the flowers were bright and happy again.

After the raindrops had saved the garden, the clouds saw that their pretty, fluffy, white dresses were soiled and gray.

"Oh, what will Mother say?" wailed one of the clouds.

"I am sure she will not mind," said one of the larger clouds. "We have found Little Cloud, and we have saved the flowers."

—Virginia B. Jacobsen.

Daddy Robin's Problem

One spring day Daddy Robin was terribly worried. For days he had been waiting patiently for Mother Robin to come from the southland. She promised Daddy Robin she would come as soon as he had found a cozy place in the old apple orchard to build a nest for their tiny bird family.

Daddy Robin had carefully inspected all the trees, finally choosing a little nook in the far corner of the orchard, high up in the forked branches of a flowering cherry tree.

For days he had worked fast and hard, collecting choice bits of straw and dried stems of grass which he wove in and out with his little brown bill, shaping and molding their tiny home.

The nest was almost built now. Daddy Robin had lined it with fresh bits of mud and was waiting for Mother Robin to come and finish lining the nest with the soft fluffy feathers which she liked to collect all by herself.

Bonnie Bluebird had arrived on time. She had finished building her nest a week ago for their babies, and Daddy Robin could tell by the happy, joyous songs that Johnnie Bluebird sang that Bonnie was kept busy these days sitting on her nest full of pale greenish-blue eggs.

Daddy Robin saw Bunny Rabbit pulling the soft fluffy fur from her stomach to line the nest that she had built away down deep in a hole in the ground under the wild currant bushes by the barbwire fence.

Reggie Squirrel was kept busy too. All day long he ran up and down the hollow trunk of an old gnarled tree to feed his babies, his fat cheeks bulging wide with the food he was carrying to them.

The Baa Baa Sheep was happy and contented, nipping the tender blades of juicy grass in the meadow close by the orchard, while her baby lambkin frisked by her side.

Bossie, the cow, had a wobbly-legged baby. He nuzzled for the warm drops of milk while his proud mother stood knee deep in sweet clover watching him and chewing her cud.

Daddy Robin saw all of these things. It made him more melancholy and worried than before. He seldom left the tree now to search for food but sat huddled and dejected with his feathers all fluffed out like a little round ball, hidden by the white, fragrant blossoms, sad and lonely.

When the merry little breezes came winging through the branches of the tree, Daddy Robin chirped, "Have you seen Mother Robin?"

"No, no," they whispered, ruffling Daddy Robin's feathers. "No, we have not seen Mother Robin."

When the busy little bees buzzed close by, Daddy Robin chirped, "Have you seen Mother Robin?"

They shook their tiny heads sorrowfully, then turning, circled around Daddy Robin's head, buzzing, "No, we have not seen Mother Robin."

When Jimmie, the red-winged blackbird, arrived from the

southland, Daddy Robin soared high up in the blue, blue sky, away up above the tall tree tops to the willow patch by the swamp where Jimmy was resting his tired wings from the long journey. Daddy Robin chirped, "Have you seen Mother Robin?"

"Yes, yes, I have seen Mother Robin," Jimmie chimed. "She was blown away out of her course by strong, heavy wind currents. She looked spent and tired, and her wing feathers were badly broken."

"Thank you, Jimmie," Daddy Robin chirped joyously, "oh, thank you!"

Daddy Robin flew back to the nest in the cherry tree. All day long he preened and watched the blue sky for Mother Robin's return, but she did not come. When the golden sun-man was going to rest behind the rugged mountain in the westland, Mother Robin had not come. When the big yellow moon rose high in the heaven and Billy the wise old owl hooted through the stillness of the night, Mother Robin had not come.

The next morning, long before the other birds began to awaken, Daddy Robin flew down to the little Singing Brook for a cool drink and a refreshing bath. He whipped the silvery drops of water over his back with his strong pinion feathers until he was dripping wet.

While he was enjoying his bath, he thought he heard a familiar "peep, peep" above him. Looking up he saw poor bedraggled Mother Robin, swaying on the tip of a blackberry bush.

Daddy Robin was overjoyed. All day he flew back and forth from the Singing Brook to the flowering cherry tree where their nest was safely hidden, bringing Mother Robin the choicest bugs and the juiciest worms he could find, while she lined the nest with soft, downy feathers that she had found in Farmer Jones's barnyard where Speckle the hen had dropped them.

A few days later, Daddy Robin sat close by Mother Robin where he could watch her from the corner of his eye and sang as though his little throat would burst, for Mother Robin had laid her first blue egg that very morning, and Daddy Robin wanted to proclaim the good news to the whole wide world.

—Celia A. Van Cott.

The wilderness and the solitary place shall be glad for them;
and the desert shall rejoice, and blossom as the rose.

—*Isaiah 35:1.*

How a Pioneer Boy Crossed the Plains

We camped at Florence, Nebraska, for nearly a month as I remember. We lived in an old shack of a house during that time, which was just enough shelter to keep some of the rain from meeting us. The house was situated right where now stand the reservoirs of the present waterworks which supply the city of Omaha with water, this water being pumped out of the Missouri River into the reservoirs and filtered. I find from Jenson's *Church Chronology* that our company left Florence on June 17, 1860, and arrived in Salt Lake City on Monday, September 3, of the same year. The company consisted of two hundred forty-nine persons, thirty-six wagons, one hundred forty-two oxen, and fifty-four cows.

Our journey across the plains was of the usual ox-team kind. There was little of special note that transpired. On the 4th of July we were near where the city of Kearney now stands, and we heard the artillery from across the river at old Fort Kearney, about two hundred miles from Omaha.

We traveled about ninety miles a week. No traveling was done on the Sabbath. It was always a day of rest and religious worship.

I remember how "green" we all were with respect to yoking up cattle or milking cows or greasing the wagon, or in doing anything that pertained to frontier or pioneer life.

At Florence, when our two yoke of cattle and wagon were turned over to us, my father got on the off side of the cattle and tried to drive them. Of course they were frightened and ran away down the hill. But we soon learned how to manage things. The little tent which we had could be folded up carefully and tied behind the wagon. The tent poles, the two props, and the roof pole were always tied together and put in the place provided for them in the wagon. Our bedding was all carefully taken care of. And we journeyed on. At noon the cattle were unhitched, perhaps not always unyoked. After they had eaten a little, we would give them drink, and in the course of an hour and a half or two hours we were plodding on our road again.

Of course there were inconveniences and more or less of hardship in such a mode of travel. But as I was a child of eleven years of age, I do not remember the hardships. On the contrary, I rather enjoyed the whole trip. Of course, to my father and mother at their time of life it must have been very difficult. I know that they suffered great inconvenience and weariness and were called upon to sacrifice much. One thing that I distinctly remember was seeing tens of thousands of buffalo on the hills west of Kearney. Sometimes the captain would have to stop the train to allow herds of buffalo slowly to cross the wagon road. As they were in large numbers, sometimes this would occupy nearly an hour. We often had buffalo meat to eat, and it was very sweet and good. We got long strips of it and hung it up to dry in the hot sun. When it was thoroughly dried, it could be kept for days and even weeks, and was much better eating than chipped beef.

Every night the wagons were formed in a circle at some level and convenient place for camping near water. Each wagon party then started its campfire and cooked supper—what little cooking there was to do, which consisted mostly of baking bread in an iron skillet, a utensil about eighteen inches in diameter, about four or five inches deep, and made of cast iron. It had a heavy lid and three or four short legs to raise the body of the skillet from the ground and to admit the fire underneath. Coals were then put on top of the heavy lid.

We often had difficulty in finding wood to burn, as there were so many trains and so many camping places, and no forests whatever. It was a question to find something with which to make a fire. The best fuel we had on the plains, where there was no wood at all, was what we called buffalo chips, being in reality simply sun-dried buffalo dung.

After the cows were milked in the morning, the milk that was not used would be put in a tin churn and strapped at the side of the wagon. By noon it would be thoroughly churned, and butter could be gathered, and buttermilk could be enjoyed for lunch.

The thunder and lightning and rainstorms that occurred periodically along the plains of Nebraska were terrific and occasioned us some inconvenience and considerable fright.

The Indians were very plentiful and sometimes a little troublesome, although we never had any conflict whatever with them. I can remember that they were a haughty and insolent lot, as they rode upon their ponies, and decked in their feathers and paint, frightening most of us who were not used to them.

We young ones walked with bare feet most of the way across the plains. We soon got used to the wagon and tent and campfire life. Our bedding was rolled in bundles in the morning, and these bundles were simply unrolled at night on the ground. Thus the beds were made again.

We suffered no loss until we reached the crossing of Green River, on the old emigrant road. At this point, one of our best oxen lay down and died. This left us with three oxen and two cows. We yoked up one of the cows with the odd ox and traveled right along, because our load was becoming lighter each day, as we consumed our provisions.

The last Sunday of the trip was spent near Parley's Park, a day's travel with oxen from Salt Lake City. George A. Smith and other leading brethren came over the mountain to greet us and to welcome us to our new country.

On Monday, September 3, we came out of the canyon and onto the bench near Fort Douglas, and I can very well remember with what joy and pleasure each one of our company, and even I, looked upon the growing little city in the wilderness. We felt that all of our troubles and trials were practically at an end, while, as a matter of fact, they had only just begun, for all the changing trials of pioneer life were yet to be undertaken and solved. Many things we were called upon to face were difficult, and many times it was hard to carry on.

Having arrived here, we did not know what to do nor where to go. Some friends of ours told us that there was quite a colony of Scottish people who had gone up into the Cache Valley that spring. They thought that might be a good place for us to go. We didn't know in the least where Cache Valley was— whether it was north or south or east or west. We didn't know anything about the elevation—whether it was too cold or too dry, or what it was. Indeed, we knew nothing about the place at all. We simply went where there were some people whom my parents had known in the Old Country. There we settled. We lived in a dugout the first winter. None of the people know now what a dugout really is, but we older ones know. I know very well about it, for we lived in a dugout, lived there in extreme poverty.

The first work I did there as a child was to help my mother

glean heads of wheat from the wheat fields, which had been cut with the scythe or cradle, for there were no mowing machines or reapers and self-binders in those days. After we had gleaned the wheat, the heads being tied in little bunches, we took a washboard and rubbed the head on it, thus threshing the wheat. This was our threshing machine. Of course there were chaff and some smut mixed in with the heads of wheat, and I had to spread the wheat on a wagon cover and take a tin pan and throw the wheat up in the air, catching it on the plate. In this manner, the little breeze that was blowing would blow the chaff from the wheat. This was our fan mill. We then ground the wheat between two millstones, for there was nothing to the gristmill at that time except two millstones. Having been ground in that way, the flour was quite dark and made a black bread, but a very wholesome bread, after all. We had that flour made into porridge for breakfast, and baked into cakes or scones for dinner and supper. That, with baked or boiled potatoes, was pretty much all the food we had to eat.

Soon I had to act as herd boy and was sent out to watch our two cows to see that they didn't stray off, and to bring them home at night to be milked, for one of the chief parts of our living was the milk from the two cows.

My suit of clothes, which my mother had made for me after we arrived in the valley, consisted of a shirt and a pair of trousers, both made out of the tent cover that we had used in crossing the plains. It was pretty stiff and hard cloth, for it was weather-beaten, but it was all I had—that and a rope around my waist to keep the suit together. That was the extent of my wardrobe.

—CHARLES W. NIBLEY.

PIONEER HOMES

Our home was in a small village named Meadowville. Primary was held in our home. Father provided some boards which were placed on the rungs of chairs to make seats; some of the lower rungs for the smaller children, on the second rungs for those a little larger, and the largest children occupied the chairs and the lounge.

It was springtime. Mother had cleaned house. The walls were fresh with whitewash. We had a beautiful new rag carpet. Since then I have seen many exquisite and costly rugs and carpets, but never one that thrilled me with its beauty to the degree that that carpet did. I can hear now the crunch, crunch of the clean, crisp straw beneath it as we walked over it. I simply cannot tell you how delightful it was to me.

It was Primary day. The rain had been falling all through the night, and it rained on relentlessly all through the day. The mud in that little town was of the kind that is so rich in stick-to-it-ive-ness. As the hour for Primary approached, I watched from the window with a heavy heart.

I asked, "Mama, why do we have to have Primary?"

"Heavenly Father wants us to," was her convincing reply.

The children came and that clinging mud with them. Primary was over, and the children gone. Can you imagine the condition of that beautiful carpet? As I looked at it, my heart was filled with anguish. I threw myself on the lounge and cried out in utter despair—"Oh, Mama, I know, myself, Heavenly Father doesn't want us to spoil our carpet for Primary."

That wonderful mother! She came and put her loving arms around me, drew me close to her, dried my burning tears, and in sweet, persuasive tones said to me: "Addie, don't you know that Heavenly Father makes it possible for us to have everything we have? Don't you think we should be willing to use it for what he wants us to do?"

EXCERPT FROM THE LIFE OF WILFORD WOODRUFF

While returning to Utah in 1850 with a large company of Saints from Boston and the East, on my arrival at Pittsburgh, I engaged a passage for myself and company on a steamer to St. Louis. But no sooner had I engaged the passage than the Spirit said to me, "Go not on board of that steamer; neither you nor your company."

The first steamer started at dark, with two hundred passengers on board. When five miles down the Ohio River, it took fire and burned the tiller ropes so that the vessel could not reach the shore, and the lives of nearly all on board were lost either by fire or water. We arrived in safety at our destination, by obeying the revelation of the Spirit of God to us.

THE TABERNACLE ORGAN AT TEMPLE SQUARE

In the great pilgrimages of the past, men and women marching to new shrines and countries have lightened their toil and eased their sorrows by song and the harp. The children of Israel in their long journey to the promised land sang and danced,

and the psalms of David indicate the elevated tone of the music
of the people of ancient Palestine. During the Middle Ages, pilgrims on their way to the shrines of saints made their tiresome
journey lighter by singing and chanting, and in later times the
great musicians of Europe idealized this custom in grand opera.
In the days of the persecution of the Huguenots, those people
found comfort not only in prayer but in hymns of praise
to God. In the eighteenth century, John Wesley gave to the
Christian world the beautiful custom of singing hymns at the
beginning of religious convocations in order "to bring the Spirit
of God into the hearts of the people congregated for worship."

So it was with the Mormon people. Song and music
became in their early history the expression of much of their
religious feelings. In the midst of sorrow they sang hymns of
thanksgiving; in their homes they sought the peace of God by
prayer and song; and in their wanderings in the wilderness, they
sang and danced and kept their lives filled with sunshine.
During the long journey over the plains in 1847, the Mormon
people never began the day's work without a song; they never
closed the day without a hymn of thanksgiving.

In their development the Mormon people have kept sacred
the greater fundamentals of art which are so expressive of religion, and they have built musical instruments in their houses
of worship at times when they have had nothing but the native
resources to furnish the materials. The history of the building
of the world-famed tabernacle organ is therefore a dramatic
story.

The people had only their native genius. Their great tabernacle was to be a place of religious gathering, where the Spirit
of God should rest upon them in their deliberations and

worship. And what could fill their souls with gladness and thanksgiving more than music? They were conquering the wilderness. This was giving them sturdiness of character and strength of muscle. They must record their idealism in not only constructing a majestic building, but in erecting a great instrument that would lift them to a finer appreciation of the spiritual life. They built an organ, and the whole world comes to hear it and to linger under its beneficent influence.

The building of the large organ is inseparably connected with the name of Joseph H. Ridges. He was a native of England but emigrated from Australia to America in 1856. In Australia, Mr. Ridges followed the trade of carpentry, working in an organ factory, where by careful observation he learned the details of organ building, which stood him well in his future work in Utah. A student of history, he was accustomed to speak on the music of the Middle Ages, and it is said that he was well acquainted with the Gregorian chants. Fascinating was his story of Ctesibius of Alexandria, who lived in the third century before Christ. It was he who invented the mechanically-blown trumpet; and Hero, his disciple, caused a row of musical pipes to be blown by mechanical means.

Mr. Ridges constructed a small pipe organ while in Sydney, and having joined the Mormon Church, he was advised to take his instrument to Utah. Years afterwards he told the story of how he emigrated to Utah. He said, in part: "And this was my first experience in organ building. I went ahead and when I had the instrument all completed, the presiding elder of The Church of Jesus Christ of Latter-day Saints, of which I recently had become a member, asked me to donate my work to the Church in Utah. I agreed to do so, and we soldered the various sections of the organ up in large tin cases and shipped them to San Pedro.

"While I was working in California, the presiding elder of the Australian Mission had reached Salt Lake. He told President Brigham Young about the organ, and the president sent word by the next party to have it brought on to Salt Lake City.

"A company was made up for the long, dangerous and tedious journey across the desert. The tin cases containing my organ—some of them as long as a wagon—were loaded up and we started out from California to Salt Lake, taking the trail now followed by the Salt Lake Route railroad today.

"Our company was made up of twelve wagons hauled by fourteen mule teams.

"From this time on, we made good progress until we struck a strip of desert, which we crossed in three days, with the sand up to the hubs and no water available, save what we carried in a barrel lashed to the side of each wagon."

The story of the travels of that organ would make a book in itself. It would include some of the history of the early days of Los Angeles, tales of the horror of thirst on the desert, the loss of Mr. Ridges's prized gold watch in the sand near Death Valley and its subsequent return to the owner in Salt Lake many months after, by a Pony Express rider, who noticed it sticking out of the sand.

In the early 1860s Mr. Ridges was selected by President Brigham Young to build an organ in the tabernacle, and the idea was endorsed by a number of leading citizens, among whom were David O. Calder, Daniel H. Wells, George A. Smith, Alexander C. Pyper, Dr. J. M. Benedict, and C. J. Thomas. After submitting preliminary drafts to President

Young and his counselors, Mr. Ridges began making arrangements for the construction of the instrument and was assisted by Shure Olson, Niels Johnson, Henry Taylor, Frank Woods, and others. Meetings were held with these men almost daily, and the reports of each man's work were listened to. While one was collecting various specimens of wood from the canyons of Utah, another was making good tools with which to carve the wood, while still a third man was experimenting in making glue. So the preliminary work went on. Specimens of wood were sent by people from all over Utah, and it was finally decided that the best wood was found in the hills around Parowan and in Pine Valley, about three hundred miles south of Salt Lake City. It was a fine grain of the soft pine variety and free from knots and without much pitch or gum. It was especially well adapted for the large pipes.

The large pipes, some of which measure thirty-two feet, required thousands of feet of timber. Over the long, lonely roads the oxen labored day after day, hauling the heavy logs to Salt Lake City. At times there were as many as twenty large wagons, each with three yoke of oxen drawing its loads. The roads were rough and dusty, and many streams had to be bridged, that the wagons might pass over them without difficulty. In crossing one stream in southern Utah, the logs were let down over the bank with ropes, and the oxen driven some miles to find a ford, where they crossed and followed on down the bank to pick up the wagons and loads again. The timber was finally unloaded in Salt Lake City. Another important article for making the pipes was glue. This was made of hundreds of cattle hides as well as buffalo skins, by boiling the strips in large pots over fires.

The organ was begun in January 1866. About one hundred men were employed constantly in its construction, and it was dedicated in October 1867. It was many months, however, before the pipes were all put in place and the instrument completed. Prior to his death, Mr. Ridges, the builder, commented on his work and the days when people did things under circumstances far different from today. Among other things, he said: "My time was taken up on making scales and various sizes and ranks of pipes, voicing them, and assigning details for the workmen. Those were busy, happy days. After many months, the great instrument upon which we had worked so long, began to assert itself. The bellows were put in place. The strong frames carrying their huge wind chests, with their multitudes of heavy pipes, the entablature, the columns and pillars, all began to rise into their positions. All was happiness and pleasure, for we felt that we had not worked in vain. Our reward was in seeing the completed instrument, for 'a thing of beauty is a joy forever.'"

On opening and dedicating the tabernacle in October 1867, the organ was nearly completed. A well-organized choir under the leadership of Professor George Careless rendered music to the accompaniment of the new instrument, which then had seven hundred pipes of the two thousand which were completed later.

In all the work of building the organ, President Brigham Young took an active interest and was on the ground daily to offer suggestions to the men. He said, "We can't preach the gospel unless we have good music. I am waiting patiently for the organ to be finished; then we can sing the gospel into the hearts of the people."

THE SALT LAKE THEATER

Upon the suggestion of President Brigham Young, plans were begun for the erection of a large theater. His declaration was, "The people must have amusement as well as religion."

Everyone was interested as preparations were started for the new building. The excavation was started in 1861. As the walls were erected, there were some who eagerly awaited the time when the first performance would be held, and there were others who complained bitterly that such a large building was another waste of time and material.

Everyone has heard of the wooden pegs in place of nails in the construction of the tabernacle. The same problem confronted the workmen for the new theater. A very clever scheme was thought of by the ingenious Latter-day Saint leaders. When Johnston's Army had come out to the west to quell the supposed uprising among the Mormons, they had with them a long train of wagons. When they left Utah after the war, which had had in it no element of warfare, most of the wagons had been abandoned along the trail. When the problem of securing nails became acute, President Young thought of those wrecked wagons along the trail. The men sent out to meet the immigrant trains were instructed to pick up the scraps of iron from the wagons and bring them back with them. From the bits of iron, nails were hammered out by hand and were used in the building of the theater.

The men who worked on the building were usually paid with written promises of future theater tickets.

When the first plays were staged, the footlights were tallow candles. If the stage was to be darkened, the lights were blown out and then relighted as the scene required.

During the first few years of the theater's existence, people coming to the playhouse loaded up their wagons with vegetables and their sweethearts and drove in from Mill Creek and Cottonwood and other places and with the garden products they purchased admission to the play.

At that time money was scarce. There was little or no medium of exchange, and patrons brought their fruits, vegetables, poultry, or wares and deposited the same in exchange for tickets. One man relates that he took a large turkey to pay for his admission, and as its value was in excess of the price of the tickets, he received two spring chickens for change.

—George D. Pyper.

The Papoose Cellar Nursery

Ann Macfarlane stood in her cabin doorway at dawn, gazing anxiously at the distant hills. Two days before, her husband had gone with others to bring the cattle in from the canyons, for rumors of thieving Piutes had traveled rapidly from one settlement to another.

Heavy-hearted, she turned prayerfully to the bed where her two babies still lay asleep. A tap at the door sent the blood racing through her heart; but it was only Sally, the young Ute woman who had befriended them often in the past hard winter. Another Indian woman crouched beside her; no, there were—three—five—eight—ten!

"Hide our papooses," whispered Sally in her native tongue.

"The Piutes are coming to steal and sell them, far away beyond the Land of the Big Water."

Ann looked at the stolid faces about her. Only their eyes, like those of hunted creatures, betrayed their fear. With a prayer on her lips her eyes sought the available hiding places about the room—beneath the bed, the granny-skirts of the cupboard, the pork barrel—not one could safely hide her little charges. Then she suddenly saw the bright strip of rag carpet that concealed the cellar door beneath. An instant later she was stooping in the dark cubicle below, scattering the contents of a wool sack over the damp, dirt floor. One by one she took the papooses from their mothers' arms, laid them in the warm wool, then climbed out and concealed the entrance.

Scarcely an hour passed after the Indian women had gone when the thundering hooves of Indian ponies pounded into the yard. With a firm step Ann advanced to meet the Piute chief, who with a dozen braves had forced his way into the room. Without a word they began their search—beneath the bed, the cupboard, the pork barrel, even the straw tick upon which her sleeping babies lay.

Meanwhile, with seeming indifference, though following the injunction of President Young, "Feed the Indians, don't fight them," she hurriedly cut huge slabs of corn bread and fairly drenched them in molasses. Forcing the unaccustomed delicacy into their hands, she brought cool water from the barrel to quench their thirst. With grunts of approval they smacked and gulped; then they mounted their ponies and galloped off in a whirlwind of dust.

Just at dusk Ann's husband returned, unharmed. A moment later Sally's anxious face appeared in the doorway. The other

Indian mothers pressed forward, wonder and relief on every face. One by one Ann lifted the cradles from their cellar nest; not a cry, not a whimper had escaped one pair of tiny lips through the long day!

The youngest sought the never-failing fountains beneath their mothers' gaudy blankets; the older ones crowded the hard corn cakes and bits of dried meat down famished little throats. Ann looked thankfully about the group, squatting on the rough floor—the first of scores that were to follow—the beginning of her papoose cellar nursery.

—Olive Maiben Nicholas.

Pioneer Schools

In the first autumn after the arrival of the Latter-day Saints in the Salt Lake Valley, a school was started by a young woman named Mary Jane Dilworth. She realized that these children needed an education. They knew how to help their parents build log houses or to tramp a dirt floor. They could hunt and fish and herd cows. The things that were vital in their lives they could do and do well—much better in fact than most children of the same age today could do.

Their parents knew that their children should learn to read and write and that they needed to know more of the geography of the country which they had crossed to come to the Rocky Mountains.

In the center of the square within the Old Fort was an old military tent to which Mary Jane Dilworth's pupils came to school. They sat on rough logs, and, when their work was completed, they carried it to an old campstool which served as their teacher's desk.

One of the pupils of that first school gave the following report of it: "I attended the first school in Utah, taught by my sister, Mary Jane. The school was opened just three weeks after our arrival in the valley. I remember Mary Jane saying to us: 'Come, children, come. We will begin now.' We entered the tent, sat down on the logs in a circle, and one of the brethren offered a prayer.

"There were nine of us that first day. We learned one of the psalms of the Bible and sang songs." There were slates and pencils, and some had paper and pens. The children were taught to write, and often they used charcoal and practiced writing on smooth logs. Sometimes the children brought colored clay and, mixing it with water, drew pictures of animals and Indians on the smooth-surfaced logs. It was not unusual in those days to dry the bark of the white mountain birch and use it for writing material.

The only schoolbooks that were available were the few that had been brought across the plains in some of the pioneer wagons. There was one book that could be found in every home—that was the Bible, and so that was the book that these children learned to read.

Can you imagine your small brother who is just starting to school this year trying to learn to read from a Bible? Can you think how it would be to do your arithmetic problems on a log with a bit of charcoal?

Sometimes all that the children in the school had for their lunch at noon was sego roots.

In spite of all the problems which made the conducting of

schools so difficult, the pioneer folk established more and more schools each year.

Although after the first winter they usually had a better place than a tent in which to hold the school, none of the schoolhouses were very comfortable or very well equipped.

One of the first buildings was sixteen by eighteen feet in dimension. It was built of logs; the roof was willows covered with earth. Other communities had small adobe buildings with two windows on each side. In one end would be a large fireplace, with a pile of sagebrush nearby, which was used for fuel. Slabs resting on wooden pegs served for benches.

The following is a description of a little school which was prominent in 1855:

"The little school that I attended was in a log cabin, the chinks of which were filled with mud. There was a rough puncheon floor. The room was uncomfortable and very cold in the winter. Pegs were thrust into the logs around the room, and on these were rough boards for seats. The smaller children sat on blocks, which they brought from home. The teacher sat at one end of the room and watched the boys and girls. She was never angry with us but always patient and kind.

"There were no blackboards or maps, neither did we have any regular system of books and study. We brought to school whatever books our parents could furnish us with. Everybody had Bibles in those days, and we children learned to read scripture at a very early age. We sang songs, and the teacher always prayed. I remember the recitation bench. The teacher prepared long lists of words and drilled us on them. We had mental exercises in arithmetic, and then the teacher read to us from a geography book. It was the only copy we had in the school.

"The girls sewed every day in school. In fact, they were taught to sew. I think it is called 'domestic art' today. The boys were organized into groups and marched off to the fields to gather sagebrush for the little stove that was in the center of the room.

"Friday afternoon was looked forward to with pleasure, for if we had been good during the week we had a 'spelling match.' To spell down the school was one of the accomplishments of which we were always proud. Lucky the boy or girl who stood first. Then there were geography matches and arithmetic problems to solve. These were extra classes and were for the purpose of 'creating interest.'

"We had to be sparing of our bread that winter. Sometimes we brought meat to school—the flesh of a deer or rabbit—and gave it to the ones that did not have such a luxury. We often danced in the schoolroom, and one of the happy events was the closing program at the end of winter or at Christmastime. Our schoolroom was nothing like the one of today, but we were happy and had every desire to learn."

—LEVI EDGAR YOUNG.

FOOD IN PIONEER TIMES

The food situation in the valley of the Great Salt Lake during early days was a serious problem. The first companies came well equipped and with sufficient provisions for one year, but they were not prepared for emergencies which might arise from unforeseen circumstances. There were about two hundred men of the Mormon Battalion who came during the winter of

1847–48. They were men who had been forced by circumstances into very straitened conditions. Their bodies had been taxed to the utmost for two years. They could not be neglected. They must be fed, so it was decided that all should share alike. An inventory of foodstuffs was taken, and everyone was rationed. A receipt was left in each house, stating how much flour had been taken and that this quantity would be replaced after the harvest in 1848. It was this willingness to share alike with their brethren and sisters that saved the lives of these men of the Mormon Battalion, who had done so much for their country and their people.

When the spring of 1848 came, nearly all the provisions were gone, so there was considerable suffering, yet the Saints continued to share one with another. Lorenzo D. Young said, "Oliver G. Workman, a Battalion man, without a family, came to Salt Lake with others from California in the autumn of 1847, and there he met his brother Jacob and family and assisted in providing food. The following spring, flour became so scarce that it was very difficult for the needy to obtain even a variety. Mr. Workman came to me twice and stated that he had tried to get a little and could not. I told him I had none to sell at any price, but I let him have a few pounds each time.

"In a few days he came to me the third time and stated that he had tried to get a little flour until he was discouraged. He expressed his regret at being under the necessity of coming again, but, said he, 'What can I do? My brother's wife is famishing.' I marked that I had only a little flour left, and I stepped into another room where Mrs. Young lay on her bed sick. I stated the case to her and asked, 'What shall I do?' The question was quite as important to us as to Mr. Workman, but she replied, 'We cannot see anyone starve. Divide to the last pound.' I weighed what I thought we might spare. It was seven pounds. As I handed the sack containing it to Mr. Workman, he put his hand into his pocket and, without counting, handed out a handful of gold. I again told him I had no flour to sell, that I would not exchange him a pound of flour for a pound of gold. He returned the gold to his pocket, and as he turned to go away he was overpowered by his feelings and shed tears."

Brother W. C. Allen of Draper, a pioneer of 1847, said: "I remember when about five years old going with my father to our field out in the vicinity of what is now Liberty Park and helping him fill a barrel full of wheat heads. We took them home to dry and shell out; later we ground the kernels with whatever we could use and then made bread."

Parley P. Pratt in his autobiography wrote: "During this spring and summer (1848) my family and myself suffered much for want of food. This was most severe on me and my family because we had lost nearly all our cows, and the few which were spared us were dry, and therefore, we had no milk to help out our provisions. We toiled hard and lived on a few greens and on thistles and other roots. We had sometimes a little flour and some cheese and sometimes were able to procure from our neighbors a little sour skimmed milk or buttermilk."

Pioneer Incident

Once there was a pioneer mother whose husband died and left her to care for several small children. The oldest boy's name was Newell. This little family was very poor; often the children left the table hungry. There was always something in the house to eat, but not a thing to spare. One day the mother was taken sick and had to stay in bed. The care of the home and the little ones was left to Newell.

The boy took the few vegetables he could find and made a soup. It looked as if there would be just enough for the family, and he felt happy. When all was cooked, he carefully took some in a bowl to his mother's bedside. It smelled good and tasted better to the sick mother.

After the first spoonful she said, "Newell, take a bowl of this over to Sister Brown."

"But, Mother," he said, "why do you give it away when we are so poor and need it ourselves?"

The mother answered, "My boy, if you wait to give until you feel you can afford it, you will never know the joy of giving."

A TRUE INDIAN STORY

The morning had been chill and clear with a stiff breeze blowing off the snow-capped mountains gleaming in the distance. Seven new log cabins stood proudly in a clearing near the point of a low hill, around which a rough trail wound its way. Over this trail, which had its beginning at Salt Lake City, Utah, had come seven pioneer families with all their worldly goods, to spend the spring and summer making butter and cheese. This was a very profitable business, for, by hauling their products regularly into Salt Lake City, they were assured a ready market and good prices. Emigrant trains enroute to California eagerly bought up all the fresh dairy and farm products available. Salt Lake City was fast becoming an oasis in a desert to these weary travelers bound for the gold fields.

The cabin farthest from the point of the hill belonged to Betsey Hambling, and the one beside it to her brother Thomas Leavitt and his young wife, Ann. Betsey had come with them to live here while her husband made a trip to San Francisco. With her two children, Billy, two and one-half years old, and Jane, only three months old, she had brought a few milk cows, also her two white oxen which had drawn her wagon from Salt Lake City.

On the morning our story begins Betsey and Ann had been washing in Betsey's cabin, while Thomas, having nothing more urgent to do, sat on the hearth making bullets for their guns. Beside him lay a powder horn and bullet mould. Over the glowing coals he held a frying pan in which a large bar of lead was slowly melting.

It was now nearing noon, and Betsey decided to build up the fire in the fireplace and prepare dinner. Needing wood and not wanting to disturb Thomas, she ran out to the woodpile a short distance away. As she bent over gathering wood, her ear caught the thud of hoofs. Heart pounding in sudden terror, she glanced toward the trail just as the first of a band of mounted Indians appeared around the point.

Although only nineteen years old and filled with the pioneers' dread of the Indians, Betsey neither screamed nor fainted, but after the first stunned moment, she snatched the two keen-bladed axes and with an arm load of wood raced for the house. "Indians!" she said in a low, strained voice to Thomas. "Indians! Lots of them." By this time the Indians had been seen by the other settlers.

Ann sat on the bed resting and thinking as she held baby Jane. It would be only a few months until she would be holding her own child in her arms. A glow spread over her sweet face, and she smiled to herself in happy anticipation. Startled, she looked up at Betsey's hasty entrance. Then she caught that dreaded word, "Indians." All the color left her face, and her big dark eyes reflected the horror that this word, as no other, instilled within her. "Dear Lord, have mercy on us!" she cried. Then she fell back upon the bed in a dead faint, the baby slipping from her arms to the bed. Thomas sprang to her side and took her gently in his arms. Meanwhile Betsey snatched Billy off the floor and placed him on the bed beside the baby. "Thomas, put Ann here beside the children, then help me push the bed into the corner so that the foot will be behind the door," said Betsey quickly.

"Now I am going to prop the door open, and you talk to them if they come to the cabin. If they are of the Ute tribe, you can talk to them if they give you a chance, and I'll keep busy running bullets. We might need all we can make." So saying, Betsey quickly busied herself at the fire. She took a long thin pole, newly sharpened at one end, used as a poker, and stirred the coals until they glowed. Then picking up the pan which held the lead Thomas had started to melt, she sat down on the hearth and went to work.

At almost the same instant Betsey had sighted the Indians; they had also been seen by the others. Amid cries from the women and hoarse shouts from the men, all rushed into their cabins. Doors were shut and bolted, and guns were snatched from their brackets above the beds. Now grim-faced men watched the approach of the band through the cabins' portholes. Strange to say, the Indians did not stop when they reached the first of the cabins, but as silent, grim, and forbidding as their chief who led them, they filed past, not pausing until they had reached Betsey's little cabin where they quickly dismounted, securely holding their horses by the lariats which were tied about the horses' necks. Their bows and arrows were held in their other hands. The chief took his place in the center, facing the white man, Thomas, now standing in the doorway.

The picture they formed as they crowded their horses together was one to chill the heart of a much older and harder man than Thomas, who was only twenty-three. There must have been a hundred Indian warriors. Their bodies, save for a loin cloth at the waist, were naked and painted. Their hair had been plastered down with black mud, and feathers were stuck in the back. But the most horrible part of the picture was the scalps dangling from the Indians' waists. Beautiful brown tresses of some unfortunate young girl and long gray hair of an elderly woman were only two of the many pitiful reminders of recent savage brutality.

It seemed to Thomas that he lived a lifetime while he waited for silence among the Indians. When the last horse was quieted, he stepped out into the circle and called a greeting to the chief. A grunt was the only answer as the chief glowered at him, hate and lust to kill in his black eyes; but Thomas started bravely on with his speech, speaking slowly and weighing each word carefully. "We are peaceful people. We have never harmed you or your people, and we ask you not to harm us."

"Ugh!" again grunted the chief. "White men liars! We kill all white men. My braves want blood—revenge for brothers killed." In his hand he held a long thin pole, sharpened at one point, not unlike Betsey's poker. Now he raised his hand and threw it to the ground with such force it stood upright, buried in the earth deep enough to hold the rest of its weight. Immediately scores of arrows from the bows of the warriors encircled it.

His brain working with lightning rapidity, Thomas stepped quickly back into the cabin. Going up to Betsey, he said, "Do you know what that means?"

Betsey answered, "Yes, I know. But, Thomas, we will not give up hope."

Laying his hand on her shoulder, he said, "That kind of courage always wins the day." Thomas seized the poker from beside the fireplace. Then standing in the doorway, he raised himself on his toes and threw it with all his strength close beside the chief's spear. The makeshift spear stood just as proud as the chief's in the circle of arrows. A surprised grunt came from the chief, and he eyed Thomas with less hostile eyes. The white man walked boldly to where the chief stood beside his horse.

Immediately the silence was broken as the Indians, keeping time with their moccasined feet, started a low, weird chanting of their war song, which when heard can never be forgotten. Thomas joined his voice with those of the warriors, singing as he had never sung before in his life. After the song ended, each warrior placed his hand over his mouth and gave a blood-curdling war whoop.

The chief, laying his hand over Thomas's heart, said, "White man brave. White man not afraid?"

Thomas spoke again. "My sister and I and the people in the other cabins do not want to die, but we are not afraid to die. We want to live and be friends with your people. Do you love your warriors?" At once the chief swept the circle with his hand, then placed his hand over his heart. Yes, he loved them very much; they were like brothers to him. Thomas immediately took advantage of this. "We may die, but some of your warriors that you say you love will also die—maybe even you will die—for inside of those cabins are men with guns watching you through little holes in the walls. If you start to kill us, they will kill many of you."

At this point the warriors started the war chant. To Thomas it seemed to hammer at his brain, and the whole thing seemed like a horrible nightmare closing in on him. The stench from the Indians' bodies, the horses, and the scalps made him deathly sick. With an effort he pulled himself together. He stepped back into the house and went quickly to Betsey's side. "Betsey," he said in a steady voice, "the chief says we are brave people and because we are so brave, he will be good to us and those who are so afraid in their locked cabins. If we will give them all our cattle, food, and clothing, they will let us go peacefully over the mountains to Salt Lake."

As the full import of the proposition struck home to her, Betsey jumped to her feet, and standing straight and bravely before him, she said with deep feeling, "No, Thomas, we will not do that. It would only mean death, if not from cold, then from starvation. We could never hope to get over that mountain—there is still snow in the pass. We will die fighting first."

"You are right," said Thomas, "but I will go and see what the others say. The chief has granted me permission to ask them." He was back in a few minutes. "Most of them say to accept these terms. They say that maybe they will not take everything."

"Thomas," said Betsey thoughtfully, "if the Lord has made these Indians merciful enough to suggest terms at all when they can take everything by killing us and the price would be the lives of only a few of their warriors, then I believe that he is opening a way to have our lives spared. Go tell them I say they can have the two white oxen and that is all. If they won't take them, tell the chief I have my gun aimed straight at his heart and that he will be the first to die. But tell him this as a last resort."

Again Thomas stepped out into the semicircle. He strode up to where the chief stood by his horse waiting. Stopping only a few feet from the Indian, he drew himself up, and, looking the chief fully in the face, he spoke swiftly in the Indian dialect. "My brave sister and I cannot accept your terms because we would all die anyway. We could not get through the deep snow in the pass with no coverings for our bodies, for we are not tough like you and your warriors. My sister says for you to take her two white oxen because they are the best we have and are fit even for an Indian chief. Take these and go in peace."

Thomas held his breath while the Indian eyed him with a grim, stolid look. Suddenly the chief seized Thomas in his long brawny arms. He hugged him as though he could not restrain his admiration for this white man's bravery. Betsy, watching from the cabin, almost fainted, for she thought surely her brother was being killed. Then she breathed again for the chief released Thomas and broke the strained silence. "White man talk brave, very brave. We no kill, take oxen and go." Over his shoulder he threw a few gutteral sentences. Immediately the warriors turned their horses and, rounding up the two white oxen, started back over the point of the hills from which they had come. Having arrived at the point, the chief stopped, turned, and raised his hand to Thomas and then vanished around the point of the hill.

—JOSEPHINE A. PURSLEY.

BLACK HAWK'S PROMISE

Bishop Kerns had been bishop of the Gunnison Utah Ward for a number of years. He was a friend of all men, black, white, or red. He was a warm friend of Chief Black Hawk and all of his tribe who used to come to his home, pitch camp, and stay as long as they liked. Bishop Kerns would order his boys to kill a beef so the Indians could have plenty to eat during their stay.

On one of these visits the chief called Bishop Kerns into his tepee and told him he wished to be alone with him as he had something of grave importance to discuss with him. When they were seated on a large grizzly bearskin, which served as a rug and seat for the chief, he began to speak:

"Bishop Kerns, you are a true friend of my people, you have done so many good things for us, and we have done nothing for you, but I see in the near future a lot of trouble coming up for both of us. My braves all love you as the great white 'God.' They trust you; they know when you speak, you speak the truth; when they are hungry, you feed them and welcome us all to come to your home and always help us, and for this I am going to make you a solemn promise. So long as I live I promise you, my white father, you or yours shall never be harmed by any of my tribe. If any of yours should be harmed by any of my

braves, if they shall kill any of your family, I, Chief Black
Hawk, swear by the great spirit that you can take my life to
repay your loss. My braves are becoming dissatisfied with the
way they are being treated in Manti and the north end of
Sanpete. Something may happen that may send us on the
warpath; and if we go, have no fear for your family and your
livestock. We all know your brand and will not forget my
promise to you."

Bishop Kerns was very much moved on hearing this solemn
promise from this grand old Lamanite and could feel a sense of
coming trouble, for back of the words of the chief was a deep
meaning. After a warm and hearty handshake these two great
men separated.

A year later a very disgraceful incident took place in Manti.
A young Indian brave rode in for some supplies. After procur-
ing these and binding them upon his pack horse, a prominent
man of Manti, a cattle and sheep man, approached the Indian
boy and accused him of stealing his cattle. The boy told him he
knew nothing about it, whereupon the white man determined
to horsewhip him unless he confessed. The young brave, who
was a grandson of Chief Black Hawk, told the man if he did he
would pay and pay dearly for his blunder.

One or two bystanders told the man he had better let the
boy go, since it might mean trouble. Not heeding their advice,
the man jerked the lad from his horse and whipped him
severely. Without a word or sign of pain, the boy was helped on
his horse, and he rode away soon to be out of sight and out of
danger of the white man.

The next morning a posse of Indians headed by Chief
Black Hawk rode into Manti and told the bishop that if he

would surrender the man who whipped the young brave there would be no trouble. The bishop told them how sorry he and his people were and asked the Indians to forgive the man who had too much "firewater," and the bishop would see that he was punished for his deed. Just then the man appeared upon the scene and offered to go with the Indians and accept any punishment they might choose to give him.

But the people of Manti said no. If nothing but war would satisfy the Indians, then let it be war. Warning was relayed all over the country that the Black Hawk tribe was on the warpath and for every outlying settlement to rush to the forts for protection.

The Indians succeeded in stealing many cattle and horses and killed several people all along the line of battle. One moonlit night a band of warriors swooped down upon some ranches and succeeded in stealing a bunch of horses, among which was a beautiful gray mare belonging to the eldest son of Bishop Kerns.

Early the next morning a runner came with the news that the Indians had been seen going up Salina Canyon near Rattlesnake Point. Immediately a posse was formed, and Bishop Kerns's son William was announced captain. They rode away in haste, much against the wishes of Bishop Kerns. They rode as rapidly as possible until they reached Rattlesnake Point. Here they halted and held a council to determine just what to do in case they should be ambushed.

Now Rattlesnake Point is at the head of a narrow canyon through which the Indians had just passed. Without warning, the ambushed Indians began sending arrows whizzing from all directions. The men made a hasty retreat back down the canyon.

William Kerns and his brother Austin were the last to leave the point. A rifle shot broke the stillness, and William slumped in his saddle, dying. Austin reached for his brother, but an arrow grazed the rump of his horse, and the rider and horse tore down the canyon, soon to overtake the rest of the posse, who, upon missing the Kerns brothers and fearing the two men had been captured, decided to return and make a fight to recover them. The Indians could be heard yelling and howling their war cry when all of a sudden it ceased; this was taken as an ill omen by the men, and they hastily returned to Gunnison with their sad news.

Bishop Kerns's grief and that of his family was beyond description. William, their eldest son and brother, had been killed and no doubt savagely scalped. In the midst of their grief, the bishop was told there was an Indian with a white flag to see him. The Indian boy, upon entering the home and seeing the grief-stricken family, fell upon his knees, and his deep sobs shook his frame terribly.

The bishop, knowing the boy was a son of his old friend Chief Black Hawk, went to him, raised him to his feet, and asked, "What do you want with me, my boy?"

"Your son William was killed by the braves who stole some of the horses from the south farmers, and among them was your gray mare," answered the boy. "I have brought her back to you, and my father says your son's body is being kept and watched so nothing will harm it until you come for it, but you must come alone."

The bishop ordered a team hitched to a buckboard, and

soon he and the Indian were on the way to recover the body of his beloved son. When they reached the head of the narrows and came in sight of Rattlesnake Point, they saw a sight which the bishop never forgot.

Old Chief Black Hawk was standing with his head bared, and his grand old frame, always so straight, was now bent. Deep lines of anguish creased his face. Tears were streaming down his cheeks as he watched the approach of his old friend and benefactor—the man who had been promised that no harm should come to him or his was now coming to claim the lifeless body of his noble son.

The old chief slowly approached the old, gray-haired, sorrowing man, and upon reaching him, bared his bosom and said, "Bishop Kerns, I have not forgotten my promise to you. My life is yours, only let it be swift as your son's death was. I am ready to go, my braves understand; and when you have finished with me, my sons will accompany you below the narrows. Your son's body is in the crevice of that rock. It is protected as much as we could protect it, and may the great God of yours, Bishop Kerns, forgive me and bless you. I am ready to go."

Bishop Kerns took the old man's hand in his and, looking the old chief in the eye, said, "Chief Black Hawk, you made the offer, but I did not say I would accept it. No, Chief, that is not the Lord's way. You would not have killed my son and neither would any of your braves if they had known it was he. Taking your life would not bring him back. All I ask, Chief, is that you end this terrible war and come back to my home again where we can be friends always."

The old chief was dazed and stood like a statue for several

minutes, then suddenly he fell upon his knees and sobbingly promised he would do all in his power to end the war.

A short while after this scene the war did end, and old Chief Black Hawk and Bishop Kerns enjoyed each other's association at regular intervals.

BISCUITS

My grandparents had a rather interesting experience with Indians while they were yet unfamiliar with Indian ways.

One frosty, early morning just as Grandmother was ready to serve breakfast, an old Indian woman came to the door to beg for white man's food, as had been the Indians' custom sometimes. She asked for "Biscuit, biscuit!"

My grandmother offered the woman the plate of biscuits, which she had just taken out of the pan to put on the table, expecting her to take one or two. The old woman reached out her hand and instead took the plate and dumped the whole pan of biscuits into her large blanket—and wasn't Grandmother surprised and chagrined! She had to go then and make more bread for her breakfast, so you see she learned not to offer any more than she expected to be taken.

—ELLA FARLEY.

THE WHITE FATHER

In the southern part of Utah, George Harrison lived with his wife, Mary, his three sons, George Jr., Paul, and Samuel, and his little daughter, Anna Mae.

George owned a sheep ranch, on each side of which lived two tribes of Indians—the Navajos and the Piutes. The Navajos were prosperous; they owned large flocks of sheep, and from the wool they made their famous blankets and rugs, which they sold or traded to the white settlers.

These two tribes were not always friendly with each other, but George could always manage to keep on friendly terms with both tribes and often managed to help keep peace between them by helping in a wise and friendly way to settle small difficulties that arose between them. The Navajos liked and respected George, but the Piutes loved him and called him the White Father.

One day trouble arose between the two Indian tribes which George was unable to settle. The Navajos said the Piutes must leave that part of the country and go into another land. The Piutes were not pleased to go into a less favorable land, so war resulted. At such a time it was not wise for white settlers to take sides or interfere with them, and George was a wise man.

One day as Mary Harrison looked down the dusty road, she saw a young Indian woman trudging along with a round-eyed, chubby baby on her back. When she reached the doorstep, she fell exhausted. Mary hastened to give her food and water, which the woman and baby ate and drank greedily, for she had not stopped for food nor water for two days.

Then she told George that the Navajos had driven the Piutes from the country, that she was a Piute, that the horse she was riding had been wounded and died, and she had taken her baby on her back and come to the White Father for help. "Me give papoose for pony," she said. "Papoose safe with White Father. Maybe I reach my people; maybe Navajos kill me."

George gave her a pony and blankets. Mary gave her a bag of goods and a canteen of water. The poor Indian mother took her baby in her arms, held him close for a minute, and then mounted the pony and rode away without once looking back. When the baby saw her leaving, he ran after her as fast as his chubby little legs would carry him; and when George tried to bring him back, he fought like a little tiger, kicking, biting, and scratching. When locked in the house, he crawled under a table in the corner and sat cross-legged, watching the family with large round eyes.

Thus he sat all day. When evening came, he fell asleep, but when Mary tried to pick him up to put him to bed, he awoke and fought her and crawled under the table again. There he stayed all night and the next day, refusing to allow anyone to touch him, nor would he take food or drink. Toward evening of the second day a low sob was heard coming from under the table. The brave spirit of the little warrior was beginning to weaken. Mary asked to be left alone with him. She offered him bread, butter, and milk. He ate the bread and butter but refused the milk. Then he allowed her to take him in her lap and rock him to sleep.

After that he completely adopted her. He would follow at her heels everywhere she went, always watching her with his big, round black eyes. He soon began to make friends with other members of the family, learned to understand and speak English, and proved to be a very good and obedient boy.

When John, for John was what they called him—was old enough, he went to school with the other boys. "I want John to have the same privileges I give my own boys," said George. John was very bright in school and a general favorite. He had long ago forgotten that his mother had ridden away and left him with the White Father. Perhaps he sometimes wondered why his hair and eyes were so black and his skin so dark, while the rest of the Harrison family were blonds, but he did not seem to think much about it.

One day an Indian woman rode up to the Harrison ranch. She was not so young as she had been ten years before, and time and trouble had left their mark on her. She asked the White Father for her child. "You may have him if he wishes to go with you, but if he wants to stay, you must leave him here," said George. John chose to stay, and the poor woman once more rode away, leaving her son with the White Father.

But this was a sad awakening for John, for now he knew he was an Indian. "I'll never marry," he told a friend. "No white girl will want to marry me, and I could never be happy to marry an Indian girl and live as the Indians do. I will spend my life taking care of the old folks and try to repay them for some of the things they have done for me."

When John was twenty-seven, Mary Harrison died. "I have lost the only sweetheart I ever had or expect to have," John said. He tried hard to make George happy. The Harrison children were all married now and tried to get their father to come and live with them, but he did not want to leave the old home and John.

One day a traveler stopped at the Harrison Ranch. "You should get you a wife," he told John. "You need a woman in the home." Then he told John about a young Indian woman who, like himself, had been reared by white people. John only smiled, but when the stranger had gone, he thought much about it.

"I don't think it would be a bad idea for you to go and see this girl," George told him, for he felt sorry for the lonely young man.

So one day John put a new coat of paint on the old shay and gave Dobbin an extra brushing down until his coat shone, put on his Sunday clothes, and started on a sixty-mile journey to see this young woman, who went by the name of Ida Sanders.

Ida, like John, was a Piute. Her father had been killed in the war between the Piutes and the Navajos. Her mother had escaped with her little baby girl, then only a few months old. When Ida was ten years old, her mother died, leaving her and her stepfather alone. The only other relative she had was an uncle. Both men considered her a nuisance, so one day they took her to the white village to sell her. They considered they had done pretty well when Mr. Sanders gave them a pony and two gallons of whisky for her. Poor little Ida was not treated like John was, for the Sanders family had bought her for a servant. She was taught to do the work as fast as she grew large enough. By the time she was fourteen she did most of the work about the house. She could wash, iron, cook, sew, and clean a house as well as any white woman in the village. The people of the village felt sorry for Ida and often invited her to parties, but Ida could never go, for like Cinderella she never had clothes good enough to wear, and so she must stay home among the pots and pans.

One day her Prince Charming rode up in his newly painted carriage, dressed in his very best. She was obliged to meet him in her old shabby clothes. No wonder she was shy. He had been told by some people where he had stopped to spend a night on his way that the Sanders family made a slave of Ida and that she never had any nice clothes, so he was prepared to see her dressed as she was. John was not long in deciding he wanted her for his wife, and asked her to marry him.

The Sanders family very much disliked losing their servant. "You can't get married," said Mrs. Sanders. "You belong to us. We bought you, and I have spent much time in teaching you to work."

But a kind neighbor came to her rescue. "You are past twenty-five, Ida, and your own boss. You can marry if you wish. They cannot prevent you."

"But I haven't any clothes good enough to get married in," she said. Then the neighbors came to her assistance. One gave her a dress, another a pair of shoes, another hose, and so on, until her trousseau was complete. So Ida and John were married and went to the Harrison ranch to spend their honeymoon. When they arrived, all the Harrisons were there to welcome John's bride into the family. Ida had never been treated so kindly in her life.

Her adopted father-in-law and her husband taught her the gospel. She had never heard of God, for the Sanders family were not a religious people. In due time a little miss came to cheer their home, and they named her Mary. "I worry so about little Mary's future," John said. "She will not want to marry an Indian, and I am afraid no white man will want to marry her."

But the White Father said, "Don't worry. Just live as you should, keeping the Lord's commandments, and he will provide her with a mate."

—Irene Merrill.

The Little Pioneer's Ride

Whoa, Buck! Whoa, Bright!" called out Stephen Harris, a young pioneer, and the glossy red oxen halted in the forest opening. "This shall be our first dinner camp today, boys," said he. "See what a fine spot!"

With their rifles on their shoulders, the pair of stalwart lads, who had been walking all the forenoon beside the big covered wagon, began to make camp for dinner. Then unyoking the oxen and turning them out to graze, they kindled a fire with dry twigs and moss and brought water from the clear brook that rippled by.

Meanwhile, children of all ages began to climb down from the wagon. There were ten of them, fine healthy children. The youngest, Martha, was a little yellow-haired girl of three, the pet and pride of them all. They were overjoyed at the prospect of running about and stretching their cramped limbs, and the forest echoed with their joyful voices. Last, the mother, a brisk, cheerful woman, alighted, and under her good management dinner was soon ready.

Every day the camp dinner was like a picnic to this family who had been thirty days on their way to the "Great West," where they hoped to make a fine farm and a good home. The wagon, which had been their traveling house for a month, was well fitted for comfort. The seats were built along the sides and so contrived as to hook back at night; then the bedding, tightly rolled up by day, was spread out on the wagon bottom. The cooking utensils were hung up on the sides. A roomy box nailed at the end held other useful articles. All of the cups, plates, and spoons were of bright unbreakable tin. Under the wagon swung the large copper kettle, the most important of all things in the households of those early times.

After dinner the bright tin dishes were washed in the brook, and the fire very carefully put out, but the travelers still lingered under the trees, so restful and lovely seemed the cool green spot. At length Mr. Harris said that the sun was fast traveling westward and that they must be doing the same.

So the oxen were yoked up, and in great spirits the pioneers scrambled to their places in the wagon. The oxen started on at a good pace. They had gone a mile or two before the fearful discovery was made that little Martha was missing! It seemed impossible that they should not have known at once that she was not with them; but so it was—not one of them had missed her!

The patient oxen were turned about, and as fast as possible the distracted family traveled back to the dinner camp, Mrs. Harris and the big brothers calling the name of the child as they went.

The camp was finally reached—but little Martha was not there, and no trace of her could be found. The forest that had seemed so peaceful an hour before was now filled with terrors. What wild animals might lurk in the thickets! The very brook seemed to murmur of dangers—quicksand and treacherous water holes.

"Baby! Oh, Baby!" called Mr. Harris suddenly, breaking into a sharp cry; and this time, in the anxious waiting pause of silence, a shrill voice from right under the wagon piped out, "Here I is!" and over the rim of the great copper kettle popped Martha's golden head. Scrambling out head over heels, she rushed into her mother's arms, as fresh and rosy from her sound after-dinner nap as though she had been rocked in the downiest cradle in the land.

There was praise and thanksgiving; there was laughter and tears; and the forest echoed with the glad shouts of the boys who could not otherwise express the joy and relief of their hearts. Then they climbed into the wagon again, and this time each one made sure that little Martha was not missing!

In after years the energy and thrift of the Harris family brought them great prosperity. Broad acres and fruitful orchards and a beautiful home became theirs, but their most prized possession was the big copper kettle in which little pioneer Martha had taken her after-dinner ride.

—ANNA E. TREAT.

A HORSE TRADE STORY

When I was about twelve years old our family lived in Kanab, Utah. A band of Piute Indians were camped a few miles away, across the wash. My father, Jacob Hamblin, the Indian missionary, said to me, "Son, I want you to go to the Indian camp this afternoon and trade that little bay pony for some blankets, which we will need this winter."

When the midday meal was over, I climbed astride old Billy, led the little bay pony, and rode bareback across the flat toward the Indian camp.

When I rode in, the chief helped me off the horse and asked, "You Jacob's boy. What you want?"

When I told him my errand, he looked at the trade pony and grunted his assent. He led me to his wigwam where there was a pile of handwoven Indian blankets. He piled out a number of them. Determined to show my father that I was a good trader, I asked for another blanket. The chief looked at me out of the corner of his eye and added another blanket to the pile. Then I asked for another and another and still another. By now the chief was grinning broadly but added as many blankets as I demanded.

Satisfied that I had really made a good trade, I closed the deal. The chief piled the blankets on the back of old Billy and lifted me up.

Father met me in the yard and looked at the blankets. Then he made two piles of about equal size. One pile he placed on the horse and put me back on, saying, "Go back and give these to the chief. You got enough blankets for two horses."

As I approached the camp, I could see the old chief. When I rode up, he laughed out loud and said, "I know Jacob send you back. He honest man. He my father as well as your father."

Several years later when Jacob was alone with a band of angry, hostile Indians, the fact that he had always been honest with them saved his life.

—LOUISE LEE UDALL, AS TOLD BY JACOB HAMBLIN, JR.

HER APRON STRINGS

Give me the very best cloth you have in the house for overalls," said Mrs. Brown to the smiling clerk, and added as an afterthought, "something that will wear those boys of mine a couple of weeks."

The clerk threw up her hands in mock consternation: "We

don't deal in boiler iron, Mrs. Brown! There's a hardware store
a block down the street, but if it's good cloth you want, we've
got the best fabric ever seen in this town since you women quit
weavin'."

They both laughed, and the clerk threw on the counter a
forty-inch bolt of cloth that smacked the board like another
piece of timber. It was a texture between canvas and regular
overall goods and very closely woven. It met Mrs. Brown's swift
approval except for color. Instead of the conventional dark blue,
it was a light, unpleasant brown, verging on yellow.

After some hesitation she bought sufficient for two pairs of
overalls, one pair for each of her boys, Gid and Sam, aged ten
and twelve years. When they saw it, they would have none of
it because it was so stiff and heavy and so displeasing in its
color. Rather than begin an argument that would prove very
wearisome even if she succeeded finally in bringing them to her
point of view, she made herself two long, wide work aprons of
it, with a belt that went around her ample waist twice and tied
in front for convenience, and to keep the boys from untying
her apron strings when she was busy.

Mrs. Brown, a widow, had taken up a homestead half a
mile or so from the town almost in the mouth of the canyon
and with her two young boys was trying to clear the best parts
of the land and bring it under cultivation. She surprised the
local agriculturalists by not always waiting for the land to be
cleared of luxuriant growth of sage and rabbitbrush but worked
around with a hoe, and in the rich virgin soil planted squash,
potatoes, and winter beans. If the season were moderately rainy,
then she would rake in a good crop. She milked a few cows,

which she pastured on the hillside that outlined the farm; but her real money crop was poultry.

One morning when she called the chickens for their feed, she thought the flock looked smaller than usual.

She called the boys: "Come out here, Gid and Sam, both of you, and tell me if you think the chickens are all here—I think I miss two or three!"

"Of course they're all here! Anyway, how in Sam-hill could you miss two or three out of a bunch like this?"

"Well, I think I do! When you boys go to town to your priesthood meeting tonight, I want you to be sure and get the gun you lent to Johnny Anderson, and get some ammunition for it."

"All right," the boys agreed, but they forgot her request.

A few nights later when the boys were in town and Mrs. Brown was engaged in some household task, she heard the chickens making a fuss.

"There!" she exclaimed. "Something is after the chickens, and of course the gun isn't here." But even as she said this, she was pulling on an old sweater and lighting a lantern. Grabbing a club, which was the first thing in the shape of a weapon that came to her hand, she ran to the coop.

There was a confused, squawking scramble among the chickens. She noticed the coop door had not been properly fastened and stood ajar. Jerking it wide open, she swung her lantern to light up the interior.

At first she could see nothing unusual, but she soon discovered a wildcat crouched in a far corner, his fiery green eyes flashing at her in the dark. She had enough experience with these common marauders to know that if she should open the door wide and get out of the way, he would be glad enough to escape, now that he knew he was detected; but she did not intend to let him go, for she knew that once having tasted chicken, he would not stop until he had eaten the entire flock.

Armed with only a club, it was rather hazardous for her to go inside, because the coop door was a bit small.

The light of the lantern had further disturbed the already frightened chickens. They were crowding and pushing, trying to get further from the menace in the corner. All at once with a fluttering squawk, one hen dropped from the roost to the floor, right in front of the hungry wildcat. His desire for chicken was greater than his fear of the person who hesitated to attack him. With a bound he left his corner and pounced on the hen.

That sight, and the sound the dying hen made, drove Mrs. Brown into action. She entered the narrow arena of the coop and, swinging the club high, brought it down on the head of the robber with all the force of her labor-hardened muscles.

If it had been any animal but a wildcat, the blow would probably have killed it, but the wildcat only wagged his head once or twice as if dazed a little. When Mrs. Brown struck again with all her might, he was not there, and the club broke in her hands.

The cat had retired to the corner, and, defenseless, she found herself facing an animal maddened by pain and fear.

Mrs. Brown, from long experience with wild animals, knew the creature was nerving itself to attack her. If she had wished to retreat now, she knew that before she could get halfway out of that low door, he would be upon her and perhaps do her horrible injury, but she would not retreat. Well she knew that the cat that kills and gets away, as this one had evidently been doing for some time, comes back and kills again and again.

Keeping her eyes on the wildcat, she very slowly lifted her hands and untied her apron strings, letting them fall; and with both hands she slowly grasped the center of the belt and slowly drew it away from contact with her person and then swiftly up to her face as the cat launched himself straight for her eyes.

The impact almost tore the apron from her hands, but she managed to hold onto it and to envelop him partly in its strong folds as they went to the floor together. She tried to pin down with arms and knees and weight that sinuous mass of fear, hate, and ferocity. He spit, bit, and clawed, and soon her wool sweater and gingham dress were torn from her breast and shoulders in a mass of rags, and blood flowed from a dozen wounds. The cat tried to reach her throat and with redoubled fury tried to bring into play those terrible hind claws, with which members of the cat tribe, when down on their backs and fighting for life, use to kill their enemies.

Mrs. Brown had her right knee on the wildcat's stomach, holding him down, and those death-dealing claws could come up only part way and rake back over the board-like surface of the apron. She was working for a purpose. Taking advantage of the twisting and turning of the wildcat's head, she finally managed to cross the strings of that apron behind the cat's neck in a strangle hold. She now planted her other knee on the writhing body and drew the strings taut with all the strength of her well-developed muscles and managed to hold on until he ceased to struggle and hung limp; then she tied the strings securely.

After resting a few moments, Mrs. Brown crawled out of the coop door backward, dragging the dead wildcat and chicken with her. Of course the marauder was dead, but the wonderful way cats have of recuperating after seeming death made her tie the apron strings in a few more tight knots.

Knowing how dangerous the bites and scratches of animals are, especially wild or enraged animals, she quickly prepared a solution of salt and, despite the terrible smarting, thoroughly cleansed her bites and scratches. She further treated them to a coating of a salve by melting equal parts of soft pine gum and mutton tallow together, and applying it quite hot, carefully stroked the torn flesh into its proper place, bandaged it all as well as she could, and went to bed.

It was not long until she heard the boys coming.

As they opened the door, she called out: "You boys did not fasten that chicken coop up properly tonight, even when I reminded you of it—go now and see to it!"

Obediently they turned, and as they went she heard the drone of their dialogue still intent on the happenings in town.

She laughed silently and listened for the shout that would tell her that they had found the dead wildcat.

But they were her sons, and the cry that sprang instinctively to their lips was suppressed before it had utterance.

"Don't you dare to act scairt," whispered Gid to Sam. "If you do, Mother will never quit making fun of us while we live." They found the coop door properly fastened and knew they had been sent out on purpose to find the dead cat. With big questioning eyes, they saw the manner of its death and went slowly back.

Going to the door, Gid called in: "What you want us to do with your dollbaby you got tied up in your apron?"

"You might put him in the woodshed till morning, and

then we'll see if the fur is worth anything. Don't take the string off!"

"All right," the boy drawled, trying to make his voice as indifferent as though finding a dead wildcat in the yard was a common occurrence, and the manner of this one's death nothing remarkable.

Mrs. Brown had hoped and expected to get a rise out of the boys and was entirely gratified when by cautiously moving to her bedroom window, she heard them talking as they dragged the dead cat to the woodshed.

"I bet that cat weighs forty pounds," said Sam to his brother.

"All of that," Gid replied, "and to think our own mother killed that fighting cyclone with her apron strings!"

"Yes, and no whining and hysterics about it, either," said the small son in a tone of intense admiration.

—Ellen L. Jakeman.

The Wooden Doll

But, Mother, I love my doll. I don't want to give it to the Indian. I don't want to—I—" Little Sarah's voice ended in a long, suppressed sob. The tears would not stay back.

"I know you don't, Sarah." The pioneer mother's voice was very gentle as she continued. "It's too bad, but I know you are a brave little girl and you always help. This will help more than any other way. If you do as the Indian says and give your doll to her baby, then they will know we are their friends, and we can stay here without being harmed. Come, dear, that's my brave little pioneer."

Sarah looked up into her mother's serious gray eyes, then with head held high walked straight over to the old Indian woman seated on the green grass. Sarah held out her wooden dolly. Quickly the woman took it, muttering, nodding her head, then placed the doll in the arms of the little Indian girl by her side.

Sarah did not wait to see the brown arms hold the doll lovingly to her but turned and walked blindly back to the big covered wagon. She climbed inside and sought refuge on the big soft quilts piled in the end of the wagon box. She could cry without Mother or the Indians seeing her. She had been asked to do many hard things all her life. But ever since her father and mother had been told to settle the Muddy it had been awful. Sarah had to leave her flower garden and little playhouse, with its hard-beaten dirt floors and the pretty rocks that formed the four sides, and now her own mother had asked her to give up her only plaything, her dear, long-loved, wooden-faced dolly.

It really was a strange doll for a girl nearly six years old to love. But Sarah did love it with all her loving little heart. She had loved it ever since her big brother had carved it out of the old pine limb, and her mother painted its face with blue and red dye. Its wooden face was just as lovely to Sarah as though it were Dresden china, for Sarah had never known or seen any other doll. Then Mother had wrapped it up in so many old clothes that it was cuddly and soft. But the prettiest thing about the wooden doll was the hood and cape made of pink and green and black print, with rose buds so real you wanted to

smell them—and now the Indian had everything, pink rose-
buds and all.

It was strange how Mother and Father always gave the
Indians everything they wanted, no matter how they had to go
without themselves. What was that Mother had said? Oh, yes.
"You can help more by doing this than any other way." She
could help. Maybe she did help. What a baby she was to cry.
She must be brave as Mother said. She would try to help; of
course, that's what all must do or they would never get to the
Muddy and have another real home.

Just as quickly as Sarah's outburst had started, it stopped.

Apparently no one noticed her as she climbed out of the
wagon box. It might have been the bright sunshine or the fact
that Sarah had been crying that made her miss the wagon
tongue and fall. Her face struck the hard wood. In an instant
blood spurted from her nose. Mother was the first one to pick
her up. She carried her to a stream of water near the camp and
bathed her face and nose in the cold water. The mother soon
realized Sarah's condition was serious, for she could not stop the
flow of blood. It looked like a real hemorrhage or broken blood
vessel. The mother knew she was far away from help, up in the
mountains with just a few pioneers heading for a new settlement and with bands of Indians ready at the least excuse to
plunder and steal and maybe kill.

Sarah was pale and weak; something must be done. Who
could help her?

Frightened, the mother ran to the Indians. She talked rapidly, motioning them to follow her. Three of the Indian women
went over to Sarah and with serious faces went to work. Two of
the Indians went to the stream of water and picked many, many

smooth pebbles, while the other Indian stripped the clothes off Sarah.

The Indians made a flat bed of the pebbles, then carefully stretched Sarah on it. They then piled them all over her, on her neck and face, and around her nose. As soon as the pebbles became warm, they went back to the stream and brought cold ones. In a short time the flow of blood stopped altogether. Sarah was cold and weak, but she knew the Indians had saved her life. She did not know the Indians had used a primitive ice pack.

All day long they watched her and helped. And all day long Sarah was glad she had given her doll to the Indians and made friends with them.

Maybe it was Sarah's kindness when she thanked the Indians, or maybe it was her pale, sad face that made the Indians feel so sorry for her. At any rate as Mother and the Indians tucked her in the warm quilts for the night in the end of the wagon box, Sarah was surprised as her beloved wooden doll was put in her arms. The Indian murmured, "Heap good girl, heap brave paleface."

As Sarah hugged her doll with the painted face and pink rosebud cape, her heart was glad. She had been brave and helped; even the Indians knew that.

—CORA CARVER RITCHIE.

HARRY'S VISIT TO GRANDMA

Harry had gone to the country to visit his grandparents. They were sitting on the porch talking when his grandfather said, "Isn't it about time you brought up the cows?" Harry was used to being called upon to help at home, but he was a little surprised this first day to be told to bring up the cows at Grandpa's. However, he started to go, but Grandma kept on talking so busily to him that he could not get away without being impolite. "We got to the valley about the first of October 1847," said Grandma, "and camped on what is now called Pioneer Square.

"Many times when a mere child, I have taken grain to the mill to be ground into flour, driving a yoke of oxen hitched to a wagon. I used to herd cows on the hills where there were sagebrush bushes, sunflowers, rabbit brush, and prickly pears, beside plenty of snakes, horned toads, lizards, and tarantulas, which were not very pleasant for bare feet. There was not a tree to shade me from the burning sun; and when it rained, I crouched down behind a sagebrush bush.

"For my breakfast," continued Grandma, "I had a little thin mush or perhaps some curds and whey, and for my dinner, a half a pint of greens with a small piece of meat. I did not herd every day, for I had to help plant and care for the crops. My Sunday dress was made out of a piece of an old tent my mother colored, and I was very proud of it." Just as Grandma finished the story, Harry saw the cows coming up, and a gray shepherd dog driving them.

"Oh!" said Harry, "I understand now. You told the dog to fetch the cows."

Grandma and Grandpa laughed. "Jack knew whom I meant. He knows his duty. He was in the kitchen and went out the back door. He always takes the cows to pasture in the morning and brings them back in the evening."

PINS AND NEEDLES

Charles W. Nibley was one of the best loved and best known of the Utah Mormon Pioneers. From the time he first arrived in the Salt Lake Valley until his death, he made friends of everybody, old and young, rich and poor. Everyone knows that in order to have friends, you must be a friend. Mr. Nibley was a friend.

The qualities that made him so beloved were encouraged in him by his mother. As poor Scottish peasants, life was a hard struggle for the Nibley family. But the home was blessed with a stalwart, courageous mother. She taught the children the value of hard work, perseverance, cheerfulness, and helpfulness to one another. And in return she reaped the love and gratitude of those children.

Charles Nibley adored her. When he was a tiny tot, he was given a penny by his Aunt Sneddon. Now a penny was an event in his five-year-old life. On the way home from his aunt's he passed a packman. These old packmen wandered from town to town, selling notions and a hard candy called rock. Much to the packman's surprise, the little boy declared, "No, I am no wantin' rock. I want pins and needles for my mother."

As early as his fifth year, Charles Nibley had cultivated those great virtues of friendship, consideration, and unselfishness.

HOLIDAY TIME

NEW YEAR

LINCOLN'S Birthday

WASHINGTON'S Birthday

Valentine Day

Easter

Mother's Day

HALLOWE'EN

FOURTH of JULY

Thanksgiving

Christmas

NELSON WHITE

And this is the gospel, the glad tidings,
which the voice out of the heavens bore record unto us.

—Doctrine and Covenants 76:40.

HAROLD'S TRIUMPH

It was February, and February in Joyville, as well as in every other American town, village, and hamlet, buzzed with the names of George Washington and Abraham Lincoln. Strange they should both be born in February! And both were so important in American history.

The school children were once more going over the stories of George Washington and his little hatchet, and of Abraham Lincoln's working long and hard to pay for a book he borrowed that met with disaster. Of course, Harold Bruce, Jr., was among the interested ones, and particularly so because his teacher, Miss Murphy, was going to have a public program to honor both great men, and Harold had been assigned an important part.

There had been many debates in the class on the subject: Who was the greater man, Washington or Lincoln?

Miss Murphy planned to have a sort of processional on the program; the boys were to represent some of the leading men of the Revolutionary and Civil War days; the girls were to represent the wives of these famous men, or prominent women such as Betsy Ross. Harold was to represent Abraham Lincoln.

It was the evening before the morning of the eventful program. The boys and girls had had a full dress rehearsal. Each pupil took his costume home so that he could come to school in the morning all ready.

In the class there was a rather tall, lanky boy older than the other members of the class. His name was Bates Hurlew. Harold had been kind to Bates, as he was to everybody, and had tried to help Bates with his problems.

This evening after school Harold was rushing home with

his costume under his arm and his Lincoln hat lovingly clutched in his hand. He had not forgotten one word of Lincoln's Gettysburg speech, and he was thrilled through and through with his part for the morrow.

Bates overtook him.

"May I carry the hat for you, Hal?" Bates asked.

A queer feeling came over Harold, and he hesitated, then finally he said, "Surely, Bates, if you'd like to."

Bates took the hat and fondled it. "It really looks like one of 'Honest Abe's' hats, doesn't it?" he commented.

"It's supposed to," returned Harold.

"Lincoln was a great guy, Hal. He was more like Jesus Christ than any other man I've read about. He was always kind to the underdog and not afraid of the big guys. He loved God too," Bates explained.

Harold looked at Bates in astonishment and exclaimed, "What do you know about him, Bates? Why didn't you get up in class and boost for him?"

"I know a lot about him, Hal. I have read every book in the library about him."

"Well, why didn't you get up in class and boost for him?" Harold repeated.

"Nobody in school wants to hear me."

The agony in Bates's voice made Harold swallow. He wanted to say something to him, but he didn't know what to say, and they walked in silence to Harold's home. When they reached the entrance, Bates said: "Hal, will you let me come in and try on this Lincoln outfit?"

"Surely," Harold replied. "Come in, and we will go right up to my room, and you can put it on up there."

"Mother," called Harold, as he opened the door.

"Yes, son," his mother answered. "How did you get along with your part?" By this time she was in the hall to greet him.

"Mother, this is Bates."

"I'm glad to know you, Bates," Mrs. Bruce said warmly.

"Tha-ank you," Bates stammered.

"We're going up to my room; Bates wants to try on my Lincoln suit," Harold explained to his mother.

"Don't you want to take Bates out and have something to eat before you do that?" she suggested.

Bates trembled with joy and fear. When they were alone in the pantry, he whispered: "Gee, Hal, your mother's got kindness like Lincoln."

Harold and Bates were in Harold's room. Bates was pulling on the Lincoln trousers. "I'm sorry they have to turn up these trousers on you, Hal, 'cause that isn't like Lincoln—his legs were always too long for his pants. Why don't you get your mother to cut them off?"

"You're funny, Bates," Harold laughed. "What difference does that make?"

"None, I s'pose," he replied.

Bates was all dressed. As he put the hat on, he turned to the mirror to be sure that he put it on just right, just like the pictures he had seen of Lincoln with his hat on. Then he faced Harold in position.

"Gee whiz!" Harold exclaimed. "You look like him, Bates."

"I wish I could be like him," said Bates sincerely. "I love him, Hal." Then he took the hat off and repeated Harold's part for tomorrow's program: Lincoln's Gettysburg Address.

Harold was thrilled. He tingled all over while Bates repeated those famous words.

"Bates, do it again," he cried. "Please let Mother hear you. Mother, Mother," he called excitedly, "do come and hear Bates say my part."

Harold's mother and two of his sisters were soon in the room. Bates went through it with the same candor, sincerity, and understanding.

"Mother, Bates will have to be Lincoln tomorrow," Harold declared, as Bates concluded.

"You can't change Miss Murphy's program," chirped one of his sisters.

"Bates, will you come with me and do it for Miss Murphy?" Harold pleaded, quite ignoring his sister's remark.

Bates was silent. In his heart he longed to, but he had little hope that Miss Murphy would even care to hear him, because he was always so bashful when near her. She was very kind to him, but her kindness increased his embarrassment.

"She'll be home by this time, and it isn't far from here," Harold continued, bubbling with enthusiasm.

"Harold, don't be silly," remonstrated his sister. "Miss Murphy isn't going to change her program at this late hour, and anyway, you have earned the right to take the part," she added.

"But he can do it so much better than I can," Harold almost shouted.

Harold's mother put her arm around his shoulder and said gently and proudly, "You are right, son, and if you wish to take Bates over to Miss Murphy, and he is willing to go, do it."

"I'd love to, Hal, but she won't let me take your place," Bates sighed despairingly.

"She may, if you will. And Harold wishes her to," Mrs. Bruce encouragingly suggested.

The hall was filled; the whole school, as well as parents, had been invited to attend Miss Murphy's program. Miss Murphy arranged for Harold and Bates not to appear until time for the Gettysburg speech. There was surprise and wonder on every face when Miss Murphy announced: Bates Hurlew will give the number assigned to Harold Bruce, Jr."

A questioning silence awaited Bates as he stepped out on the platform. The silence increased as he proceeded. Before he finished, men and women were brushing tears from cheeks and lashes. He took his seat in a breathless silence. Then there burst forth a thunderous applause.

THE PLAYMATES CELEBRATE ST. VALENTINE'S DAY

Today is Valentine's Day! Today is Valentine's Day!" said Dixie, as she dressed. Then she ran to the kitchen and looked out the window. That is she tried to look out, but it was so foggy that she could not see a thing outside.

"I don't like fog," she pouted. "I can't see a thing, and I wanted the weather to be nice on Valentine's Day."

"Wait a while and see," her mother smiled. "Now hurry and set the table, Dixie. Daddy will soon be ready for breakfast."

Dixie was so busy helping her mother and thinking about the valentines she had for her friends that she forgot about the fog. They had eaten their breakfast when she heard a tap on the door. Dixie knew that little knock and ran to let Patsy in.

"I brought all my valentines so we could take them around together," said Patsy, smiling. "And look what Mother made for me to take to Jimmie White, because he broke his leg and has to stay in bed for weeks and weeks."

Patsy lifted the cover from her basket and showed Dixie the heart-shaped cookies all covered with pink icing.

"Oh, how lovely!" said Dixie. "Mother, may I take something to Jimmie for Valentine's Day?"

"How would you like to take some of these nice oranges?" her mother asked.

"Jimmie would like those," Dixie said. She and Patsy made room in the basket for the oranges.

Then they started out to show Jay and Jackie.

"I want to take something to Jimmie too," said Jay when they reached his home. So Jay went into the cellar and picked out the very biggest and the very rosiest apples he could find and filled the basket. They put the cookies on top of the apples and oranges.

"Let's go and show Jackie," said Jay, but just then there was a knock on the door and in came Jackie.

"I want to take something to Jimmie too," he said, when he saw their gifts. "What can I take?" He thought hard for a minute, then he said, "I have a new dime at home. I will run and get it and buy Jimmie a big chocolate heart with his name on it. I was going to get me a pocketknife, but I would rather get Jimmie a valentine present."

By the time the playmates were ready to start on their way, the sun had come through the clouds, and the fog lifted. The children gasped with delight when they went outside, for every tree, bush, and weed was covered with thick, shining white frost that glistened and glittered in the bright sunshine. The snow on the ground covered everything, and it glittered too.

"How beautiful!" gasped Patsy. "It looks like fairy land!"

"Or a lacy valentine trimmed with diamonds," said Dixie. "And to think that I was cross this morning because it was foggy."

They stopped at the store, and Jackie got the big chocolate heart with Jimmie's name on it. There was no room for it in the basket, so they asked the clerk in the store to wrap it in red paper and tie it to the handle of the basket.

"Let's take the things to Jimmie first and deliver our other valentines later," said Patsy, and they all agreed.

Jimmie White was feeling very lonely and sorry for himself that morning.

"This is not a happy Valentine's Day for me," he thought, "even if Daddy and Mother did give me such nice presents. I wish I had never broken my leg, and I would not have to lie in bed all the time."

Just then a knock came on the door. Jimmie called, "Come in," and in walked Patsy, Dixie, Jay, and Jackie.

"Happy Valentine's Day, Jimmie," they called and came over and gave him the basket.

How happy Jimmie was to be remembered by his playmates! He thanked them for their gifts, and after they had played some games with him and were getting ready to go, Jimmie's mother said, "You children have the real Saint Valentine spirit. You have made Jimmie very happy."

"And making Jimmie happy has made us happy too,"

laughed the children as they waved goodbye and continued on their way.

—Geneva H. Williams.

The Valentine That Made Friends

The children came running into the house one Saturday morning early in February.

"Oh, Mother," said Jane breathlessly, "some people are moving into the house next door."

"The moving van is out in front of the house now," added Bill.

"The new people have a baby," said five-year-old Pam.

"There is a boy in the family," said Bill.

"Yes, and a girl and a dog," said Jane.

"Well, well," laughed Mother, "and how did you find all this out? Did you see the children?"

"No," said Pam, "but I saw a baby carriage, so there must be a baby."

"And nobody but a boy would have such a fine tricycle," answered Bill.

"Girls ride tricycles too, remember," said Mother.

"Yes, and nobody but a girl would have a little trunk for doll clothes, and no one but a puppy could use such a fine dog house."

"I do hope they will be a nice family," said Mother. "The children will be lonesome in a new neighborhood. We must be friendly with them."

That night at the dinner table Bill said, "We were right, Mother. In the family next door there is a boy. His name is John. He will be in my room at school."

"Peggy is just as old as I am," said Jane, "and in the second grade. And, Mother, you should see the baby. He's so sweet. Mrs. Harris said I could tend him sometimes."

"Well, I can see you are all acquainted with the new family. I'll have to call on Mrs. Harris very soon," said Mother. "Now, if you get your faces and hands washed quickly and teeth brushed, we'll have time for a story before you go to bed."

Soon the children were ready for the story. Pam climbed on Mother's lap and snuggled down while Bill and Jane sat at Mother's side.

"What story will it be this time?" asked Mother.

" 'Ask Mr. Bear,' 'William and His Kitten,' 'Snip, Snap and Snurr and The Red Shoes,'" they called out.

"Dear me," said Mother, "one at a time. How would you like a new story? Perhaps you have heard it before, but it's one we all like to hear just before St. Valentine's Day."

"A valentine story, please, Mother," they coaxed.

So Mother told the children the story of good Saint Valentine, and she ended with, "And because the people loved Saint Valentine so, for all the kind deeds he had done, they decided to remember him each year by sending messages of love and good cheer to their friends."

"I like that story," said Jane. "In our room at school this year we are going to send valentines and letters to Bobby, who has been ill."

"That's a lovely thing to do," said Mother. "We can remember even those about us with kind deeds and fine thoughts."

"Oh, Mother, I have an idea," said Bill. "The Harris children don't know many children in our neighborhood. Couldn't we make them some valentines for St. Valentine's Day?"

Mother smiled. "You surely could. I hope to have some willing hands ready to go to work Monday evening."

Monday evening Mother put wallpaper samples on Pam's little table and paper lace doilies, paste, scissors, red paper, drawing paper, and bits of ribbon.

"Now let's see what fine valentines you can make," said Mother. "I'll help Pam cut out a paper heart." Mother showed Pam how to fold the paper and cut a heart.

Soon Pam called out, "See my red paper heart. I made it all myself."

"Pam could fasten a lot of hearts together with ribbon and make a heart chain," said Jane, looking up from her work.

She and Bill had been busy too.

"Look, Mother! See my valentine man all made of paper hearts. Isn't he funny?" said Jane. "I'm going to make a beautiful one now with a lace paper doily."

"And what a fine one you're making, Bill. It looks like a snowflake," said Mother.

"It is. My teacher taught us how to make snowflake valentines. You fold the paper like this and cut along the edge." And Bill showed Mother just how to do it.

"It will soon be time for bed," said Mother. "You can finish these and make more tomorrow."

The days passed slowly for the three children, but St. Valentine's Day came at last. In the evening the children put on their coats, caps, mittens, and overshoes and started out to deliver their valentines.

Just before they left the house Mother said, "I made some little heart cookies yesterday. Perhaps you would like to take them as my valentine."

When the children were close to the Harris home, Jane said, "Bill, you're the oldest; you take your valentines first." So Bill crept softly up to the door, put his valentines down, gave a loud knock, and ran away. From the corner of the house the children could see the door open, then the Harris children came out.

"Oh, look, Mother, valentines! Here's one for John, one for me, and one for Bubbles."

Then it was Jane's turn. In her package was the valentine man, a valentine lady, and the beautiful valentine made of the lace paper doily. She knocked softly at the door and ran away. The children laughed when the door opened again and they heard cries of, "Isn't this one beautiful? See the funny man and woman! Who's it from?"

Last of all went Pam with the package of cookies and her own precious red paper heart for the baby.

"Now, Pam, remember to put your valentine and package down first and then knock, or they'll surely see you."

But little Pam was so excited when she got to the door that she knocked first. The door was opened quickly.

"We have caught you," they said. "Come on in."

Pam called to Jane and Bill, and they went into the house.

"I've never seen such beautiful valentines," said Mrs. Harris, "and to think you made them all yourselves."

"I like the funny man and lady," said John.

Peggy smiled, "The snowflake valentine is lovely," she said.

"See, the baby likes his valentine," and they all laughed to see him wave the red heart and try to put it into his mouth.

"You must stay a while and have some popcorn and apples," said Mrs. Harris. "Perhaps we could try one of these fine cookies too."

That night before the children climbed into bed, Jane said, "Mother, they liked our valentines."

"Peggy and John said they were glad to have us for friends," said Bill. And Pam said sleepily, "And the baby liked my red paper heart best of all."

—HAZEL WEST LEWIS.

THE STORY OF ST. VALENTINE

Once upon a time there lived in a country, a great many miles from here, a very old man; he was older than a great many of our birthdays added together; he had beautiful snow-white hair and beard and such kind, gentle eyes. He was noted in all the country round for his kindliness and devotion to his fellow men. He nursed the sick, went to those who were poor, taking supplies and good things, and comforted those who were sorrowing. He never was in trouble of any kind. The people began to call him Saint Valentine, because he was so very kind.

Often on cold winter evenings, when the north wind blew and all the snowflakes came down to visit the earth, Valentine would gather the little children of the neighborhood around his bright log fire and tell them beautiful stories of winter and summer, the birds and flowers, and many other things.

But this fine man gradually grew old, and he couldn't leave

his home to visit those who needed him. This was the saddest part of his life, for St. Valentine could not be happy unless he was spreading happiness too.

However, one day he discovered that he could still perform many kindnesses by writing letters of encouragement and love to those whom he could not visit. He wrote lovely verses too and sent them to the children and young people to make them happy. People who received his verses were truly made happier. They began to watch for the old man's kind words. When children were sick, they would say, "I know Father Valentine will send me a letter today."

The years went by, and then word was received that the old priest had died. People grieved deeply. When his birthday came along, which was February 14th, they remembered it by exchanging kind words or letters. Verses expressing sympathy and love for friends became a habit. Finally it became a custom in several countries, and Saint Valentine lived in the hearts of the people.

—SARA O. MOSS.

THE EASTER STORY FROM THE BIBLE

Then took they the body of Jesus, and wound it in linen clothes with the spices, as the manner of the Jews is to bury.

"Now in the place where he was crucified there was a garden; and in the garden a new sepulchre, wherein was never man yet laid.

"There laid they Jesus therefore because of the Jews' preparation day; for the sepulchre was nigh at hand. . . .

"The first day of the week cometh Mary Magdalene early, when it was yet dark, unto the sepulchre, and seeth the stone taken away from the sepulchre.

"Then she runneth, and cometh to Simon Peter, and to the other disciple, whom Jesus loved, and saith unto them, They have taken away the Lord out of the sepulchre, and we know not where they have laid him.

"Peter therefore went forth, and that other disciple, and came to the sepulchre.

"So they ran both together: and the other disciple did out-run Peter, and came first to the sepulchre.

"And he stooping down, and looking in, saw the linen clothes lying; yet went he not in.

"Then cometh Simon Peter following him, and went into the sepulchre, and seeth the linen clothes lie,

"And the napkin, that was about his head, not lying with the linen clothes, but wrapped together in a place by itself.

"Then went in also that other disciple, which came first to the sepulchre, and he saw, and believed.

"For as yet they knew not the scripture, that he must rise again from the dead.

"Then the disciples went away again unto their own home.

"But Mary stood without at the sepulchre weeping: and as she wept, she stooped down, and looked into the sepulchre,

"And seeth two angels in white sitting, the one at the head, and the other at the feet, where the body of Jesus had lain.

"And they say unto her, Woman, why weepest thou? She

saith unto them, Because they have taken away my Lord, and I know not where they have laid him.

"And when she had thus said, she turned herself back, and saw Jesus standing, and knew not that it was Jesus.

"Jesus saith unto her, Woman, why weepest thou? whom seekest thou? She, supposing him to be the gardener, saith unto him, Sir, if thou have borne him hence, tell me where thou hast laid him, and I will take him away.

"Jesus saith unto her, Mary. She turned herself, and saith unto him, Rabboni; which is to say, Master.

"Jesus saith unto her, Touch me not; for I am not yet ascended to my Father: but go to my brethren, and say unto them, I ascend unto my Father, and your Father; and to my God, and your God.

"Mary Magdalene came and told the disciples that she had seen the Lord, and that he had spoken these things unto her.

"Then the same day at evening, being the first day of the week, when the doors were shut where the disciples were assembled for fear of the Jews, came Jesus and stood in the midst, and saith unto them, Peace be unto you.

"And when he had so said, he shewed unto them his hands and his side. Then were the disciples glad, when they saw the Lord."

—JOHN 19:40–42; 20:1–10.

POLLY'S EASTER SERMON

Early in the fall one year, the year that Polly was going on ten, her Sunday School teacher had told her class that it

would be beautiful if each girl would buy a bulb and tend it
herself and on Easter bring the plant to school and then all go
together to the children's hospital and make glad the holy day.

Polly lived in an apartment house, and her mother, who did
washing and sweeping, worked hard mornings and nights to
keep their two rooms tidy and comfortable, and little Polly had
learned that a patch of brightness will grow and spread in
almost any place, if you try for it.

"But I have only three pennies!" she sighed. "Now what can
I do with three pennies?"

Polly went to Mr. Smith, the florist, and she found him
sorting bulbs. She asked him if he had a fine bulb for three
cents.

"No, but you can have this little crooked one for nothing,"
said Mr. Smith, "and I'll sell you a pot of earth for your three
cents."

Polly took the offering, and then she told Mr. Smith of her
plan. "I'll come in and tell you how it turns out!" she cried glee-
fully, and away she ran with her prize.

Now the window of Polly's back room was always sparkling,
and the sun shone in every morning when it was clear. Then
Polly stood the pot with the Easter bulb on a little stand, and
every morning before she went to school, she paid the little
bulb a short visit and sprinkled the dark earth, breathed a wee
prayer over it, and then left it to the sunbeams.

The warm sun always kissed the earth, and away down
deep the little bulb stirred and dreamed.

The dear little crooked bulb! It always dreamed the same
dream. It was always of a rare white blossom, and the songs of
birds, and golden light.

And one day the little bulb straightened out and sent two small green sprouts up through the earth to tell Polly and the sun that it was doing its best.

Polly was wild with joy at this message, and that same day, full of fresh faith in the bulb and in the sun, she had an inspiration. She knew that the Queer Lady and old Daddy Nolan had the sunlight a part of the afternoon in their windows. Right after dinner the Queer Lady had it, and later came Daddy Nolan's turn. So, although she was almost frightened at her own daring, she took the little pot in her arms and trotted across the dark passage to the Queer Lady's door.

Polly knocked softly. A cross woman opened the door.

"What do you want?" she asked.

"Please," faltered Polly, "may I borrow your sunshine?"

"My—what?" then the Queer Lady laughed roughly. "Come in and see if there is any here," she said.

Polly tripped in and looked about the dirty room. "Oh, plenty!" she replied, "if—we could wash the window a little bit."

The Queer Lady was not angry at all, and after she heard Polly's story she went to work, and soon a part of the window fairly shone, and when the sun passed on, the little girl gathered the pot to her heart and thanked her new friend.

"Bring it every day," whispered the Queer Lady. "I'll have the window bright."

With a brave heart and her plant in her arms, Polly toiled along up to Daddy Nolan's room. He lived at the top of the house and had quite a fine lot of sunshine until the day was gone.

Tap, tap, tap! Tap, tap, tap! very softly.

"Who's there?" cried a gruff voice.

"Just little Polly from downstairs," quivered the visitor.

"What do you want?"

"It's to know if you will please lend my plant your sunshine, Daddy?"

"Well, come in, then." The gruff voice was softer.

Polly went in, all smiles and dimples, right over to Daddy, where he was by the window, and with the little pot in her arms she told the story.

Daddy got up and took the pot and put it where the sun shone warmest, and then he and Polly had the time of their lives.

The little girl tidied the room and sang as she pattered about. Daddy watched her, and his heart grew tender, and the sun shone on the pot with the little green sprouts.

So it was the days and weeks passed, and you should have seen that plant grow! The Queer Lady's room became as neat as wax, and every afternoon, when the sun shone, she waited for Polly's step and knock with a glad, warm heart.

The sky was gray some days, and there was no sunshine to lend, none at all.

At the rooms that had only sunless windows Polly stopped every day on her way to Daddy Nolan's to let the tenants see how warm and strong the leaves were!

The Saturday before Easter when Polly opened her eyes, a wonderful sight greeted her.

There stood the plant on the window ledge with its dream come true! A glorious white lily shone in the dim room, a lily with a heart of pure gold. Polly stood before it, and the sun, peeping in just then, sent a blessing down in long, warm rays of light.

Polly's mother was standing there, in her shawl and bonnet, ready to go to her day's sweeping.

"I can hardly bear to leave it," she said, "only that you will have it all, dearie."

And then Polly went up the stairs, bearing the plant in her arms and calling with her little knock at every door. "Come out and see the lily! Come see the lily!"

And what an Easter Sunday the morrow brought! Polly, carrying her lily went through the streets towards the Sunday School, and after her followed her mother, the Queer Lady, Daddy Nolan, and others, all in their Sunday best, to celebrate the blooming of Polly's lily.

Then Polly's teacher said, "Now, Polly, tell the school the story of the crooked bulb."

Forgetting herself, and still holding her lily close, Polly began with the little crooked bulb, and went on to tell of the sunshine she had borrowed from the Queer Lady and Daddy Nolan.

"They all helped!" she ended radiantly. "They lent me their sunshine, so that my lily had sunshine all day long. Just see it now—and it was such a helpless little bulb!"

And then—oh! You should have seen that joyous procession going to the children's hospital.

AN EASTER SURPRISE

Spring was coming! Grandpa knew it as soon as he stepped outside and smelled the fresh little breeze that came out of the canyon. It had a different feel from the winds that had blown all winter.

Carol knew spring was coming when she heard the robin call, and LaVonne and David knew it as soon as they heard the bluebird's song. Baby Neta knew it when her daddy brought her the first snowdrop that pushed its way through the moist earth so early it was a wonder Jack Frost did not nip its nose. But Grandma knew it when she heard her old red hen clucking proudly to tell everyone she was setting on a nest of eggs so she could hatch some little baby chickens.

"I wonder where she hid her nest?" said Grandma.

"Let's find it for Grandma," cried six-year-old Carol and LaVonne to four-year-old David and Baby Neta, who was not yet two.

So all four of the little cousins hunted and hunted. They looked everywhere. Carol and LaVonne looked under the granary, around the woodpile, under the trees and bushes, and even in the maple groves where they played house. David looked in the cellar, and in Grandpa's machine shop, and even in the wood box. Baby Neta toddled first with one little cousin and then with another and looked with round, blue eyes everywhere.

The little cousins hunted almost every day. The new little leaves came out on the maple trees. Buttercups raised their yellow heads in the hollows where snow had lain a little while before. The robins built a nest in the maple grove; and the bluebirds, in Grandma's plum tree. Still no one found the nest of that old red hen. David even told Grandpa's old dog Toots about it and had her help him hunt. He thought sure she could find it, because she was so old and wise and had lived around the chickens for such a long time.

At last the bluebirds had three pretty eggs in their nest, and the robins had four blue eggs in their little cradle that swung in the maple tree. Grandpa's apple orchard was white with blossoms and so very fragrant, and still no one—not one soul—knew where that old hen had hidden her nest.

At last Easter came, and the little cousins were so happy and excited because they were going to have a picnic. Aunt Bee had sent them each a lovely Easter basket filled with candy eggs and chickens and bunnies and everything.

They were so happy they almost forgot about the old red hen and her nest.

"Where shall we have our picnic?" asked LaVonne, as they climbed the pasture hill.

"By that big serviceberry bush," said Carol.

"Oh yes, by that bush!" said David, running for the spot.

"By bush!" cried Neta, raising her chubby hands and running until a colored egg rolled from her basket.

They soon had their picnic spread, and how those children did eat! The baskets that had been full were nearly empty when they heard a little sound that made them stop eating. The little girls looked at each other with round, excited blue eyes, while David looked at them all with brown eyes full of questions.

"Did you hear something say, 'peep'?" asked Carol.

"It did say 'peep,'" cried David.

"Peep! Peep!" gurgled Baby Neta.

"Sh—," softly whispered LaVonne.

"Sh!" said David, very loud.

"Shoo!" yelled Baby Neta.

They all laughed, and then they heard it again:

"Peep! Peep! Peep!" it said.

"Baby chickens!" cried LaVonne.

"Baby chicks!" cried David.

"Chick!" cried Baby Neta.

Then they all started to hunt. They looked here, there, and everywhere, under brush and bushes and around the rocks.

Then they heard more peeping and followed the sound around the serviceberry bush. They tried to peek between the green leaves but could not see, so they took hold of the branches and parted them, and right before their surprised eyes sat that old red hen, as calm as you please.

"Oh! Oh!" they all gasped.

"We've found the old red hen," cried Carol.

"And a nest full of chicks," cried LaVonne.

"There's one black chick," shrieked David, and while they watched, four little fluffy chickens poked their yellow heads from under the old red hen's soft feathers.

Then they all laughed and called until their mothers and fathers and uncles and aunts and even Grandma and Grandpa came to see what all the excitement was about.

When they found out, they came up to the nest. Grandpa reached into the bush and lifted the old red hen carefully from the nest. There in a bed of soft leaves and feathers were ten of the prettiest, fluffiest, yellowest, little chickens you ever saw.

"Every egg hatched," said Grandpa. "Now help me catch these little ones before they get away; be careful not to squeeze them."

So everyone tried to catch them before they could hide in the grass and bushes.

Carol caught one and held it in her little hands. LaVonne caught one and held it to her little face. Neta's mother caught one and put it in her baby's apron. David looked everywhere, even under rocks, trying to find one. Then he looked up and found one hiding in his Easter basket, so he held it.

Then Grandpa took the old red hen and put her and her ten pretty chickens in a crib in the dooryard so Carol, LaVonne, and David, and even Baby Neta could feed and water them every day and watch them grow.

—GENEVA H. WILLIAMS.

FLOPPY AND THE EASTER BUNNY

Floppy crouched down behind a large burdock plant hoping that her mother wouldn't see her and call her out with the other children. She wasn't hiding because she had done something wrong and was afraid of a scolding, not in the least. Floppy was hiding because Mrs. Gray Rabbit and all her children were visiting Mother White Tail.

The last time Mrs. Gray Rabbit had come she had been most unkind and had said, "What a tiny little rabbit, and what a queer floppy ear! Whatever is the matter? Doesn't she eat her carrots and lettuce?"

Mother White Tail had assured Mrs. Gray Rabbit that Floppy had a very good appetite and ate her vegetables every day. In fact, she had said that she herself couldn't understand why Floppy was so much smaller than any of her other children.

"It's in the family somewhere," said Mrs. Gray Rabbit,

helping herself to another cabbage leaf. "Now you take my family, for instance. All of us are very large, and we can all run unusually fast. Because of that we have many famous rabbits in the family. I have even heard it said that we are second cousins to the Easter Bunny."

Mother White Tail mumbled something about that being very nice. Soon afterward Mrs. Gray Rabbit took her six children and went home.

As soon as Floppy was sure that they were out of hearing, she scampered in to her mother and asked, "What are famous rabbits?"

"Famous means having done something very good and great so that everyone knows and tells about it," answered Mother White Tail, sorting over the greens for supper.

"And who is the Easter Bunny?" asked Floppy.

"The Easter Bunny is the most famous of all the rabbits," replied Mother White Tail. "He brings colored eggs to the children, and they love him very much."

Floppy went outside and sat and thought for a long time. All at once she said, "That's just what I'll do." She jumped clear across the ditch and scampered down the long lane that led to the woods. There on a branch of the very first tree sat Mrs. Bluejay, chattering so hard and fast that Floppy began to fear she would never stop long enough to be asked a question. Finally, when she simply had to stop for breath, Floppy said, "Do you know where I can find the Easter Bunny?"

Mrs. Bluejay stared at Floppy for a moment and then said, "Dear me, you're so little I can scarcely see you. No, of course I don't, and by the way, whatever makes your ear flop down like that?"

Floppy didn't stop to answer any questions but hurried on into the woods. She almost bumped into a squirrel who was stirring busily among last year's dead leaves looking for something to eat.

"Excuse me," said Floppy, "but I didn't see you until just this minute. Do you happen to know which way I might look for the Easter Bunny?"

"I've seen hundreds of rabbits in these woods at one time or another," said the squirrel, pouncing upon an acorn. "How would I know which one is the Easter Bunny?"

"Oh, he's large and beautiful and carries a basket of colored eggs," Floppy answered. "I'm sure you'd know him if you had ever seen him."

"Yes, I'm sure that I would, and I'm also sure that I haven't, but if you'll follow the trail to the big tree near the edge of the woods you'll find Mr. Owl. He can tell you anything, or at least that's what he claims. By the way, what happened to your—?"

But Floppy was already scampering down the trail so that she could get away before the squirrel asked about her floppy ear.

She found the owl dozing in the tree and had such a hard time waking him up that she was about to go on without ever asking him. But finally he blinked one eye and said, "Whatever are you doing here this time of the day? Can't you see that the sun is still up, and I want to sleep?"

"I'm looking for the Easter Bunny, and, if you'll tell me where he is, I'll go away. Then you may sleep as long as you wish," said Floppy.

"That's simple. He isn't in these woods, so he must be somewhere else. It's likely that if you take that road you'll run

on to him in no time," and the owl turned his head around and
went promptly back to sleep again.

Floppy traveled on down the road until she came to a big
white house. It was getting dark now, and she was very tired
from her long journey. The green lawn looked so cool and
inviting that she decided to stop and rest there. "Besides," she
thought, "if the Easter Bunny brings bright-colored eggs to
children, he may be stopping here tonight. Then I can meet
him and find out how to become famous."

So Floppy ran across the green lawn and up close to the
house. There didn't seem to be anyone around. She crept up on
the porch and curled up in a small ball to wait. She was so tired
that in less than a wink she had gone fast asleep. When she
opened her eyes again, the sun was shining brightly, and two
children were laughing and talking near her.

"Isn't she a darling rabbit!" cried the little girl. "And wasn't
it kind of the Easter Bunny to bring her to us?"

Floppy blinked her bright eyes in wonder and looked
about. Yes, sure enough there was a big basket of colored eggs
that the Easter Bunny had brought during the night. Now he
had gone again, and she would never learn how to become
famous so that folks wouldn't make fun of her floppy ear.

She looked up at the little boy as he said, "She sure is a
dandy. We'll make a nice house for her and feed her carrots and
lettuce and cabbage every day. I think that she's the most beautiful rabbit I ever saw."

Floppy quit worrying about the Easter Bunny right that
minute. Why should she care about being famous? She had
plenty of fresh vegetables and two children who thought she
was beautiful. Even a floppy ear didn't matter now. Then

Floppy settled down and started to nibble daintily on the large lettuce leaf that the little girl had just brought from the house.

—MABEL S. HARMER.

THE SELFISH GIANT

Every afternoon as they were coming home from school, the children used to go and play in the giant's garden.

It was a large, lovely garden, with soft, green grass. Here and there over the grass stood beautiful flowers like stars, and there were twelve peach trees that in the springtime broke out into delicate blossoms of pink and pearl and in the autumn bore rich fruit.

The birds sat on the trees and sang so sweetly that the children used to stop their games to listen to them. "How happy we are here!" they cried to each other.

One day the giant came back. He had been to visit his friend the Cornish ogre and had stayed for seven years. After the seven years were over he had said all that he had to say, for his conversation was limited, and he determined to return to his own castle. When he arrived, he saw the children playing in the garden.

"What are you doing here?" he cried in a very gruff voice, and the children ran away.

"My own garden is my own garden," the giant said. "Anyone can understand that, and I will allow no one to play in it but myself." So he built a high wall all around it and put up a notice board:

TRESPASSERS
WILL BE
PROSECUTED

He was a very selfish giant.

The poor children now had nowhere to play. They tried to play on the road, but the road was very dusty and full of hard stones, and they did not like it. They used to wander around the high wall when their lessons were over and talk about the beautiful garden inside. "How happy we were there," they said to each other.

Then the spring came, and all over the country there were blossoms and little birds. Only in the garden of the selfish giant it was still winter. The birds did not care to sing in it, as there were no children, and the trees forgot to blossom.

Once a beautiful flower put its head out from the grass, but when it saw the notice board, it was so sorry for the children that it slipped back into the ground again and went off to sleep. The only ones who were pleased were the snow and the frost. "Spring has forgotten this garden," they cried, "so we will live here all the year round."

The snow covered up the grass with her great white cloak, and the frost painted all the trees silver. Then they invited the north wind to stay with them, and he came. He was wrapped in furs, and he roared all day about the garden, and blew the chimney-pots down. "This is a delightful spot," he said. "We must ask the hail on a visit."

So the hail came. Every day for three hours he rattled on the roof of the castle till he broke most of the slates, and then he ran round and round the garden as fast as he could go. He was dressed in gray, and his breath was like ice.

"I cannot understand why the spring is so late in coming," said the selfish giant, as he sat at the window and looked out at his cold white garden. "I hope there will be a change in the weather."

But the spring never came, nor the summer. The autumn gave golden fruit to every garden, but to the giant's garden she gave none. "He is too selfish," she said. So it was always winter there, and the north wind, and the hail, and the frost, and the snow danced about through the trees.

One morning the giant was lying awake in bed when he heard some lovely music. It sounded so sweet to his ears that he thought it must be the king's musicians passing by. It was really only a little linnet singing outside his window, but it was so long since he had heard a bird sing in his garden that it seemed to him to be the most beautiful music in the world.

Then the hail stopped dancing over his head, and the north wind ceased roaring, and a delicious perfume came to him through the open casement. "I believe the spring has come at last," said the giant, and he jumped out of bed and looked out.

What did he see?

He saw a most wonderful sight. Through a little hole in the wall the children had crept in, and they were sitting in the branches of the trees. In every tree that he could see there was a little child. And the trees were so glad to have the children back again that they had covered themselves with blossoms and were waving their arms gently above the children's heads. The birds were flying about and twittering with delight, and the flowers were looking up through the green grass and laughing.

It was a lovely scene; only in one corner it was still winter. It was the farthest corner of the garden, and in it was standing a little boy. He was so small that he could not reach up to the branches of the tree, and he was wandering all around it, crying bitterly. The poor tree was still quite covered with frost and snow, and the north wind was blowing and roaring above it. "Climb up! Little boy," said the tree, and it bent its branches down as low as it could, but the boy was too tiny.

And the giant's heart melted as he looked out. "How selfish I have been!" he said. "Now I know why the spring would not come here. I will put that poor little boy on the top of the tree, and then I will knock down the wall, and my garden shall be the children's playground forever and ever." He was really very sorry for what he had done.

So he crept downstairs and opened the front door quite softly and went out into the garden. But when the children saw him, they were so frightened that they all ran away, and the garden became winter again. Only the little boy did not run, for his eyes were so full of tears that he did not see the giant coming. And the giant strode up behind him and took him gently in his hands and put him up into the tree.

The tree broke at once into blossom, and the birds came and sang on it, and the little boy stretched out his two arms and flung them around the giant's neck and kissed him. And the other children, when they saw that the giant was not wicked any longer, came running back, and with them came the spring.

"It is your garden now, little children," said the giant, and he took a great axe and knocked down the wall. And when the people were going to market at twelve o'clock, they found the giant playing with the children in the most beautiful garden they had ever seen.

All day long they played, and in the evening they came to the giant to bid him good-bye.

"But where is your little companion?" he said, "the boy I put into the tree." The giant loved him the best because he had kissed him.

"We don't know," answered the children. "He has gone away."

"You must tell him to be sure and come here tomorrow," said the giant. But the children said that they did not know where he lived and had never seen him before, and the giant felt very sad.

Every afternoon when school was over, the children came and played with the giant. But the little boy whom the giant loved was never seen again. The giant was very kind to all the children, yet he longed for his first little friend and often spoke of him. "How I would like to see him!" he used to say.

Years went by, and the giant grew very old and feeble. He could not play about anymore, so he sat in a huge armchair and watched the children at their games and admired his garden. "I have many beautiful flowers," he said, "but the children are the most beautiful flowers of all."

One winter morning he looked out of his window as he was dressing. He did not hate the winter now, for he knew that it was merely spring asleep and that the flowers were resting.

Suddenly he rubbed his eyes in wonder and looked and looked. It certainly was a marvelous sight. In the farthest corner of the garden was a tree quite covered with lovely white blossoms. Its branches were all golden, and silver fruit hung down from them, and underneath it stood the little boy he had loved.

Downstairs ran the giant in great joy and out into the garden. He hastened across and came near to the child. And when he came quite close, his face grew red with anger, and he said, "Who hath dared to wound thee? Tell me, that I may take my big sword and slay him."

"Nay!" answered the child, "but these are the wounds of love."

"Who art thou?" said the giant, and a strange awe fell on him, and he knelt before the little child.

And the child smiled on the giant and said to him, "You let me play once in your garden; today you shall come with me to my garden, which is Paradise."

And when the children ran in that afternoon, they found the giant lying dead under the tree, all covered with white blossoms.

—OSCAR WILDE, FROM *THE HAPPY PRINCE*;
USED BY PERMISSION OF J. B. LIPPINCOTT COMPANY.

SPRING, THE LITTLE YELLOW-HAIRED PRINCE

One year when Spring, the little yellow-haired prince with eyes like violets, came much earlier than usual, he found none of the children in the woods to meet him.

He asked the birds if they knew why the children were not there. "You are so much earlier than usual," they said, "that we do not think they know you have come, but we are glad they are not here, for last year the boys stole our eggs and broke up our nests."

"Yes," said the meadowlark, "and one little girl stepped on my nest hidden away so carefully in the grass, and all my eggs were mashed."

The trees heard the birds talking, and they began: "We were treated badly too; some boys with great sharp knives cut deep gashes in our sides, and how it hurt us!" And one tiny little tree told how its tallest branch had been broken right off, so that it would take a whole year to grow another half so tall.

"Well, well!" said Spring, "that is too bad! We must see what we can do to help matters." And he sent word around by the bluebird, calling all the birds to a meeting next day.

The following morning Spring said, "I have thought of a plan. Suppose we send all the children presents and tell them I have come. Then they will know that we love them, and they will love us in return."

"What shall we send?" the birds asked, and such a twittering and chirping began that you would have thought a dozen music boxes were going at once. At last the dove flew down and told Spring that all the birds had agreed to send an egg—they could easily spare one each from their nests.

Away they flew to get them, and back they soon came. There were all colors and sizes from the robin's tiny blue egg to the big, round white one of the old screech owl who lives in the hollow elm tree near by. Even the humming bird had brought her tiny egg from her nest like a bunch of moss.

"Now," said Spring, "who will be our messenger and carry the eggs to the children?"

The birds did not think they could carry them, so Spring looked about to see which one of the animals would act as messenger. The bear and the wolf said they would go willingly, and they were certainly strong enough, but they were sure the children would be afraid of them, so it would not do for them to go.

The fox came up with a sly look on his face and offered to be the messenger. Spring looked at him a moment and said, "Mr. Reynard, you would travel fast enough, I know, but I fear I couldn't trust you with the eggs."

The turtle was careful and steady, but as they were in a hurry to send the presents, they could not choose such a slow-moving creature as she to take them.

At last they chose an animal that was swift, yet gentle, but very timid. Can you guess what one it was? Yes, the rabbit. He could carry them quickly, yet gently, and not break or jar even the tiniest.

The rabbit, however, was afraid to go. He was afraid of the children—of the dogs—of everything.

"But," said Spring, "suppose you go early in the morning before it is light, when everything is asleep, and slip the eggs into the yards where the children live; would you be afraid to do that?"

"No," said the rabbit.

But now came another difficulty. How could the little rabbit carry them?

"I know, I know!" said Robin-Red-Breast, away up in a tree, and down he flew; perching upon the shoulder of the little prince, he whispered something in his ear, "Carry them in a bird's nest!"

"That is good," said Spring. "Which of you will weave the nest?"

Up came the old black crow. "I will!" he cawed, but all the

birds and animals burst out laughing and said he would never
do. "Why," said Spring, "isn't that careless bundle of sticks in
yonder tree your nest? Do you think such a fellow could weave
a nest fit to hold such pretty eggs as these?"

The crow hung his head and stood aside while the noisy
jaybird in his blue and white suit came up, with his saucy cap
cocked back on his head.

"Do you think you could weave the nest?"

"Oh, yes!" said he.

"Wasn't that your nest in the ash tree with the dirty old
pieces of rags and strings hanging from it, and the rough straws
and sticks almost dropping off its sides? I'm afraid your nest
wouldn't be much better than the crow's," said Spring, shaking
his head.

At length up came a little bird dressed in orange and black.
She had been sitting on the highest branch of an elm tree near
by, swinging in the nest that she had hung away out on the end
of a limb. It was the oriole. Her nest would be best of all, for it
is long, and deep, and strong; it swings in the wind, and never
an egg spills out.

So the oriole was chosen to weave the nest.

Now the trees said they would like to help too, and they
offered to give twigs for the nest, so that it would be strong and
not break the load of eggs.

The cottonwood's twigs were so thick and short and
snapped so easily that they would not do. The pine tree's twigs
were so covered with sharp needles that they would not suit to
make the nest, and the elm's twigs were long and slender, but
they did not bend to and fro.

At last a tree that grew near the river's bank was found. Its branches swept down to the water's edge, and so limber were they that with every breeze they swayed to and fro.

It was the willow.

So the oriole wove the nest of the willow's twigs and made it deep and long, with a piece to go around the rabbit's neck, and a sheep gave some of his wool to make a soft lining for the eggs to rest upon.

The rabbit started long before the sun was up, and he slipped into the yard and hid the pretty eggs, and away he ran before anybody saw him. Early that Easter morning the children found the beautiful colored eggs which the birds had sent. And every Easter morning they still find the eggs. And so they know that the birds love them, and they love the birds in return.

A TALE OF A TAIL

Reynardita Fox emptied her much-worn purse on the table. Ten, twenty, thirty, forty, fifty cents, she counted. How she had economized to save that sum! It was every penny of her spending money for ten weeks.

Tomorrow would be Christmas. That fifty cents was to buy a present for her best-loved, Reynard Fox. It was to be a sensible gift this year—five inches of the best gray fox fur to mend a tear in his tail, for one day some brambles had caught in Reynard's exquisite tail and had torn off the top, leaving a ragged, shabby end. It had been a sore trial for Mr. Fox to wear so jagged a tail, but he had uttered not one word of complaint. He had just made the best of it.

So, tomorrow Reynardita meant to surprise him! She had found a shop that sold a marvelous five-inch length of fur for fifty cents. It was gray and silky and of exquisite quality. Would half-past eight ever come so the store would be open? Reynardita could hardly wait to go out and buy her best-beloved a gift.

With beaming face she gathered up the coins and jingled them. "Tomorrow will be Christmas!" she sang joyously. "Tomorrow will—"

In the midst of her song the doorbell rang. What could it be so early in the morning? She hastened to the door to admit a messenger with a note from Widow Muskrat. During the night her home down the river had been flooded, and the water had carried away all her possessions. She herself had caught a severe cold.

Renardita Fox put on her hat, buttoned her fur coat, slipped her precious purse into her muff, and went straight to Mrs. Muskrat.

The very first thing to be done was to search for a safe hole. They found one high on the bank. But what is a house with nothing to eat in it? Mrs. Fox thought of her Christmas savings. She had dreamed how Reynard's eyes would sparkle at the sight of that five inches of marvelous gray fur, but if she used one coin, she could not buy it.

But poor Mrs. Muskrat was hungry. And it was Christmas time. Reynardita could not see her starve. She could find some cheaper fur for Reynard's tail! After all, Reynard did not need such expensive fur, whereas Mrs. Muskrat *had* to have a home and a Christmas dinner. So, with half her savings Reynardita brought warmth and food to put into the new house.

Then, leaving Mrs. Muskrat safe in her warm home with a fine Christmas dinner in her pantry, Reynardita set off to find her best-beloved's gift.

"The Christmas spirit will be in the cheap fur just the same," thought Mrs. Fox as she entered a fur shop on the corner. But no inexpensive fur was to be found there. Reynardita tried another shop, and another, and still another, but not a bit of gray fox fur could she buy for her price.

There was one store left. It was a department store way off at the very end of Nowhere. Reynardita had to walk. She could spare not one penny for a ride. But she hummed to her heart all the way, and the cheer of coming Christmas made her forget she was tired.

It was almost dark when at last she stood before the gaily dressed windows of the store. "If I don't find it here," she said softly to herself, "I'll have to make the best of it and buy something else. Reynard would love whatever I give him. But I *do* want five inches of gray fur to mend his poor torn tail!"

The fur-by-the-inch counter was crowded. So, until her turn Mrs. Fox amused herself by looking at the powders, perfumes, and sachets on the next counter.

At length the clerk was able to wait on her. He brought out several kinds of fur. With trembling paws Mrs. Fox examined them. And there it was, the shade of gray she wanted, and at her price! Reynardita bought five inches.

"Now," thought she, as she hugged the box to her heart on the way home, "every morning when he goes to business he can wave to me over the bushes, as he used to do. Tonight I shall sew it on for him!" Her heart felt so light that the box of fur seemed to grow lighter than air.

Finally she reached home. At the foot of the stoop she stopped to take out her key. But the door opened from the inside. Reynard was home early and had seen her coming up the path. The candles were lighted and the kettle was on. But Reynardita just couldn't wait until after supper to show her gift. "See what I have for you, Reynard," she said. "I have bought some gray fur to mend your raggedy tail."

Reynardita untied the string. She took off the cover. Then she gave a little scream of disappointment. Instead of the five inches of gray fox fur, there was a white powder puff! The wrapper in the store had made a mistake. But Reynard snatched up the gift, and with the cheer of Christmas in his heart, just for fun, he clapped it on the end of his torn tail. The magic of Reynardita's love was in the powder-puff, and it stuck. Reynard did the fox-trot around the room, waving his tail with its power-puff tip. Reynardita shook with laughter at the antics of her very best-beloved. But it really did look gorgeous—that white tip in the midst of the gray.

"Why, my dearest," said Reynard, when he stopped for breath, "this is better than sewing a piece on my tail. When I wave to you now, this will shine through the bushes until I am quite out of sight. It's wonderful, the best Christmas present I've had! Now here is yours."

From his inside pocket Reynard drew a brand new purse filled with bright coins for Reynardita to get whatever she wanted most.

"Buy me a powder-puff tip for my tail too," she said.

Reynard did—that very night!

Ever since that Christmas Eve, foxes' tails have had white powder-puff tips. Love can put magic in everything.

—MARY J. J. WRINN.

THE FIRST AMERICAN MOTHER'S DAY

Miss Anna Jarvis of Philadelphia was the founder of the American Mother's Day. Wishing to honor her own mother and seeing the need of designating one special day of the year for all mothers, Miss Jarvis worked hard to bring the idea before the public. For many years she traveled over the country, making speeches, writing letters, and giving her time and effort to the cause. At last, on May 8, 1914, Congress signed a resolution to set aside the second Sunday in May as the national Mother's Day. Flags were to be displayed in public places, programs and gatherings were to mark the occasion, and a white carnation was chosen as the emblem. President Wilson, himself, wore this pure, white flower in his lapel as a token of respect to all the mothers in America.

One reason Miss Jarvis made the carnation the emblem of Mother's Day was that her own mother, an ardent flower lover, found much joy in distributing the blossoms to those who had none. She was known all about town for her kind heart and always remembered the sick, the poor, and the shut-ins. She was an ideal mother, having eleven children of her own. In its pure whiteness, the carnation symbolizes a pure heart and the unselfishness of motherhood.

In observing Mother's Day we express love, not only for our own mothers, but for all mothers everywhere.

—SARA O. MOSS.

MOTHER'S GIFTS

Under a big tree in a beautiful meadow little Ann sat crying. "Oh, I'm so unhappy," she said, and she cried and cried.

"What did you say?" asked a tiny voice.

Ann gave a start. "Where are you? Who is talking?" she said.

"Here I am, Queen Maybelle, queen of all the meadow fairies."

"But I can't see you."

"Hold out your hand, and I'll come closer."

Ann held out her hand, and a beautiful little fairy no larger than her thumb stood right in the middle of it.

"Why are you crying?" the fairy queen asked.

"I want to give my mother a present, and I have no money."

"Money! What's money?"

"You don't know!" exclaimed Ann, looking so surprised. "You buy things you want with it, especially a present for Mother."

"You could give your mother many things that wouldn't take money," said Queen Maybelle. "Come with me, and I'll show you."

Swish! Swish! went the tall grass as Ann and the fairy walked through the meadow.

"Look over there," said Maybelle, pointing with her wand.

Ann looked and saw a group of little fairies all dressed in yellow, smiling and dancing.

"They seem to be having such a good time," said Ann. "May I play with them? What are their names?"

"They are the Smile Fairies, and to play with them one must be happy and glad. Perhaps they could tell you what present you could give Mother."

Ann joined the fairies and danced in the ring.

"Come," said Maybelle a little later, "we must be going now. There are other fairies I want you to see or hear."

Maybelle hopped up on Ann's shoulder as they walked along.

Ann put her head to one side and whispered in Maybelle's ear. "I found out one present I could give Mother. It's a big smile." And as she said that last word, a big smile spread from ear to ear.

By and by they came to a little bubbling brook that ran through the meadow.

"Listen, Maybelle! I hear voices, little tiny fairy voices."

"The voices you hear are those of the song fairies. Can you tell what they are singing?"

From afar off came little voices singing:

> We sing because we're happy;
> We sing because we're glad;
> We sing to help each other
> Do kind things every day.

"Isn't that lovely?" said Ann. "I could sing my mother a song," and Ann hummed the tune. As she hummed it she began making up her own words to the lovely melody.

> I sing because I'm happy;
> I sing because I'm glad;
> I want to help my mother
> In every kind of way.

"It is getting late now," said Queen Maybelle. "We must be getting on."

They left the meadow and came to a beautiful garden.

"Why, this garden looks very much like our garden at home," said Ann. The fairy queen smiled and waved her wand over all the flowers in the garden. They began to dance and sway in the breeze.

"Aren't they beautiful?" said Ann. "My mother loves flowers."

"Perhaps you have thought of another gift," said Maybelle.

Ann turned to thank her, but the fairy queen had vanished.

"Aren't you ever going to wake up?" said Mother as she kissed Ann.

Ann opened sleepy eyes and smiled.

"Oh, I had the best dream. The fairy looked just like you, Mother."

And on Mother's Day, Ann gave to her mother the three gifts Mother liked best of all—a smile, a song, and a lovely red rose.

—HAZEL WEST LEWIS.

BIRTHDAY OF THE STARS AND STRIPES

This is a story about the birthday of the flag of the United States of America.

Many, many years ago the members of the Continental Congress met in the city of Philadelphia and gave the thirteen United States a flag. Independence Hall was the place where the congress met, a famous old building that had seen the signing of the Declaration of Independence and had heard the stirring words that great men spoke when a new nation was formed.

On the 14th day of June, 1777, the Stars and Stripes was selected as a flag of great beauty to wave over the world's newest nation.

There had been other American flags before this one. Back in 1775 there had been several flags lifted to the breeze to wave over some town or some colony or some ship at sea. Among these were two blue flags, a white flag, and a red flag. There were three flags that had pine trees in their pattern to represent the forests on the high American hills. One flag had a rattlesnake stretched across its stripes, and upon another banner was written this wonderful word—LIBERTY.

But not one of these flags was a Star Spangled Banner; not one was a flag with both stars and stripes in a new design. And not one of these flags represented all the colonies united together, to work all for one and one for all.

A new nation needed a new flag. The men who met in the city of Philadelphia on that summer day in 1777 have been called "The Makers of the Flag," for they chose the design and the colors, and they passed a resolution that has become famous all over the world.

"Resolved, that the flag of the thirteen United States be thirteen stripes, alternating red and white; that the union be thirteen stars, white in a blue field, representing a new constellation."

Why are there stripes in the flag? Where did we get the pattern of stars?

John Paul Jones, who commanded the ship of the new nation, unfurled a striped flag before the year 1777, and when George Washington took command of the American soldiers at Cambridge, Massachusetts, in January 1776, a striped flag waved over that place. The flag of Washington and the flag of John Paul Jones had red and white stripes in the design, but in the corner of these banners there was a double cross of red and white lines, a cross that stood for England and Scotland.

A new nation needed a new banner. So "The Makers of the Flag" chose red and white stripes. But, instead of using a cross that represented countries across the sea, they chose stars to be the emblems of a new country.

"We take the stars from heaven," declared George Washington, "the red from our mother country, separating it by white stripes, thus showing that we have separated from her, and the white stripes shall go down to posterity representing liberty."

A grouping of glorious white stars in a flag was a new design, and, as Washington said, they took the stars from heaven. Stars have always been the emblems of high thoughts and high ideals. Very beautiful are the stars in the dark blue sky, glowing with their calm and steady light.

Many people think that stars are a sign of the love our

Heavenly Father has for us and an emblem of the eternal life that he has promised all his children.

Many people believe that the blue-white stars are the most beautiful of all the heavenly lights, more beautiful even than the yellow stars, and those that glow with a flaming red light. Sirius, called the King Star, is the brightest "lantern of the sky" and its light is blue-white and splendid beyond any earthly thing.

It was these wonderful blue-white stars that gave the fathers of our country a pattern for the flag.

> And that is how the flag was made,
> And how it came to be,
> The stars and glorious stripes arrayed
> To wave on land and sea.

When the 14th day of June comes, remember that it is the birthday of the flag. Remember that it is the day for all of us to salute the bright banner of the United States of America. All of us should remember that one who loves the flag will always honor the law, whether the law of his home, his church, his town, or his state. He will be loyal and "true blue."

> Your flag and my flag—
> And how it flies today
> In your land and my land
> And half a world away.

> —VESTA P. CRAWFORD.

THE LITTLE SILK FLAG

It was quite the most beautiful flag that Peter had ever seen. It hung in the toy shop window, and it was made of silk with red and white stripes like a peppermint candy stick, and it had more white stars in its blue corner than Peter could count.

"How much does it cost?" Peter asked the man who kept the toy shop and who was a very unusual kind of shopkeeper indeed.

"It isn't for sale," said the shopkeeper. "I am going to give it away next Monday to the bravest boy that I see through my window."

"Oh," said Peter, his eyes very big, and then he went on to school; and before the last bell rang, he had told all the boys.

"The queer, funny old shopkeeper is going to give away the beautiful silk flag on Monday, Washington's birthday, to the bravest boy he sees through his window," Peter said; so of course, everyone was excited indeed.

All the week before Washington's birthday the boys strutted up and down in front of the shop window, trying to do brave things and to look brave, and hoping, oh, so much, that the queer old shopkeeper, with his twinkling eyes hidden behind a pair of large bone spectacles, would see them.

Halmar fell off a stone wall which his mother told him not to climb, and although he cried very loudly when the doctor put on the splints, he stood one whole afternoon in front of the shop window, hoping that the shopkeeper would see him and think him very brave indeed.

Burton put on his Indian suit and waved his tomahawk high above his head and ran up and down the street in front of the shop, giving war whoops, which at least sounded brave. Wilmont had a fight with a boy who was not so large as he, in the street near the shop, but at all these sights the shopkeeper shook his head.

"I wonder which little boy knows how to be truly brave," he said on the morning of Washington's birthday.

There was a wonderful parade planned for the day. The soldiers were going to march first, and after them the firemen and then a brass band, and last of all would come the policemen in their blue coats and brass buttons. All the boys were most excited watching for the parade; and when it came swinging down the street, the pretty colors of the uniforms shining in the sunlight and the music of the band ringing out upon the air, the boys shouted in delight and ran behind, forgetting all about the little flag in the shopkeeper's window.

Peter was the last boy of all to try and catch up with the parade. It was a long way from his house to the street down which the parade marched, and the band was just passing out of sight when he saw a lame child sitting on the curbing, his crutches lying on the sidewalk at his side.

"Hurry, I'll help you along!" Peter cried, helping the lame child to rise and putting his crutches in place. But the lame child walked very, very slowly, even when Peter helped him. Peter had to lift him over some of the rough places, and the parade swept farther and farther away through the street, and the band grew fainter and fainter. Try as hard as they could, the lame child and Peter helping could not catch up with the policemen, even. They missed every bit of the parade.

Presently, though, they came to the shop and the shopkeeper stood inside, looking out at them through the window. Then Peter had a thought, as he saw the beautiful flag flying so pretty and gay in the window.

"Here's a brave boy, Mr. Shopkeeper," he cried. "He says

that his leg often aches at night, but he never cries. I think that he is brave enough to have your flag. Will you give it to him?"

"He certainly is a brave little lad," said the queer old shop-keeper, smiling down at the two little boys through his bone spectacles.

"I will give him a drum to beat upon and help him to keep up his courage," he said, and he hung a fine little red drum across the shoulder of the lame child. Then he took the flag from the window and held it up in the light so that its colors shone and shimmered.

"I have found another brave child," the shopkeeper said, "a child who forgets himself in helping a friend," and he gave the beautiful red, white, and blue flag to Peter.

—CAROLYN SHERWIN BAILEY.

OLD GLORY'S BIRTHDAY

Hurry and finish your breakfast, Timmy," Mother said, "so you can help raise the flag this morning."

Timmy poured more cream over his cereal. "Oh, Mother," he laughed, "you're fooling. Today is not the Fourth of July."

"No," she said, "but today we honor the birthday of the Stars and Stripes. Today is June 14th."

"I didn't know our flag had a birthday."

"Of course, Timmy. In 1776 George Washington asked Betsy Ross to make America's first flag, thirteen stars and thirteen stripes; and the next year on June 14th, the Congress adopted it and made it officially the flag of the United States."

"But, Mother," Timmy asked, "didn't we have a flag before then?"

"Oh, yes. There were many flags, but none of them exactly suited the Fathers of our country."

"What were they like?"

"There were the 'Pine Tree,' also known as the 'Green Tree' flag, the 'Beaver' flag, the 'Hope,' the 'Rattlesnake,' and many others."

Timmy reached for a slice of toast. He chuckled. "That's funny," he said. "Imagine a 'Rattlesnake' flag."

"The rattlesnake has no eyelids and was meant to symbolize the constant vigil it would keep, being on guard at all times against enemies," Mother explained. "Others thought the warning message of 'Don't Tread on Me' and the deadly bite of the rattlesnake were more significant."

"Oh, I didn't know that," Timmy said.

Mother went on talking. "The 'Beaver' flag denoted the industry of the colonies and the great fur trade. The busy beaver depicted the people of America as being ambitious and always going forward."

"That's interesting! What did the 'Pine Tree' flag mean?"

"It was to honor the memory of an old tree in Boston, under which the Sons of Liberty met, and an oak tree in Charleston, South Carolina. The Declaration of Independence was read to the people of Charleston under that old tree." Mother poured Timmy another glass of milk. "The 'Pine Tree' flag had the inscription 'An Appeal to Heaven' written on it. That meant the tree was lifting its branches toward heaven asking for the blessings of God on the people of the colonies who came to America to worship as they pleased."

"America is a wonderful place, isn't it, Mother?"

"Yes, indeed."

"What was the 'Union Jack'?"

"It was a flag of thirteen red and white stripes and in the corner was the cross of St. George of the British flag. It represented the thirteen colonies and their connection with the mother country."

"The mother country was Great Britain, wasn't it?"

"Yes. The American colonies were under the rule of England until the Revolutionary War," Mother explained.

"That was when George Washington got the idea for a flag of our own. I remember studying in school about it. The thirteen stars and stripes represented the thirteen colonies, united for the cause of liberty."

"That's right," Mother said.

"And when new states were added to the Union, a new star was added to the field of blue." Timmy was talking so much he wasn't finishing his breakfast.

"Drink your milk now," Mother told him.

"Okay," Timmy said. "We want to have our flag out first this morning. We Americans are proud of our flag, aren't we, Mother?"

"Yes, Timmy, and we are proud of everything it stands for too."

Timmy drained his glass and pushed his chair away from the table. "I'm finished, Mother," he said. "Let's hurry. Today is really a day to celebrate. It's Old Glory's birthday!"

—MYRTLE C. NORDE.

A HALLOWEEN STORY

Once upon a time a big orange pumpkin was growing just outside a stone wall, far off in a field, all alone. The farmer had gathered all his pumpkins and stored them carefully in his great barn. But no one knew of the big orange pumpkin growing just outside the wall, all alone. The big orange pumpkin was lonely.

"I wish I belonged to someone," he said.

"Mew, mew! I do too," cried the little black pussy cat, stretching herself and jumping down from the stone wall where she had been sleeping.

"It will soon be winter," said the big orange pumpkin. "Let's go find someone to belong to."

"Yes, let's do," said the little black cat eagerly. "I want to belong to a little girl with a sweet face and shining eyes."

"And I," said the big orange pumpkin, "want to belong to a jolly little boy who whistles and sings while he works. Let's hurry right away to find them."

"Yes, let's do," said the little black cat.

So they started off—the big orange pumpkin rolling and tumbling along and chuckling to himself as he went, and the little black cat pit-patting along on her soft little cushions, purring because she was happy.

On and on they went, over the fields and through the woods. It began to grow cold, oh, so cold, and dark too. The little black cat shivered as the wind whistled through the trees.

"See here," said the big orange pumpkin, "you can't sleep outdoors tonight. What shall we do?"

Just then they saw a man coming along the path with a bundle of wood on his back.

"Ho, Mr. Woodcutter," cried the pumpkin, "have you a knife?"

"That I have," said the merry woodsman. "What can I do for you, my fine fellow?"

"Just cut out a piece of my shell where the stem is and scoop out some of my seeds, if you please," said the pumpkin.

No sooner said than done.

"There, my little black pussy cat," said the pumpkin, "when you wish to sleep tonight, you may curl inside and be as warm as a sunbeam."

"But will you not come home with me?" asked the woodsman.

"Have you a little girl with a sweet face and shining eyes?" asked the little black pussy cat.

"Have you a jolly little boy who whistles and sings when he works?" asked the big orange pumpkin.

"No, ah, no," said the woodsman, "but I have a pig and some hens."

"Then we'll go on," said the pumpkin, "but thank you kindly."

So on they went, and on, until the stars began to shine. Then the tired little pussy cat curled in her hollow nest, put on the cover, and went to sleep.

In the morning they went on again, but before long it began to rain. The pussy cat's soft fur was soon very wet.

"You poor little thing," said the big orange pumpkin, "curl inside your house and I will trundle you along."

"But it's so dark inside, and I couldn't see where we were going," cried the pussy cat, holding up a tiny dripping paw.

"Windows!" cried the pumpkin. "Of course, windows! How stupid of me! Wait here under this fence, my little friend, until I come back."

Then off he hurried across the road to a carpenter's shop.

"Ho, Mr. Carpenter," cried the pumpkin, "have you a knife?"

"That I have," said the jolly carpenter. "What can I do for you, my fine fellow?"

"Just cut some windows for me, if you please."

So the carpenter took a sharp knife and cut four windows—just like a face he made them, two for eyes, one for a nose, and one for a mouth, and he laughed as he did it.

When he finished the mouth, the pumpkin laughed too. "Ha, ha, ha!" cried he. "What a relief to have a mouth to laugh with! Ha, ha, ha!" And he laughed all the way back in the rain to where the little shivering pussy cat was waiting.

And she laughed too and climbed inside her coach and put on the cover. So on through the rain they went, and on and on. Just as dark was drawing near, they came to a wee brown house by the side of the road. In the yard was a little boy picking up chips and then putting them into a big basket. He whistled as he worked, and then he began to sing:

> If wishes were horses,
> Then beggars might ride;
> If turnips were watches,
> I'd wear one by my side.

Then the door opened, and a little girl with a sweet face

and shining eyes stood on the threshold. "What do you wish, John?" she called.

"Oh," laughed the boy, as he came in with the chips, "I wish I had a pumpkin for a jack-o'-lantern, for this is Halloween."

"And I wish I had a pussy cat to love," said the little girl.

"This is the place for us," whispered the big orange pumpkin; and he rolled up to the door, bumpity bump!

"Look, John!" cried the little girl, "here's your jack-o'-lantern! The fairies must have sent it. Isn't it a beauty?"

"There's something inside," said John, snatching off the cover, and out jumped a tiny black pussy cat, straight into the little girl's arms.

"Oh, oh!" they cried.

And when Mother came home in the dark, a jolly jack-o'-lantern with a candle inside was shining out of the window at her, and close beside it sat a little black pussy cat.

—ELIZABETH THOMPSON DILLINGHAM,
FROM *TELL IT AGAIN STORIES*, BY DILLINGHAM AND EMERSON;
USED BY PERMISSION OF GINN AND COMPANY.

LITTLE JOHNNY PUMPKIN

Little Johnny Pumpkin lived in a garden patch on Farmer Ned's place. He knew that it would soon be Halloween. Jack Frost had been to see him, and Jack had told him so. Johnny Pumpkin could see the moon coming too. There was always Mr. Moon, as round as could be on Halloween. Each night he grew rounder and brighter.

"I am so happy," thought Johnny Pumpkin. "Now I can join the boys and girls in the fun of Halloween."

One day Farmer Ned came to the garden patch and took all of the pumpkins, except Johnny Pumpkin, to the city and sold them to the stores. This made Johnny very sad and lonely. He was afraid he would not share in the Halloween fun.

"Why did not Farmer Ned take me too?" he thought.

At night Johnny Pumpkin would look up at the man in the moon, and Mr. Moon would look right down at him. "Please help me find a nice little boy or girl, so I can make funny faces for them on Halloween," Johnny would say. He always smiled when he looked at the man in the moon, and Mr. Moon always smiled at him.

When the day before Halloween came, Johnny Pumpkin heard voices coming into the garden patch. As they came near, he could hear Farmer Ned saying, "Here he is. He is the finest pumpkin that grew in my garden. I have kept him for you."

Johnny Pumpkin looked around and saw a little boy with bright eyes and a big smile. "Oh, thank you, Uncle Ned," said the happy boy. "He is as round as the moon. He will be great fun at our party."

That evening when the moon came out, he saw Johnny Pumpkin with a big smile and shining eyes. He is sitting in Farmer Ned's window. Inside were happy girls and boys. They were dancing and playing games. It was Halloween.

—EUNICE BUCK.

KENT'S HALLOWEEN PRANK

W e leaned the scarecrow up in his door. We stepped back, and with a long stick we knocked three times. Old Man Todd opened the door. The scarecrow fell in on him. Did he jump? Oh, boy!"

"We lifted Sam Jones's gate off the hinges and carried it down the lane."

Kent listened to these stories of old Halloween pranks as told by Uncle Dan. It must be fun to do things like that. Then he wondered what he'd do if he opened a door and a scarecrow should fall on him. Well, that would be "a cat of another color." He couldn't bear to hurt anyone, but he felt he would like to give some folks the surprise of their lives tonight. He wished he could think of a way to do so. First, however, he must help Aunt Ella pit the last of her vegetables.

When everything was in the cellar, Aunt Ella picked out her very biggest pumpkin and gave it to Kent.

"This is your bonus. You've been such a very good helper."

"Oh! Thank you!" He remembered the apple in his pocket. "Do you want an apple, Aunt Ella?"

"I'll say I do."

Kent tugged and pulled away at his pocket. Out came a hard green apple.

"Oh, Kent! I got my mouth all ready for a sweet, juicy apple. I'm afraid I can't eat that one. Thank you, just the same."

Kent was sorry. He felt as though he had hurt Aunt Ella. He took his pumpkin and started across Mrs. Selby's lot toward home.

Mrs. Selby and Aunt Ella had been very dear friends for

many years. Their lots joined at the back, and there they had a
little gate through which they went back and forth, visiting and
exchanging products. But some time ago they had a bitter quar-
rel. Angry words were spoken. Each vowed she would never do
a favor for the other again. Aunt Ella nailed up the little back
gate.

"Why did you do that?" asked Kent.

"Because Mrs. Selby and I are not on speaking terms," she
had answered.

Kent didn't know what the gate had to do with speaking
terms. He didn't mind, though, because he had climbed over
the gate more often than he had opened it.

This time he easily vaulted over the gate and into Mrs.
Selby's orchard, then over the division fence into his own yard.
He put his pumpkin on the screen porch.

As he walked around the house, Mrs. Selby called, "Kent,
here's a sack of apples for you."

"Thanks, Mrs. Selby."

"You've been a good boy to help me this fall."

Kent's mother came out and gave her neighbor a squash
pie. Mrs. Selby was very grateful. She expressed her liking for
pumpkin and told of her failure to raise any this year.

Kent carried his apples out on the screen porch. Here an
idea, a plan came into his mind. He knew now what he would
do this Halloween night. Yes, sir. He would surprise someone
"good and plenty."

When all the chores were done and darkness had set in,
mother said he could run to the neighbor's and play a little
while. So he took his pumpkin and the bag of apples over to
the back fence. After hunting up Daddy's hammer, he climbed

over the fence, then over the gate into Aunt Ella's backyard. With the hammer he pulled the nails out of the gate. They squeaked. It seemed to Kent they made an awful noise. He waited to see if anyone was coming to investigate. No one came. The gate opened easily. He took the sack of apples over to Aunt Ella's doorstep, placing it between the screen door and the frame door. Aunt Ella probably wouldn't open it until morning, but her surprise would be just as great then.

Creeping quietly back to the fence, he found his pumpkin. This he carried to Mrs. Selby's kitchen and stood it so it would fall in when she opened her door. No one seemed to have heard him, so he climbed over the fence into his own lot and put the hammer away.

That night Kent slept as only happy children can, not waking up until almost time for school. Could he only have known what happened in his neighbors' homes as a result of his prank, he would have been very happy indeed.

As Ella opened her back door, the red delicious apples rolled in. Kent would have been well satisfied with his night's work if he could have seen her stare of astonishment. She knew very well where those apples came from. For many years she had eaten fruit from Mrs. Selby's garden, and no other apples tasted as good as these. She knew that her foolish pride had kept her from being friends again with her neighbor. Now it looked as though Mrs. Selby had proved herself the better character of the two by forgiving Ella's bitter words and by bringing over this gift of peace.

Remorse burned Ella's soul. She determined to make amends. She knew that Zina Selby liked pumpkins and that she did not raise any this year. Ella picked out a big one and started toward the little back gate.

As Mrs. Selby opened her kitchen door, the largest pumpkin she had ever seen rolled in upon her floor. She started in amazement.

"Why, that is from Ella King's garden."

She thought of all the angry words she had spoken to her old friend and of how unforgiving she had been. But Ella had shown the greater heart. She must have forgiven all and in the night brought over this pumpkin as a token of love. Tears filled Mrs. Selby's eyes as she thought all those things. Hastily she filled a sack with the apples which she knew Ella liked so well. She too started toward the little back gate.

There they met—two appreciative, humble souls. Each was so overjoyed to see the other's friendly smile that she hardly heard the spoken words. Gifts were exchanged and plans made for a visit to a mutual friend. Then each returned to her household duties.

Aunt Ella was sweeping her floor as Kent rushed in on his way to school.

"Did you get surprised this morning, Aunt Ella?"

"Surprised! What about?"

Kent stared at her. "Didn't the apples fall in?"

"Apples! What apples?"

Aunt Ella surely was dumb or else those apples were lost.

Kent explained, "Why, I played a trick on Mrs. Selby and you. I took the nails out of the back gate and put apples in your doorway and my big pumpkin in hers. Didn't they fall in, Aunt Ella?"

Many thoughts flashed through Aunt Ella's head. She now

realized she had made a mistake. But as she thought it over, she knew that she was glad. She wouldn't go back to that mean, hateful feeling of being angry at her friend again for any price.

Kent was speaking again. "I kept only one apple for myself."

Aunt Ella understood. "You're a darling, Kent. I surely was surprised this morning when those apples rolled in. Just pick out the one you want and come in whenever you want another."

She watched the happy youngster run down the street, so unaware of the joy his kindly Halloween prank had brought to two aching hearts.

—PEARL W. PETERSON.

THE FIRST THANKSGIVING DAY

There was one group of people, called Pilgrims, who decided to leave their native land and go to Holland where they would be free to worship God as they desired so much to do.

After the Pilgrims had lived in Holland for about ten years or so, they wanted to move again because their children were growing more and more like the Dutch children in their habits of living. This made the Pilgrim parents very sad because they did not want their children to forget the things they had learned in their own native land.

The Pilgrims learned that the king was letting some of the people of England go to the land of America to live if they

would send part of the crops which they raised back to their
native country.

The Pilgrims sent several men back to England to ask per-
mission to go to this new country. Their request was granted.
When the men brought the good news back to Holland, the
Pilgrims rejoiced and were soon on their way to bid farewell to
England, their native land.

They left the shores of their beloved country in a sailing
vessel called the *Mayflower*.

Not many days had passed before great storms arose. The
waves rolled up over the deck, and the lives of the people were
in great danger, but the stout-hearted Pilgrims went on and on.

On November 20, 1620, over three hundred and fifty years
ago, the courageous band found themselves looking with glad
hearts upon the shores of the new country, America. How they
poured out their hearts in gratitude that they had crossed the
stormy sea in safety.

All were anxious to go ashore, but before they were allowed
to go, an exploring party went out in search of a suitable place
to build their homes.

They found springs and ponds of fresh water and some
Indian mounds containing stores of corn. What should they
do, take the corn, or leave it and run the risk of starvation?
They decided to take only enough to plant in the spring. They
afterwards paid the owners double for what they had taken.

The men began at once to chop down trees and build a
large house which could be used as a storehouse, a hospital, and
a church.

Then they built their own homes.

The first winter was a hard one for these brave Pilgrims

because they had not experienced such cold weather before. Before the warm days of spring came, one-half of the little band had perished, but not a man or woman among those left went back to the old home when the *Mayflower* sailed away.

At first they were afraid of the Indians, but they later found them to be friends in their need.

One day while the leaders of this new colony were talking together, a fine-looking Indian came toward them and said in their own language, "Welcome! Welcome!" This Indian was Samoset, who had already saved the lives of two white men taken by the Indians. He brought other Indians to sing and dance for the Pilgrims.

Even the great Indian chief, Massasoit, with twenty other Indians without bows and arrows came to visit their strange neighbors. They agreed not to harm each other and to be friends forever.

One of the Indians named Squanto taught the Pilgrims many new things. He showed them how to raise corn by putting dead fish in the hill when planting the corn, how to hoe the corn while it was growing, and how to pound the corn to make meal. Indian corn proved to be the Pilgrim's best food crop.

Squanto also taught them how to catch eels by wading into shallow water and scaring them out with their feet. The Indians also taught the white men to make Indian shoes, or moccasins, snowshoes (like skis), birch bark canoes, and many other useful things.

The first summer was now over, and the Pilgrims' first harvest had been gathered. Their houses had been repaired, and there were no sick among them. Fish and wild game were plentiful. They decided that the time for rejoicing and thanksgiving had also come. They invited Massasoit, the great Indian chief, and his warriors to join them in the celebration.

The Pilgrims first went to church to give thanks to their Heavenly Father who had blessed them so bounteously. After they returned home they heard a lusty Indian war whoop which was the signal for the arrival of their guests of honor.

The Indians thought they had never tasted anything so good as soup with biscuits in it and the turkey stuffed with beechnuts. Then the chief poured a bushel of popcorn on each table and said that not one of his tribe should harm them.

THE FIRST THANKSGIVING STORY FROM THE BIBLE

Make a joyful noise unto the Lord, all ye lands. Serve the Lord with gladness: come before his presence with singing.

"Know ye that the Lord he is God: it is he that hath made us, and not we ourselves; we are his people, and the sheep of his pasture.

"Enter into his gates with thanksgiving, and into his courts with praise: be thankful unto him, and bless his name.

"For the Lord is good; his mercy is everlasting; and his truth endureth to all generations."

—PSALM 100.

How Patty Gave Thanks

It was Thanksgiving Day.

Patty was at the farm.

Tom was there too.

What a good dinner they had!

After dinner Patty said, "Come, Tom.

We will go to the barn.

We will take some cookies and apples with us."

Patty and Tom went to the barn.

They saw Gray Pony.

"Hello, Gray Pony," said Patty.

"You are a good little pony.

You give us rides.

This is Thanksgiving Day.

Thank you for the rides, Pony.

Here is a big apple for you."

Then they went to White Cow.

"Hello, White Cow!" said Patty.

"You are good to us.

You give us milk.

This is Thanksgiving Day.

Thank you for the good milk.

Here is a big red apple for you."

"Here is Red Hen," said Patty.

"Come, Red Hen, come.

You are good to us too.

You give us eggs.

This is Thanksgiving Day.

Thank you for your good eggs.

Here are some cookies for you."

Then the children went into the house.

Soon Grandfather came in.

"I was in the barn," he said.

"I saw something funny.

It looked like a party.

Gray Pony and White Cow had big red apples.

Red Hen had cookies.

It was a funny party."

Patty laughed.

"We had a Thanksgiving party in the barn," she said.

—EMILIE POULSSON, AS PRINTED IN THE
ELSON READER BY SCOTT, FORESMAN & COMPANY.

A HAPPY THANKSGIVING

Once upon a time, in a big white house on the hill, there lived a very old man. He was always wondering what he could do so that he could make some people happy.

It was the day before Thanksgiving. Little flakes of snow were making the ground white.

Gentleman Gray, for that was the name of this fine man, looked out of his window. "What a beautiful Thanksgiving Day we will have. I'm wondering if everyone will have a good dinner tomorrow."

Just then he heard the doorbell ring. When he opened the door, Mr. Thomas, the shoemaker, was standing there.

"I didn't get your shoes finished till late," said Mr. Thomas, "so I thought I would bring them over."

"That was very kind of you," said Gentleman Gray. "Here's

an extra dime for your trouble. By the way, could your family eat a fine fat turkey tomorrow?"

"That we could," said shoemaker Thomas with a smile.

"Well, you take this one," said Gentleman Gray, handing him a big fat bird. "You know, I've always said:

> If the day be sunny,
> If the day be gray,
> If you want to be happy,
> Give something away.

"I'll remember that," said the shoemaker, and closed the door.

When the shoemaker returned home, his children met him at the door.

"What have you there, Daddy?" asked small Jim.

"A surprise?" asked wee little Patty.

The shoemaker opened the big package.

"Oh, oh! How nice!" said the shoemaker's wife.

"What a big, big bird!' cried Patty.

"Suppose you put on your hat and coat, Jim, and take Mrs. Lee the chicken we were to have for our dinner," said the shoemaker.

When Jim knocked at Mrs. Lee's door, he heard a cheery voice say, "Come in."

Mrs. Lee was making pumpkin pies. "Father sent this chicken to you for your Thanksgiving dinner," said Jim.

"What a fine man!" said Mrs. Lee. "He has made me happy indeed."

"Won't you have a piece of pie before you go out into the cold again?"

Now if there was anything Jim liked, it was pumpkin pie, so there in Mrs. Lee's cozy kitchen, Jim ate his pie.

After Jim had gone, Mrs. Lee said, "Now, Mrs. Jones has worked so hard washing clothes for other people that I believe I'll take her one of my pumpkin pies."

When Mrs. Jones saw the pumpkin pie, she exclaimed, "What a lovely pie! It is the finest one I've seen. Its yellow face makes me happy. I can hardly wait to taste it. Now it's my turn to make someone happy."

She sat down in her rocking chair by the warm kitchen fire and thought and thought. "I know what I can do," she said. "I can make some gingerbread for the Murphy children. They have no mother, poor dears."

So Mrs. Jones made some spicy gingerbread that smelled so good!

The Murphy children, Joyce, Pat and Kathleen, were seated at the table having supper of bread and milk when Mrs. Jones knocked at the door.

"Here's some gingerbread for your Thanksgiving Dinner," said Mrs. Jones. "I do hope it is good."

"Oh, thank you," said Joyce.

"My, it smells so good," said Pat.

"I can hardly wait to eat it," said Kathleen.

After Mrs. Jones had gone, Joyce spoke up, "Let's take a slice to Jack, the little lame boy, who lives next door."

So they cut off a nice big piece of the sweet-smelling gingerbread, wrapped it in paper, and carried it to the house next door.

Little Jack was seated in a chair by the window. His face lighted up when he saw the children.

"This is for you," said Joyce.

"It's gingerbread," said Kathleen.

When Jack opened the package, he gave a little squeal. "Oh, what lovely gingerbread. Such a big piece! Thank you and thank you," he said. And the next day when little Jack was eating his lovely gingerbread, he saved the crumbs and scattered them on the window sill.

The sparrows twittered as if to say, like old Gentleman Gray:

> If the day be sunny,
> If the day be gray,
> If you want to be happy,
> Give something away.

(Adapted from the poem "A Good Thanksgiving," by Marian Douglas and Annie Douglas Robinson)

—HAZEL WEST LEWIS.

EDWARD'S THANKSGIVING DINNER

Late in the afternoon of the day before Thanksgiving, Edward went up the hill to the big house to carry some things that his mother had ironed for the people who lived there. He had to wait in the kitchen while the maid went to get the money to pay him, so he just looked around a bit.

"Turkey, sweet potatoes, cranberries, celery, doughnuts, and squash," he said to himself. "My, what a lot of things they must have bought today. I wish I lived in this home for tomorrow."

He took the money and started back down the hill. He was not feeling as happy as he had been when he went up the hill. He was thinking of the things that he had seen in his own home for the Thanksgiving dinner, and it did not seem fair that Bob, who lived with his father in that big house, should have so much, while he had so little. Edward's father had been out of work for many weeks, and so there was only the money that his mother earned with which to buy food.

"Potatoes, turnips, and sausage—sausage for a treat—a queer Thanksgiving dinner!" he said aloud, as he opened the gate of the yard.

"Will you get me some wood as soon as you can?" called his mother, as he opened the door.

"I suppose so," he answered with a frown.

"What is the matter, son?" asked his mother.

"Nothing, only I wish that I lived in the house on the hill tomorrow. They have lots of good things to eat, and we can't have any," said Edward.

His mother went back to her ironing, but she said nothing. It was hard to make him understand. What was the use of trying?

The wood was in the yard. When Edward went to get it, he found that some had to be split, so he started to work at it. Then he heard a whistle. Bob had come to ask his help on some school work.

"I was up at your house a little while ago. What a big Thanksgiving dinner you are going to have! Seemed to me you had everything there in the kitchen. Father's been out of work so long that we can't have much," said Edward later as they stood at the gate.

"Give me your mother, and I will give you my dinner," said Bob quietly. "Mother was here last year. I don't care whether we have any dinner or not," and he went off up the hill.

That night when Edward went to bed, he could not go to sleep. He kept thinking of Bob with no mother to tuck him in bed or to kiss him goodnight. After all, what did it matter what they had to eat as long as mother was home to cook the meal? She would make everything taste good. He was ashamed to think he had grumbled at her.

Thanksgiving Day was a very cold one. Edward tried to help as much as he could around the house, but about ten o'clock he slipped out and went up the hill. He whistled for Bob to come out. Then he said, "I've been thinking about what you said. We would miss Mother at the table today, but if it would make you any happier, I'll ask her to come up and sit at your table instead of ours. She likes you, you know. I don't want to be selfish."

"Father had just told me that I could run down and ask you all up to help us eat our dinner," said Bob. "I told him what you said about your dinner. You will all come, won't you? It won't be so lonesome then."

So the two boys went together down the hill to the little house. Later they wrapped up the good apple pie which Edward's mother had made as a surprise for him and carried it with them up to the big house. Soon they were followed by Edward's father and mother.

Such a happy party it was! Edward's eyes were very big when he saw all the good things to eat. Bob's eyes were very happy when he looked at the smiling lady at one end of the table. Mother's eyes were very kind as she looked at the two boys eating their dinner.

"What is the best part of Thanksgiving dinner?" asked Bob's father, as he watched the boys finishing their apple pie and ice cream.

"A mother," said both boys at once.

—MARGARET W. EGGLESTON.

CHRISTMAS STORY FROM THE BIBLE

A nd it came to pass in those days, that there went out a decree from Caesar Augustus, that all the world should be taxed.

"(And this taxing was first made when Cyrenius was governor of Syria.)

"And all went to be taxed, every one into his own city.

"And Joseph also went up from Galilee, out of the city of Nazareth, into Judaea, unto the city of David, which is called Bethlehem; (because he was of the house and lineage of David:)

"To be taxed with Mary his espoused wife, being great with child.

"And so it was, that, while they were there, the days were accomplished that she should be delivered.

"And she brought forth her firstborn son, and wrapped him in swaddling clothes, and laid him in a manger; because there was no room for them in the inn.

"And there were in the same country shepherds abiding in the field, keeping watch over their flock by night.

"And, lo, the angel of the Lord came upon them, and the glory of the Lord shone round about them: and they were sore afraid.

"And the angel said unto them, Fear not: for, behold, I bring you good tidings of great joy, which shall be to all people.

"For unto you is born this day in the city of David a Saviour, which is Christ the Lord.

"And this shall be a sign unto you; Ye shall find the babe wrapped in swaddling clothes, lying in a manger.

"And suddenly there was with the angel a multitude of the heavenly host praising God, and saying,

"Glory to God in the highest, and on earth peace, good will toward men.

"And it came to pass, as the angels were gone away from them into heaven, the shepherds said one to another, Let us now go even unto Bethlehem, and see this thing which is come to pass, which the Lord hath made known unto us.

"And they came with haste, and found Mary, and Joseph, and the babe lying in a manger.

"And when they had seen it, they made known abroad the saying which was told them concerning this child.

"And all they that heard it wondered at those things which were told them by the shepherds.

"But Mary kept all these things, and pondered them in her heart.

"And the shepherds returned, glorifying and praising God for all the things that they had heard and seen, as it was told unto them."

—LUKE 2:1–20.

CHRISTMAS AT OUR HOUSE

We believe in Christmas. To us, the George Albert Smith family, Christmas is one of the most blessed and precious days the year brings. We are striving to make each Christmas as loving and living as our parents made them for us.

The first Christmas I remember was spent in the home of my great-grandfather, where the fireplace was so large that Santa Claus actually stepped out of the fireplace, where the Christmas tree was so tall that it touched the ceiling, and where the long banisters, slick and polished, let us ride two stories without getting off. I shall never forget the great crocks of spicy doughnuts and the shelves of fat mince pies in the pantry, nor the beds made all over the floors throughout the huge house where all of us slept, or tried to sleep, until Christmas morning. Even now I see the doll, with its real hair wig, that was mine this first remembered Christmas!

The next Christmas, I remember, we spent in the new house which Father and Mother had built for their family. This Christmas my best present was a new baby sister who had come since Thanksgiving, in time for Mother to be up and around by Christmas. This sister was my extra special gift and always will be because she is the only sister I have.

Preparations for Christmas at our home have always been very special. Our plans were extensive and carefully laid, the money budgeted, the gifts painstakenly chosen. Father and Mother always insisted that whatever means we had to use for Christmas must be spread over a wide territory, for they planned that we should learn for ourselves that it's always "more blessed to give than to receive." We began with the wonderful box that Mother always prepared for the Relief Society and into which she put all of the goodies that we planned for ourselves, including mince pies and plum puddings with a wonderful buttery sauce. We assembled the contents of this Relief Society Christmas box for days. After everything was ready, it was loaded on the sled and dragged on top of the crisp, icy snow to the Relief Society room at the 17th Ward. Thus began our custom, one that has always been Father's, of providing Christmas for those persons that others forgot. He has always considered the fact that where people were well remembered, they might well do without his remembering them in a substantial way, other than to extend his sincere good wishes, while gifts and fancy holiday foods should be taken to those too frequently overlooked.

Christmas Eve at our house began family festivities. We hung our stockings in front of the fireplace in the dining room. Father always hung a great, huge stocking, because he assured us that Santa never could get all the things he wanted in just a regular sock. And then, to add to the gaiety of the occasion, each year he brought his tall rubber boots up from the basement and stood one at either side of the fireplace in the dining room.

After stockings were hung, we spread a table for Santa Claus's supper—a bowl of rich milk and bread and a generous wedge of mince pie. We wrote a note to encourage him on his way and went to bed, but it seemed morning would never come. The length of Christmas Eve night and the shortness of Christmas Day was something we could never understand.

No matter how excited we children were, we never were permitted to go downstairs until we were washed, combed, and

fully dressed. Then we had morning prayers and sat down to
breakfast, the worst breakfast of the year because it took so
much time and seemed to hinder our getting to our stockings.
Always there was something very unusual and very special
down in the toe. First, we laughed and laughed over the things
Santa Claus put in Father's boots—coal and kindling and vegetables; and then we were offended because we thought Santa
was not very kind to our father, who is always generous with
everyone else. After this first experience with boots full of jokes
on Christmas, we bought something very special for Father the
next year to make up for the slight Santa Claus had made.

After we had enjoyed our toys and gifts in the stockings, the
folding doors into the parlor were pushed aside and we beheld
our twinkling candle-lighted Christmas tree. Under the color-
ful, green tree were the packages for friends and the rest of the
family. These were distributed and all had a very happy, festive
time.

After our own mirth and merriment had partially subsided,
Father always took us with him to make the rounds of the forgotten friends that he habitually visited on Christmas. I was a
very little girl when I went with Father to see how the other half
of the people lived. I remember going down a long alley in the
middle of a city block where there were some very poor houses.
We opened the door of one tiny home and there on the bed lay
an old woman, very sad and alone. As we came in, tears ran
down her cheeks, and she reached over to take hold of Father's
hand as we gave her our little remembrances. "I am grateful to
you for coming," she said, "because if you hadn't come I would
have had no Christmas at all. No one else has remembered me."
We thoroughly enjoyed this part of our day.

Christmas dinner was another high spot in our Christmas celebration. We always had very wonderful Christmas dinners, usually turkey dinners served on our beautiful blue-lace plates.

One Christmas that I shall never forget is the one when Father was very seriously ill. Expenses had been extremely high and it seemed that we were not going to be able to afford much of a Christmas. Mother longed to provide our usual happy Christmas, but she knew she could not do so and still pay the tithing due before the end of the year and which had accumulated as a result of Father's illness. She felt that her children were entitled, as are all children, to a happy Christmas. If she bought the usual gifts and dinner for them, however, she couldn't possibly pay her tithing. If she paid her full tithing her children could have no Christmas. It was a difficult decision, but she finally decided that she must pay her tithing before she gave it further thought, as the desire of doing something for her children might tempt her too greatly. Hurriedly, she put on her wraps and went to the bishop, where she paid her tithing in full.

On her way home her heart was very heavy. She was convinced that her children could have nothing for Christmas, and she dreaded our disappointment. She was walking through the snow, head down, when Mark Austin, her good neighbor, said, "Just a moment, Sister Smith. I have been thinking that your expenses have been exceedingly heavy during Brother Smith's long illness, so I should like very much to have you take this little gift and buy yourself something very special for Christmas. I am sure you haven't had anything for yourself in a long, long time." Mother, choking with tears, tried to thank him. She took the check, folded it, and went home, her heart fairly pounding with joy and thanksgiving. When she entered the house and turned the light on, she found he had given her one hundred dollars, the exact amount that she had paid in tithing.

When that Christmas morning arrived, Mother said, "This is really your Tithing Christmas, children," and she told us the story as the day progressed. Bit by bit the blessing of tithing was thus deeply impressed upon us.

Since that Tithing Christmas, we have spent Christmases in many different lands. Some have been spent in England and some in many states within the United States. We have had plentiful Christmases and meager Christmases, happy Christmases and Christmases that have not been so joyous. Irrespective of what our personal sorrows may have been, Father has always seen to it that those who needed Christmas, who were not of our particular family, were not forgotten. All of our holiday celebrations at Christmastime have been motivated by the thought impressed upon us in early childhood. "It is more blessed to give than to receive." In fact, not only Christmas, but every day of our father's life has stressed this philosophy, the practicing of which has made a lifelong impression upon our minds. We believe in Christmas!

—EMILY SMITH STEWART,
A DAUGHTER OF PRESIDENT GEORGE ALBERT SMITH.

WEE BEAR

Mamma," asked Woofski Bear a few days before Christmas, "where are they taking all the trees in those big trucks?"

"Those, dear, are Christmas trees for boys and girls in the city. Keep away from the road so the men won't see you or one might pick you up for a present," said Mother Bear.

This was to be Woofski's first Christmas, so he did not understand about Christmas trees and presents. He wondered just what it all meant. He marched down to the road to find out.

The very next truck stopped when it saw the cunning bear, and a big man reached down and whisked Woofski into the truck. The man tossed Woofski Bear high on the pine trees, exclaiming as he did so, "Won't my children love him! How fortunate I saw him!" Poor little Woofski Bear perched up on the pines felt suddenly all lonesome and afraid. The truck was moving so fast there was no way of escaping. What—oh—what could he do!

Then they came to the city. Woofski had never seen the city before. He was all wonder and amazement as they drove through the lighted streets with so many cars on them and past gaily-lighted and decorated shop windows. In all the windows were trees decked in strands of silver and gold. Those must be what Mother Bear had called Christmas trees.

Suddenly they stopped at a house. The man gathered Woofski up in his arms and went into the house. "Here, children, see what I have brought you," he called.

Two little children bustled around Woofski, exclaiming with joy. Woofski was all atremble with fright. When the children attempted to stroke him, he growled and acted peevish. "Such a cross grizzly baby!" they exclaimed.

"Perhaps he is lonesome for his mommie," Marilyn Jane put in.

"Maybe he is hungry," said Eleanor Joan.

Marilyn Jane brought some warm milk and bread. Then she fixed a small basket with a down pillow for a comfortable bed for such a wee bear. All night he cried and all the following day.

Now Mommie and Daddy Bear were most concerned. They looked all over the Green Forest. Then Mommie Bear sent Daddy to Santa to ask him for help. Santa promised that when he took his toys about that night he would keep his eyes open for Woofski.

As Santa was about to go down the chimney of Jane and Joan's house, he leaned over and listened. Then he exclaimed, "Who could be crying here! I have gifts for all of them. Someone must be sick."

Like a flash he darted down the chimney. "Hello . . ." he shouted. "Woofski! I do believe! What are you doing here? Your mother is sick worrying about you."

"Oh, Santa, dear kind Santa, please take me home to Mommie and Daddy!" sobbed tiny Woofski.

"Grumpy little bear, certainly, if you will help take the rest of my toys about."

"Yes, Santa," Woofski answered weakly.

"Hop into my pocket—we're off! If you are hungry, you will find a cracker or so there too," said Santa.

Woofski had not eaten since he left home, so he munched every crumb of cracker. At each house he helped Santa. When they started back to the Green Forest, he was so weary he fell sound asleep all cozily tucked away in Santa's very big fancy pocket.

When Santa arrived at Woofski's house, the stockings were

hung awaiting him. He lifted Woofski from his pocket. "Humph! Bear!" he exclaimed, "Yes, sir, and asleep!" Then a smile crept over Santa's face, and it seemed to say that Santa would give Mommie Bear a surprise.

Well, a surprise it was, for next morning when Mommie looked into her stocking, there snoozing comfortably was wee Woofski! She drew Woofski, stocking and all, to her and kissed him many times. Papa Bear did the same. Woofski was a real Christmas gift to them. After this they all looked at their gifts, but sly old Santa left in Woofski's stocking a long, long, long, long rope with a Christmas card that said:

Dear Woofski,

Again when you stray, have one end of the rope tied to your house and the other end to yourself, and then you may easily return.

Happy Christmas,
SANTA CLAUS.
—Verona Toronto Bowen.

The Christmas Legend

A long, long time ago on the night just before Christmas, a little child, all alone, wandered the streets of a large city. There were a great many fathers and mothers hurrying home with bundles of presents for their little ones, and some rolled past in fine carriages, one after the other, bound for home to celebrate the happy time with their children.

This little child seemed to have no home but wandered up

and down, looking into the windows and watching the lights. No one seemed to notice the little one except Jack Frost, who bit the bare toes and fingers, and the North Wind, who almost brought tears to the child's eyes with his blowing. It was cold, oh, very cold that night.

Up and down the street the little child passed, and the walks were all snowy and icy. The child had on neither shoes nor stockings; but, though it was cold, the little one was glad, for it was Christmas Eve, and the whole world seemed glad too.

Everywhere the light was streaming out of the windows, and if one looked in, there could be seen the beautiful candles and the Christmas trees. In some of the houses, the trees were loaded with presents for the children, and in one place into which the little child looked, the boys and girls were playing and skipping, and their merry laughter rang so loudly through the house that it could be heard through the thick walls and doors out into the street.

The little child was glad with them and clapped its hands and said, "Oh, they are so happy in there! Surely they will share with me, and let me come into the warm, bright room and sing and play."

And the little feet tripped up the great, wide staircase, and without a fear the child tapped softly at the door.

And the door opened. There stood the tall footman. He looked at the little child but sadly shook his head and said: "Go down off the steps. There is no room in here for you." He looked sorry when he said it, for he probably remembered his own little ones at home and was glad that they were not out in the cold.

Through the open door a light—oh, such a bright light—shone, and it was so warm!

But the child turned away into the cold and darkness, not knowing why the footman spoke so; for surely the children would have loved to have another little companion to join in their joyous Christmas evening festival.

But the children did not know that the child had knocked.

The street seemed colder and darker to the child than before, and the bright windows were not nearly so bright, because the child was sad. But all along, on both sides of the wide street, the light streamed out, and it was almost as bright as day; and the beauty all about made the little child glad again.

The great city was full of happy homes that night, and the cold outside was entirely forgotten. All remembered only the happy time, and no doubt thought that every single person in the whole wide world was happy too.

Farther and farther along, down where the homes were not quite so large or beautiful, the little child wandered. There seemed to be children inside of nearly all the houses, and they were dancing and frolicking about; there were Christmas trees in nearly every window, with beautiful dolls and toys; there were trumpets and picture books, and all sorts of nice things; and in one place a sweet little lamb made of white wool was hanging on the tree for one of the children.

The child, stopping before this window, looked and looked at the beautiful thing and, creeping up to the glass, gently tapped upon the pane. A little girl came to the window and looked out into the dark street and saw the child. But she only frowned and shook her head and said, "Come some other time, for we cannot take care of you now," and then she went away.

The little child turned back into the cold again and went sadly on, saying, "Will no one share the beautiful Christmas with me? The light is so bright, and I love it so!" The child wandered on and on, scarcely seeing the light now, on account of the tears.

The street became darker and narrower; farther and farther the little one traveled. It grew late. Scarcely anyone was out to meet the child as it walked, and all the outer world was still and cold.

Ahead there suddenly appeared a bright, single ray of light that shone right through the darkness into the child's eyes. The child smiled and said, "I will go and see if they will share their Christmas with me."

Hastening past all the other houses, the little one went straight up to the windowpane from which the light was streaming. It was such a poor, little, low house, but the child saw only the light in the window, for there was neither curtain nor shade. What do you suppose the light came from? Nothing but a tiny tallow candle! But it seemed to the little wanderer almost as bright as the sun. That was because the child was glad again. The candle was placed in an old cup with a broken handle, and right in the same cup there was a twig of evergreen, and that was all the Christmas tree they had.

And who do you suppose was in the house?

A beautiful mother with a baby on her knee and a little one beside her. The children were both looking into their mother's face and listening to her words. A few bright coals were burning in the fireplace, which made it light and warm within. The child crept closer to the pane and knocked. They all listened.

"Shall I open the door, dear mother?" the little girl asked.

"Certainly, my child. No one must be left out in the cold on our beautiful Christmas Eve. Open the door and let the stranger come in."

The door was thrown wide open, and the little girl looked into the darkness; when she saw the child she put out her little hand to help. The child went in—into the light and warmth. Then the mother put out her hands and touched the little child. The children said: "Dear little one, you are cold and naked; come and let us warm you and love you, and then you shall have some of our Christmas."

The baby crept out of its mother's lap, and she gathered the little stranger to her, and the children stood at her knee, and warmed the cold hands and feet, and rubbed them and smoothed the tangled curls, and kissed the child's face. The mother put her arms about the three little ones, and the candle and the firelight shone over them all, and everything was so still.

And the mother's sweet voice spoke in the stillness: "Little ones," she said, "shall I tell you the real Christmas story?"

The children said, "Yes," so the mother began:

"Many, many years ago, this very night, some shepherds were out on the plains watching their sheep. The wee little lambs were asleep, and the large sheep were sleeping too. The stars shone bright and clear above, and all was very still below.

"The shepherds sat beside each other without a word, leaning on their crooks and hardly moving.

"Suddenly a great light shone all around about them right through the darkness; they did not know what it was, and they were all afraid.

"Then an angel, white and beautiful, came to them from

out of the light, and told them not to fear, for great joy and gladness had come to the whole world. It was a little babe who was to become their king and save them from all wrong and suffering and do great good for them and all mankind. The angel then showed the shepherds where to find him, saying that he would be wrapped in swaddling clothes and lying in a manger.

"'And suddenly there was with the angel a multitude of the heavenly host praising God, and saying, Glory to God in the highest, and on earth peace, good will toward men.' And a wonderful light was all about them, and when the angel had gone away from them into the heaven, the shepherds said one to another, 'Let us go and see this child of whom the angel told us.'

"So they left their lambs sleeping on the plains and took their crooks in their hands and started out.

"It was a long way, but a shining star was before them, and they followed it even up to the place where the angel had told them. And they found the babe lying in a manger; and when they had seen him, they told all the people that came to see the child of what they had seen that night on the plains, and how the angel had told them to come to the child, and of the wonderful light which had made them afraid, and how the multitude had sung. All they that had heard it wondered at the things which were told them by the shepherds. The mother of the little babe was very glad and remembered all these things.

"The kind shepherds departed and went back to their flocks, telling everyone they met of the young child.

"They called the child Jesus, and the child grew and was strong and beautiful; and Jesus taught the whole world how they should love one another and be good, even as our Father in Heaven is good and loves us."

The sweet voice of the mother ceased. The light in the room had grown brighter until now it shone like the sun; from the floor to the ceiling, all was light as day. And lo, when the little ones turned to look for the child, the mother's lap was empty; there was nothing to be seen; the child was gone, but the light was still in the room.

"Children," the mother said quietly, "I believe we have had the real Christ Child with us tonight." And she drew her dear ones to her and kissed them, and there was great joy in the little house.

THE TEN-CENT CHRISTMAS

The doctor was whistling merrily as he rang the doorbell, but the tune died on a long note of dismay when Florence opened the door.

Her face was puffed and streaked from crying, and she held a little wet ball of handkerchief in her hand.

"What's the matter here?" said Dr. Thompson. "Is your father worse?"

Mrs. Gray came down the stairs. "Good morning, Doctor," she said. "Florence is crying herself sick because we are not going to have a very grand Christmas this year."

"All I have to spend is t-ten cents," interrupted Florence, "and how can I buy presents for Mother and Father and Grandma with ten cents? And I wanted to get something 'specially nice for Father because he's been sick so long, and now he's just beginning to enjoy things."

Dr. Thompson's first impulse was to put his hand in his pocket, but he knew that Mrs. Gray would not like to have him interfere in that way. He thought rapidly; then his eyes twinkled as he said gravely, "I don't know that I ever had a patient with just this trouble before, but perhaps I can help a little. I'll see you, Florence, after I've been up to see Father."

Florence waited for him on the stairs. She wiped her eyes several times, but the doctor's words had aroused her curiosity, and she did not feel quite so bad. He stayed upstairs a long time. She could hear them talking and laughing. At last she heard him say, "See you tomorrow, Gray," and saw him coming down the stairs. He was tearing a leaf off his prescription pad.

"I'm in a great hurry, Florence," he said. "There are lots of sick folks waiting for me, so I can't stop to talk to you. But there is a prescription, and you are to take it according to directions, and I'll see you tomorrow."

He let himself out, and Florence hurried away to find Grandma and read the prescription with her.

This is what it said: "Work out the following on your slate; show it to me tomorrow: If twelve Christmas bells cost five cents, how many bells will ten cents buy? If one crib has four posts, how many posts will six cribs have?"

"What does it mean?" cried Florence.

"I'm sure I don't know," replied Grandma, "but I'd do it if I were you."

Mrs. Gray found Florence eagerly figuring on her paper.

"Mother," she said, "do you know what this means?" But her mother only laughed and would not answer her.

Florence quickly found that the answer to both questions was the same, but she could not guess why Dr. Thompson had given her such a queer prescription.

Next day a radiant little girl let him in. He looked at the paper in her hand and pronounced the answers correct but would not explain. Once more he gave her a folded paper when he went away. This one said, "Dr. Thompson begs the honor of Miss Florence Gray's company tomorrow morning at ten o'clock. P. S. He very much wants Gladys to go too." Gladys was Florence's doll. Florence showed her the note and told her all about it. That afternoon Grandma washed and ironed Gladys's best dress, and Florence and she were all ready and waiting when Dr. Thompson came for them.

It was the day before Christmas. Dr. Thompson stayed upstairs with Father such a long time, and they laughed and talked more than ever, but at last he was ready to go.

"All right," he said. "Be sure to take your ten cents. We're going to have a Christmas."

Florence hadn't thought much about her ten-cent Christmas since he had given her the mysterious prescription, but now her doubts appeared again. Before she could say anything, she found herself hurried out into the doctor's sleigh and wrapped up warmly in a great buffalo robe with Gladys in her arms.

"Where are we going?" she asked.

"You'll see," replied the doctor.

He clucked to the horse, and away they went over the snow, down the busy streets among the hurrying people till they came

to the ten-cent store. Its windows were bright with Christmas
tree ornaments and tinsel, and around its doors surged a great
throng, pushing its way in and out.

"Do you suppose you can get in there?" asked the doctor.

"Of course I can."

"Run along, then, and buy—let me see—how many
Christmas bells was it?"

"Two dozen—twenty-four—oh," gasped Florence, realizing for the first time that this ride had something to do with
the questions she had worked out on her slate.

The doctor held Gladys until, after a while, he saw Florence
struggling back through the crowd, a flat paper bundle in her
hand. Off they went again, leaving the shoppers behind them.
They stopped on a quiet street before a huge brick building.
Through the windows Florence could see many white iron
beds, and women in blue and white dresses bending over them.

"Why, it's the—"

"Hospital—yes," said the doctor. "Get out now. Look out
Gladys doesn't slip on that ice."

They went in. Florence saw a long corridor stretching
ahead of her, with many doors on each side. Men in white coats
were walking softly about in rubber-soled shoes. She clasped
Gladys to her and clung to the doctor's hand.

They walked down the corridor. In one of the rooms
Florence saw a little boy in bed.

"There's a little boy," she whispered.

Dr. Thompson turned into the room. The little boy smiled
at him.

"Well, sonny, how's the leg today?" said the doctor.

The little fellow twisted himself and sat up but did not

answer. He was a little Italian boy and could understand only the doctor's friendly manner—not his strange words. Florence watched him closely.

"Let's see," said the doctor to himself. "How many posts has this crib?"

"Four," cried Florence. "Four, I know," and she pulled at the string on the flat bundle. The little boy watched with eager eyes.

"I'll be back in a few minutes," said the doctor, but Florence scarcely heard him. She was busy unfolding a red paper bell and fastening the metal clamps that held it open. As the last one slipped into place and the little bell hung from her fingers, a cry came from the crib, and two little hands reached out imploringly. She gave him the bell, but he put it aside shaking his head and motioning for the parcel. "Why, he wants to do it himself," she told Gladys. When the doctor returned, he found Florence guiding Pietro's fingers, while three merry bells adorned his crib. As she leaned over to hand the fourth one, she touched something hard in the bed.

"Oh," she exclaimed, "did I hurt him?"

"No," replied the doctor and turned away the sheet to show her the heavy plaster cast that encased Pietro's leg.

"Doesn't it hurt dreadfully to wear a thing like that?" she asked as they went down the corridor.

"No, it's uncomfortable, of course, but it's going to make him well. He will have to stay here a long time, though."

"Hasn't he any father and mother? Hasn't he any home?"

"Yes, but his father and mother work. They come to see him on Sundays."

Florence thought of her own pleasant home, of her

grandmother who cooked and sewed and did so many things for her while her mother nursed Father, who was getting well fast now.

Four other little cribs were hung with bells before they came to the one in which little Mary lay. One arm was wrapped close to her body, which was swathed in bandages. Toys and books lay unnoticed about her, and a sweet-faced nurse bent over her, trying to coax her to drink some milk.

"I can't. It hurts," she moaned and turned her curly black head from side to side on the pillow. Dr. Thompson looked very grave. The nurse straightened up, her face troubled.

"If we could only get her to eat," she said. "She isn't giving herself a chance. And she bears the pain so bravely too."

The little black head still tossed on the pillow. As the nurse moved, the big black eyes caught sight of Florence—and Gladys in her clean white dress. Little Mary's well hand reached for the bars of the crib, and she slowly pulled herself up, a new expression on her face. Dr. Thompson touched the nurse on the arm. They left the room. "Pretty dolly," said bandaged little Mary.

Florence looked at her—at the stiff, angular little body under the coarse nightdress—at the thin little face, scarred with newly healed burns.

"Mary wants dolly."

Florence moved Gladys's arms. They reached toward Mary.

"Dolly wants you too," said Florence.

Mary sank painfully back, with Gladys clasped close to her side. She kicked the surrounding playthings. "Take 'em away," she commanded.

Dr. Thompson and the nurse, coming back, heard a faint

laugh. The discarded playthings were on the floor. Florence was taking off Gladys's coat and hat, while Mary watched.

"She could do it herself if she had two hands," Florence explained. "She does a whole lot with just one."

"How would you like to have a tea party?" asked the doctor. "I find that I shall have to stay here quite a while."

"Oh," cried Florence, "that would be just splendid."

The nurse brought a tray with a pitcher of milk, a plate of thin bread and butter, and some custard pudding. There were three mugs and three plates and three spoons. She raised Mary in the bed and made her comfortable with pillows; then she sat outside the door where the children could not see her.

"Now, Mary," said Florence, "I'll be the lady this time, 'cause I've got two hands to wait on the table, and you and Gladys can be the company. Will you have some of this bread and butter, Mrs. Smith? Do let me give you some of this tea. I made it myself. Will you have some too, Miss Gladys?"

The nurse heard the rattle of dishes, then Florence's voice again. "You know, after we eat ours, we must eat Gladys's too, and play she ate it herself."

And Mary ate. Dr. Thompson, coming after Florence, was met by a thankful nurse who told him all about it.

"Doctor," said Florence, "do you suppose you could bring me here again tomorrow? Because if you did, and if I could find something for a nightdress for Gladys, I'd let her stay all night with Mary. She wants her to."

Dr. Thompson gravely produced a large clean handkerchief. "Will this do?"

Gladys, wrapped in the doctor's handkerchief and tied with a bit of bandage, lay open-eyed all night in the arms of a little burned and bandaged girl, who slept as the nurse had prayed she would.

Dr. Thompson carried a very happy little girl home in his sleigh. "Florence has had her ten-cent Christmas," he said to Mrs. Gray, "and I don't believe it was such a bad one either."

The words simply tumbled over each other as Florence tried to tell about the little burned girl at the hospital, but Dr. Thompson's few quiet words told Mrs. Gray what Florence did not dream of—that probably she had saved Mary's life. And when, next day, they carried Gladys's nightdress and the rest of her clothes in a "truly trunk" and left her to visit Mary until she was able to go to her own home, Doctor Thompson told Florence what she had done.

"You have given yourself for a Christmas present," he said, "and you can always do that as long as you live, even if you don't have any money to spend. And if you have a happy self, you can give happiness to everyone, and happiness is a great deal more precious than pin cushions and handkerchiefs."

And Mother and Father and Grandma all agreed with Doctor Thompson—and so did Florence and Mary and Gladys.

—BERTHA CURRIER PORTER.

THE PROMISE: A CHRISTMAS WONDER STORY

There was once a harper who played such beautiful music and sang such beautiful songs that his fame spread throughout the whole land, and at last the king heard of him and sent messengers to bring him to the palace.

"I will neither eat nor sleep till I have seen your face and heard the sound of your harp." This was the message the king sent to the harper.

The messengers said it over and over until they knew it by heart, and when they reached the harper's house, they called: "Hail, harper! Come out and listen, for we have something to tell you that will make you glad."

But when the harper heard the king's message he was sad, for he had a wife and a child and a little brown dog, and he was sorry to leave them, and they were sorry to have him go.

"Stay with us," they begged, but the harper said, "I must go, for it would be discourteous to disappoint the king; but as sure as holly berries are red and pine is green, I will come back by Christmas day to eat my share of the Christmas pudding and sing the Christmas songs by my own fireside."

And when he had promised this, he hung his harp upon his back and went away with the messengers to the king's palace.

When he got there, the king welcomed him with joy, and many things were done in his honor. He slept on a bed of softest down and ate from a plate of gold at the king's own table; and when he sang, everybody and everything, from the king himself to the mouse in the palace pantry, stood still to listen.

No matter what he was doing, however, feasting or resting, singing or listening to praises, he never forgot the promise he had made to his wife and his child and his little brown dog; and when the day before Christmas came, he took his harp in hand and went to bid the king good-bye.

Now the king was loath to have the harper leave him, and he said to him, "I will give you a horse that is white as milk, as glossy as satin, and fleet as a deer, if you will stay to play and sing before my throne on Christmas day."

But the harper answered, "I cannot stay, for I have a wife and a child and a little brown dog, and I have promised them to be home by Christmas day to eat my share of the Christmas pudding and sing the Christmas songs by my own fireside."

Then the king said, "If you will stay to play and sing before my throne on Christmas day, I will give you a wonderful tree that summer or winter is never bare, and silver and gold will fall for you whenever you shake this little tree."

But the harper said, "I must not stay, for my wife and my child and my little brown dog are waiting for me, and I have promised them to be at home by Christmas day to eat my share of the Christmas pudding and sing the Christmas songs by my own fireside."

Then the king said, "If you will stay on Christmas day one tune to play and one song to sing, I will give you a velvet robe to wear, and you may sit beside me here with a ring on your finger and a crown on your head."

But the harper answered, "I will not stay, for my wife and my child and my little brown dog are watching for me, and I have promised them to be at home by Christmas day to eat my share of the Christmas pudding and sing the Christmas songs by my own fireside." And he wrapped his old cloak about him and hung his harp upon his back and went out from the king's palace without another word.

He had not gone far when the little white snowflakes came fluttering down from the skies.

"Harper, stay," they seemed to say. "Do not venture out today."

But the harper said, "The snow may fall, but I must go, for I have a wife and a child and a little brown dog, and I have promised them to be at home by Christmas day to eat my share of the Christmas pudding and sing the Christmas songs by my own fireside."

Then the snow fell thick, and the snow fell fast. The hills and the valleys, the hedges and hollows were white. The paths were all hidden, and there were drifts like mountains on the king's highway. The harper stumbled and the harper fell, but he would not turn back; and as he traveled he met the wind.

"Brother Harper, turn I pray; do not journey on today," sang the wind, but the harper would not heed.

"Snows may fall and winds may blow, but I must go on," he said, "for I have a wife and a child and a little brown dog, and I have promised them to be at home by Christmas day to eat my share of the Christmas pudding and sing the Christmas songs by my own fireside."

Then the wind blew an icy blast. The snow froze on the ground, and the water froze in the rivers. The harper's breath froze in the air, and icicles as long as the king's sword hung from the rocks on the king's highway. The harper shivered and the harper shook, but he would not turn back; and by and by he came to the forest that lay between the highway and his home.

The trees of the forest were creaking and bending in the wind, and every one of them seemed to say:

> Darkness gathers, night is near.
> Harper, stop! Don't venture here.

But the harper would not stop. "Snow may fall, winds may blow, and night may come, but I have promised to be at home by Christmas day to eat my share of the Christmas pudding and sing the Christmas songs by my own fireside. I must go on."

And on he went till the last glimmer of daylight faded, and there was darkness everywhere. But the harper was not afraid of the dark.

"If I cannot see I can sing," said he, and he sang in the forest joyously:

> Sing glory, glory, glory!
>> And bless God's holy name;
> For 'twas on Christmas morning,
>> The little Jesus came.
>
> He wore no robes; no crown of gold
>> Was on His head that morn;
> But herald angels sang for joy,
>> To tell a King was born.

The snow ceased its falling, the wind ceased its blowing, the trees of the forest bowed down to listen, and lo! dear children, as he sang, the darkness turned to wondrous light, and close at hand the harper saw the open doorway of his home.

The wife and the child and the little brown dog were watching and waiting, and they welcomed the harper with great joy. The holly berries were red in young green pine; the Christmas pudding was full of plums; and the harper was happier than a king as he sat by his own fireside to sing:

> O glory, glory, glory!
>> We praise God's holy name;

For 'twas to bring his wondrous love,
The little Jesus came.

And in our hearts it shines anew,
While at His throne we pray,
God bless us all for Jesus' sake,
This happy Christmas day.

—MAUD LINDSAY, FROM *THE STORY TELLER*, PUBLISHED BY LATHROP,
LEE & SHEPARD CO., INC.; REPRINTED BY SPECIAL PERMISSION.

CHRISTMAS IN PIONEER TIMES

I remember our first Christmas in the valley. We all worked as usual. The men gathered sagebrush and some even plowed; for though it had snowed, the ground was still soft, and the plows were used the entire day. Christmas came on Saturday. We celebrated the day on the Sabbath, when all gathered around the flagpole in the center of the fort, and there we held a meeting. And what a meeting it was. We sang praises to God, we all joined in the opening prayer, and the speaking that day has always been remembered. There were words of thanksgiving and cheer. Not a pessimistic word was uttered. The people were hopeful and buoyant, because of their faith in the great undertaking. After the meeting, there was handshaking all around. Some wept with joy. The children played in the enclosure, and around the sagebrush fire that night we gathered and sang:

Come, come, ye saints,
No toil nor labor fear,
But with joy wend your way.

That day we had boiled rabbit and a little bread for our dinner. Father had shot some rabbits, and it was a feast we had. All had enough to eat. In a sense of perfect peace and goodwill, I never had a happier Christmas in my life.

•   •   •

The principal thing was to get together enough food for a dinner, for it was very scarce that winter. I think the people met as families and friends in the fort. I went to my mother's house. She lived in a little log room behind where the Beehive House now stands. To me that one log room looked like a palace. It was so grand to have a home with a roof over our heads. I remember that we gathered all of the good things we could to make a dinner. Mother made a cake which was a very unusual thing to have. Little Isaac Perry Decker, about seven years old, ate so much dinner before the cake was cut and served that he looked at it almost crying and said, "Mother, what shall I do? I can't eat it!" His voice was full of regret, for he loved cake and had not had a piece for a long time. Mother said, "Well, you can save it until tomorrow." Little Perry's face brightened with the thought that he could really eat the cake another time.

The Christmas of 1848 found the Saints with much more of a variety of things for their Christmas dinner. Some had wild duck or prairie chicken and a little cake. Although sugar was scarce, some molasses had been made by squeezing cornstalks and making what they called cornstalk molasses. Serviceberries and chokecherries had been gathered from the canyons, and pies were made of these. Some gingerbread was mixed and made into various shapes to please the children. They were indeed happy with this cake and did not even think of looking

for more. The families in the fort generally organized themselves into groups for dinner so that all might have a share of
the good things.

•   •   •

My first Christmas dinner in Utah was partaken of in 1848
in the old fort, at my Uncle Daniel's table. It was customary for
everybody to cook the best they had on such occasions.

Plenty of vegetables had been raised and corn dried in the
fall, and I am sure there must have been some kind of dessert.
Our fruit consisted of serviceberries and chokecherries, which
we gathered in the canyons.

In the early days, sugar was scarce, and molasses was made
from sugarcane, watermelons, and frozen squashes, the juices
having been boiled down into a syrup.

Our amusement consisted mostly of dancing and having
concerts. These exercises were always opened and closed with
prayer. We never lacked for music or musicians, for we had
both brass and martial bands.

As there was not money to buy presents, suitable mottoes
were worked out on cardboard, gloves and mittens were knit-
ted, and crochet work was done. Rag dolls were made and
dressed for the little girls, and sleds and wagons were made for
the boys. The stockings were generally filled with homemade
molasses candy, popcorn, sometimes a popcorn ball, or a fried
cake. These made the children very happy.

Our neighbors were remembered on that day by sending
them some of our fare or inviting them to eat with us. The poor
were always remembered in a substantial way. The people raised

their own beef and pork, and I think there was never a pig or a beef killed without a piece being sent to the nearest neighbors.

As the years went by, food and money were more easily obtained, and as a result the Christmas celebrations were a little more elaborate. As the menu for Christmas dinner in the various homes differs at the present time, so did it in the early days. Some had chicken or duck, others had pork or rabbit pie. Some had pumpkin pie or squash pie for dessert, others had currant or vinegar pie, while others had plum pudding made with spices, dried currants, and serviceberries. For years, however, there were many families that did not have stockings to hang up on Christmas Eve, and the presents they received were laid on the mantel or by the plates at the breakfast table. In the families where the children did have stockings, they were hung on the mantel or on a string extending from the mantel to some article of furniture. The presents consisted of dried serviceberries, and a little molasses candy, popcorn, etc. In later years the children found a few dried peaches, or apples, or a bow of ribbon. Sometimes the girls received hair ornaments made of velvet ribbon trimmed with beads. Hats made of braided wheat straw and toys carved out of wood were also among the presents.

The fried cakes which were also important at Christmastime were made of saleratus, sour milk, and flour. The saleratus was obtained by the fathers and brothers from the shores of the Great Salt Lake. This was placed in water so that the sand which was scraped up with it would settle to the bottom. A certain quantity of this water was poured with sour milk and mixed with the flour and rolled out on a board. The dough was cut in long strips, twisted, the ends fastened together and put in the hot fat to brown. The fat used was carefully saved bit by bit for days and days before Christmas. While the most fortunate Saints were enjoying the Christmas day with their families, they were not forgetting those in poverty or sickness. A bag of flour, a piece of pork, or a bit of cake was sent to the poor. The sick were given extra good food and special attention. The children ran from house to house shouting, "Christmas gift! Christmas gift!" although they did not expect a single gift to be given. They loved the joy that comes from mingling with each other.

FATHER TIME'S VISIT

Just tonight," pleaded Charlie. "I have never sat up to see the New Year come in yet."

"Very well, dear," said mother, "but I am afraid you will get very sleepy."

"No, indeed, I shall not be sleepy. Besides that, this is such a good chance to read the book I got for Christmas."

Outside the cold wind was blowing around the house, and the snow was drifting, but in the room where Charlie and his mother sat there was a bright, warm fire burning. Winter could not get in there, but they could often hear the wind whistling and were glad that they were out of the storm.

Charlie was soon reading his book. When he got tired of it, taking his chair over by the gate, he sat looking into the fire and thinking of the New Year that was just coming.

Soon an old, old man came into the room. His hair was

long and white and he was covered with snow. Under his arm he carried a large, flat parcel. He walked over beside Charlie.

"Don't you know me?" he said to Charlie with a smile.

"No," answered Charlie, "I think I have never seen you before."

"Well, well, that is strange," said the old man. "I know you well. I have seen you many, many times. I am old Father Time. Perhaps you have heard of me. I saw you were waiting for the New Year, and I thought I would come and talk to you and show you something."

As he said this, he took from under his arm the parcel he carried and handed it to Charlie, who was so astonished and excited that he could scarcely unwrap the parcel. Finally he got the paper off and found a large book.

"Come to the table, and we will look at it," said Father Time.

They both drew their chairs up to the table, and Father Time opened up the book. Charlie looked at the first page in wonder. He rubbed his eyes and looked again. In the center of the page was a picture, painted in bright, beautiful colors, of a large room with many children in it, all looking very happy. Charlie knew it was a picture of a party that he went to last New Year's Day. Yes, sure enough! There was Charlie himself just giving his place in a game to a timid little boy whom nobody else had noticed. The little boy had given him such a sweet smile of thanks, and that same smile was on the face in the picture.

"I think that must have been a very happy day," said Father Time, looking kindly at Charlie.

"It was," said Charlie, and then Father Time turned to

another page. There were no bright colors on this page; the picture was dark and gloomy. Charlie could see a hill and boys coasting down it. There coming down the hill, with his sled running into a large rock near the track was Charlie himself. As he looked at the picture his face saddened. Yes, he remembered it. It was last winter. Mother had told him not to coast on that hill, but he thought he knew more about hills than his mother did. He meant to go down just once; but in going down that one time, the sled went so fast he could not tell how to steer, and he had run into the rock. He was hurt and was taken home to Mother. Even now he could see her face, so sad, but so sweet, and as Charlie thought of it the tears came into his eyes so that he could scarcely see the picture.

"Here is a brighter picture," said Father Time, turning over the leaves.

Charlie looked. It was another brightly colored picture. Now it was springtime and a little boy stood by a bird's nest, just putting back in the nest a poor little bird that had fallen out. Charlie thought nobody knew of this.

Father Time turned page after page. Some of the pictures were beautiful, and others were dark and gloomy. Charlie found himself in each picture and remembered what he had done.

"That was a fine day," he said, as they turned to a picture of the procession of the Fourth of July. "What a good time we had that day."

Father Time kept turning the pages, and Charlie found that all of the little things he had done, and had almost forgotten, made the pictures either beautiful or dark and sad. It made him sorry to see the dark ones, and Father Time looked sad too.

They were getting near the end of the book. It was winter again. Here was a page with a large, beautiful picture on it. A smile came to Charlie's face. How did Father Time find all these things out? It happened only last week. He had such a nice, new sled that Santa Claus had brought him and was going out one morning to try it when he met a little girl, poorly clothed, with large holes in her shoes, and the saddest face Charlie had ever seen.

"Do you want a ride?" he asked her.

"Would you give me one?" she had said.

"Of course, I will. Just get on." She looked so happy. He had meant to give her a little ride and then go with the boys, but when he ran fast, she laughed and clapped her hands, so he thought he would take her for a long, long ride. He could go coasting some other time, and perhaps she could not have another ride.

Father Time looked at him and smiled. "We like the bright pictures the best, don't we?"

"Charlie, Charlie! Wake up. It is almost time for the New Year to come," Charlie heard his mother saying. He got up, rubbed his eyes, looked at the table and all around the room. Where was the book, and where was Father Time?

"I was afraid it would be too long for my boy to sit up," said Mother.

Just then the bells began to ring, and Charlie knew that the old year had gone and that the New Year had come. When the bells stopped ringing, he went to his mother, and putting his arms around her neck, he whispered: "Mother, I am going to try to have more beautiful pictures next year."

"More beautiful pictures!" said mother. "I don't know what you mean."

Charlie thought of Father Time and said, "I am going to try to make this year a happy one."

SUBJECT INDEX

ALPHABETICAL INDEX